Foundation Core GCSE Maths 1–3

Michael White

Elmwood Education

First published 2015 by
Elmwood Education
Unit 5
Mallow Park
Watchmead
Welwyn Garden City
Herts. AL7 1GX
Tel. 01707 333232

ISBN 9781 906 622 442

Preface

This book covers the material mainly required for grades 1 to 3 of the GCSE Foundation Tier.

Nowadays there is a wealth of enriching resources available to teachers, particularly on the internet. This book can be used alongside these to enable students to work at topics in a systematic way which helps to build up their confidence.

The 'M' exercises cover the main part of the syllabus. Exercises are labelled as 'E' when the author believes the content is particularly difficult relative to the other material in this book.

Constant revisiting of topics is essential for mathematical fluency and success. Throughout this book, the author provides 'Can you still?' sections to encourage this continual reviewing process. This material is designed for short (e.g. 5 to 15 minutes) sessions within lessons to keep ideas 'fresh' in students' minds.

Questions are provided at the end of each unit for students to test themselves against each learning objective stated at the start of the unit. These are then backed up with a selection of GCSE examination questions.

The author has chosen to retain a functional 'Use your maths' section in each unit. These sections are designed to encourage discussion and to highlight the maths required in a variety of situations. There is also an additional unit devoted to raising students' awareness of money matters.

Each unit in this book is designed to match up with the corresponding unit in the 'Essential GCSE Maths 4–5' book. This provides many extension possibilities.

The author hopes that the contents of this book will contribute towards each student developing a greater mastery of this subject.

Thanks are due to AQA, CEA, EDEXCEL, OCR and WJEC for kindly allowing the use of questions from their past examination papers. The answers are solely the work of the author and are not ratified by the examining groups.

The author is indebted to the contributions from Hilary White and Peter Gibson.

Michael White

Contents

Unit 1

Number 1

Unit 2

Algebra 1

Unit 3

Number 2

Unit 4

Geometry 1

Unit 5

Number 3

Unit 6

Watch Your Money

Unit 7

Algebra 2

Unit 8

Statistics 1

Unit 9

Geometry 2

Unit 10

Statistics 2

Unit 11

Geometry 3

NUMBER 1

1

In this unit you will learn how to:

– understand place value in numbers

– round off numbers

– add and subtract whole numbers

– multiply and divide whole numbers

– use negative numbers

– do calculations in the correct order

– use powers

– find factors and prime numbers

– find HCF and LCM

– break down numbers into prime factors

– use standard form

– USE YOUR MATHS! – win the premiership

Place value

M1.1

1 What is the value of the underlined digit in each number below?

(a) <u>6</u>75   (b) 71<u>4</u>   (c) 137<u>8</u>   (d) <u>3</u>619   (e) 40<u>6</u>

(f) 5<u>7</u>14   (g) 37<u>8</u>1   (h) <u>5</u>369   (i) 5<u>1</u>8   (j) 3<u>6</u>72

(k) 372<u>6</u>   (l) <u>5</u>064   (m) 4<u>1</u>07   (n) 8<u>7</u>10   (o) 691<u>5</u>

2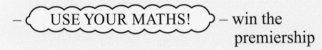

(a) Using all the 3 cards above, what is the *largest* number you can make?

(b) Using all the 3 cards above, what is the *smallest* number you can make?

3 Write down a number which is one hundred more than

(a) 8712   (b) 6498   (c) 3925

4 Write these numbers in order of size, starting with the smallest:

(a) 4163, 4089, 4158, 4080

(b) 7481, 7492, 7396, 7377, 7365, 7418

5 ⬛ 7   ⬛ 1   ⬛ 4   ⬛ 6

(a) Using all the 4 cards above, what is the *largest* number you can make?

(b) Using all the 4 cards above, what is the *smallest* number you can make?

6 (a) Which number is one thousand less than 52 498?

(b) Is your answer to part (a) greater or less than 51 500?

7

Use all the cards to make
the smallest possible *odd* number.

8 (a) Write down a number which is one thousand more than 68 734.

(b) Write down a number which is one thousand less than 70 735.

(c) Which answer is larger and by how much?

Tenths, hundredths, thousandths

0·6̲ the 6 means $\frac{6}{10}$ 27·1̲8̲ the 8 means $\frac{8}{100}$ 27·348̲ the 8 means $\frac{8}{1000}$

M1.2

1 What is the value of the underlined digit in each number below.

(a) 0·82̲   (b) 0·9̲13   (c) 0·5̲86   (d) 0·307̲   (e) 0·9̲

(f) 0·517̲   (g) 0·368̲   (h) 0·42̲8   (i) 7̲·89   (j) 5·2̲38

(k) 28̲·6   (l) 1̲5·37   (m) 17·82̲6   (n) 26·108̲   (o) 3̲6·029

2

2 Dan thinks that 0·7 is larger than 0·08.
Is he correct?
Explain your answer.

3 Which number is the larger:

$\boxed{0\cdot1}$ or $\boxed{0\cdot01}$?

Give a reason for your answer.

4 Which number is the largest:

$\boxed{0\cdot09}$ or $\boxed{0\cdot5}$ or $\boxed{0\cdot008}$?

5 The number 39·4 can be written as $30 + 9 + \frac{4}{10}$.
Write the number 84·73 in this way.

6 $\boxed{A}\ \boxed{B}\ .\ \boxed{C}\ \boxed{D}\ \boxed{E}$

(a) Tom has 5 cards: $\boxed{7}\ \boxed{3}\ \boxed{8}\ \boxed{4}\ \boxed{6}$

Tom must place the cards on spaces $\boxed{A}\ \boxed{B}\ \boxed{C}\ \boxed{D}\ \boxed{E}$ above to make the *largest* number possible. Write down the number he makes.

(b) Tom must now place the cards on spaces $\boxed{A}\ \boxed{B}\ \boxed{C}\ \boxed{D}\ \boxed{E}$ above to make the *smallest* number possible. Write down the number he makes.

(c) Sasha has 6 cards: $\boxed{4}\ \boxed{9}\ \boxed{1}\ \boxed{6}\ \boxed{5}\ \boxed{8}$

Sasha must place 5 of her cards on spaces $\boxed{A}\ \boxed{B}\ \boxed{C}\ \boxed{D}\ \boxed{E}$ above to make the *largest* number possible. Write down the number she makes.

(d) Sasha must now place 5 of her cards on spaces $\boxed{A}\ \boxed{B}\ \boxed{C}\ \boxed{D}\ \boxed{E}$ above to make the *smallest* number possible. Write down the number she makes.

Rounding numbers

M1.3

Round to the nearest 10

1 64 **2** 47 **3** 307 **4** 289 **5** 1324 **6** 6149

Round to the nearest 100

7 230   **8** 610   **9** 673   **10** 747   **11** 896

12 1350   **13** 2715   **14** 4582   **15** 2193   **16** 5417

Copy the sentences in questions **17** to **22**, writing the number to the nearest 1000.

17 The van costs £16 580

18 Jack flew 2813 miles to New York

19 Hale Brewery sold 16 293 bottles of beer last week.

20 The 'Harry Potter' book has 678 pages.

21 Ramesh won £38 625 last month.

22 482 301 people live in Bristol.

Round to the nearest whole number.

23 7·8   **24** 3·2   **25** 2·5   **26** 12·3   **27** 8·34

Round to the nearest pound.

28 £3·17   **29** £2·91   **30** £7·36   **31** £12·81   **32** £24·50

Round to the nearest kilogram.

33 7·2 kg   **34** 3·5 kg   **35** 14·3 kg   **36** 8·72 kg   **37** 23·26 kg

A headteacher says there are 800 students in Sand High School. This number is rounded off to the nearest 100.

Which of the numbers below could be the exact number of students in Sand High School?

820   701   791   752   861   850   831   750

Answer

820   791   752   831   750

are all possible answers.

Round off each number below to:

(a) the nearest 10   (b) the nearest 100   (c) to the nearest 1000

1 2317   **2** 4628   **3** 6278   **4** 4191

5 997   **6** 3283   **7** 8169   **8** 17451

9 A golf club has 600 members. This number is rounded off to the nearest 100.

Which of the numbers below could be the exact number of members of the golf club?

550   610   650   619   583   529   665

10 The table below shows the population (in millions) of some countries:

Population (millions)	
China	1131
India	871
USA	251
Brazil	153
Pakistan	126
Japan	124
Mexico	90

Write down each country and round off the number to the nearest 100.

11 The home of Chelsea football club is Stamford Bridge. One Saturday around 50 000 people watch a game at Stamford Bridge. This number is rounded off to the nearest 1000.

Which of the numbers below could be the exact number of people at Stamford Bridge?

50 351   50 564   49 681   50 018   49 394   50 500   49 499   49 899

12 Lauren has sent 1800 texts in the last month.

This number has been rounded off to the nearest 100.

What is the least number of texts that Lauren may have sent last month?

5

M1.5

Copy and complete.

1   376
     − 128

2   829
     − 463

3   3718
     + 587

4   581
     − 273

5   8172
     + 3218

6   2160
     − 1317

7   5863
     − 2194

8   86148
     + 31683

9

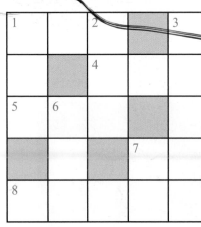

Copy and complete the crossnumber using the clues.

Clues across	Clues down
1 737 + 187	**1** 382 + 576
4 471 − 228	**2** 561 − 137
5 1274 − 390	**3** 13 872 + 9417
7 387 − 329	**6** 417 + 417
8 27 383 + 36 876	**7** 826 − 771

10 Find the sum of 318 and 187

11 Find the sum of the four numbers
    49, 386, 172 and 563

> The *sum* of 51 and 38 means 51 + 38
> The difference of 51 and 38 means 51 − 38

12 Find the difference between 268 and 189.

13 Find the difference between 637 and 476.

14 What is the total of the three numbers 58, 124 and 186?

M1.6

1 Sparrow Electrical Goods sell the following:

Washing machine	£389
Fridge	£225
Dishwasher	£412
Microwave	£87
Freezer	£149

(a) What is the total cost of all 5 items?

(b) How much more does the Dishwasher cost than the Freezer?

(c) What is the difference in the prices of the Fridge and the Microwave?

2 Joe has £383. He needs to save £760 to buy a laptop. How much more money does he need?

3 Tina wants to raise £300 for a charity. She collects the following money from a sponsored run:

£22, £39, £21, £6, £18, £54, £31, £28, £42.

How much more money does she have to collect to meet her target?

Copy and complete the squares below:

4

+	38	87		66
109	147			
326			571	
			229	
				512

5

+		148	516	
384	827			
			400	
87				331
226				

6 A rock concert was supposed to be watched by 80 000 people maximum. One night the Police estimate that 112 350 people have managed to watch the concert. How many *extra* people were able to see the concert that night?

7 The table below shows how many students were absent from school one week.

Year	Monday	Tuesday	Wednesday	Thursday	Friday
7	11	12	7	13	16
8	3	7	6	4	9
9	10	13	13	7	11
10	17	13	14	19	21
11	16	14	21	22	18

(a) How many students in total were absent on Monday?

(b) How many students in total were absent on Wednesday?

(c) What is the difference in the total number of students absent on Wednesday compared to Monday?

(d) What is the difference in the total number of students absent on Friday compared to Tuesday?

8

Cakes

40p each

Buy 2 and

get 1 free

Tanya buys some cakes at a school fair. She hands over £4. How many cakes does Tanya get?

9 Last year Sid travelled 13 912 miles in total in his car. At the start of this year Sid's car showed 52 487 miles

on the milometer. At the end of this year it shows 68 279 miles. How many more miles did Sid travel in his car during this year compared to last year?

Multiplying and dividing whole numbers

Multiplying and dividing by 10, 100 and 1000

$586 \times 100 = 58\,600$ $\times 100$ digits move 2 places to the left

$79\,000 \div 100 = 790$ $\div 100$ digits move 2 places to the right

M1.7

Write the answers only.

1 31×1000 **2** $81\,700 \div 10$ **3** $527\,000 \div 100$

4 $31\,600 \times 10$ **5** 530×100 **6** 70×30

7 80×50 **8** 9×400 **9** 300×90

10 800×700 **11** $180 \div 90$ **12** $400 \div 50$

13 $7200 \div 900$ **14** $32\,000 \div 4000$ **15** $4200 \div 70$

16 400×600 **17** $21\,000 \div 700$ **18** $32\,000 \div 800$

19 Ned earns £100 each week. How much money does he earn in one year (52 weeks)?

20 Molly does a sponsored swim. Her total sponsorship money is £13 for each length of the swimming pool. How much money does Molly get if she swims 100 lengths?

21 A factory makes 110 000 sweets during one week. The sweets are packed equally into 1000 boxes. How many sweets are there in each box?

22 A school buys 30 boxes of drawing pins. Each box contains 200 drawing pins. How many drawing pins are there in total?

Copy and complete.

23 ☐ × 100 = 46 000   **24** ☐ ÷ 1000 = 49   **25** 710 × ☐ = 71 000

26 ☐ × 30 = 150   **27** ☐ × 800 = 56 000   **28** ☐ ÷ 30 = 50

29 ☐ ÷ 500 = 70   **30** 25 000 ÷ ☐ = 500   **31** 7000 × ☐ = 210 000

32 60 people share a Lottery win of £300 000. How much does each person get?

33 20 people each save £400.
Another 30 people each save £600.
They need to save £25 000 in total.
Have they been successful? Give reasons for your answer.

Copy and complete questions **34** to **37**.

34 316 → ×10 → ☐ → ×100 → ☐ → ÷10 → ☐ → ÷100 → ☐

35 ☐ → ×100 → 864 000 → ÷100 → ☐ → ÷10 → ☐

36 20 → ×40 → ☐ → ×30 → ☐ → ÷600 → ☐ → ÷10 → ☐

37 300 → ÷10 → ☐ → ×50 → ☐ → ×30 → ☐ → ÷90 → ☐

9

1   Copy and complete the grids below. Time yourself on the first grid. Try to improve your time on the second grid.

×	7	2	10	8	6	3	11	9	4	5
7	49									
2										
10										
8										
6				48						
3						9				
11										
9										
4										
5										

×	2	9	6	3	5	11	0	8	7	4
2										
9										
6										
3										
5										
11										
0										
8										
7										
4										

Work out

2
$$\begin{array}{r} 416 \\ \times\quad 4 \\ \hline \end{array}$$

3
$$\begin{array}{r} 513 \\ \times\quad 3 \\ \hline \end{array}$$

4
$$\begin{array}{r} 216 \\ \times\quad 6 \\ \hline \end{array}$$

5
$$\begin{array}{r} 436 \\ \times\quad 8 \\ \hline \end{array}$$

6   208×5

7   9×246

8   6×3152

9   6384×7

10   One night 73 people watch a film at the cinema. They each pay £7.
How much money do they all pay in total?

11   A fast-food restaurant sold 326 'special meals' at £4 each. How much money did they get for all 326 'special meals'?

12   Ralph likes collecting fossils. Each month he collects 8 new fossils. How many fossils will Ralph collect in 3 years?

13   Sandra and her 5 friends are going to Spain on holiday. They each have to pay £418. One month before their holiday they are each told that they must pay an extra £47 each.
How much do Sandra and her friends have to pay in total?

14   Work out $39 \times 6 \times 7$

Long multiplication

Using grids
38 × 26

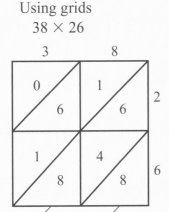

Traditional method

$$38 \times 26$$

add
along
the
diagonals

$$
\begin{array}{r}
38 \\
\times\ 26 \\
\hline
228 \ (38 \times 6) \\
760 \ (38 \times 20) \\
\hline
988 \\
\end{array}
$$

The answer is 988

M1.9

Work out

1 23 × 16   **2** 16 × 35   **3** 93 × 27   **4** 68 × 46

5 76 × 52   **6** 59 × 34   **7** 64 × 28   **8** 417 × 76

9 398 × 59   **10** 68 × 409   **11** 623 × 67   **12** 518 × 43

13 28 × 338   **14** 81 × 716   **15** 543 × 728

16 64 people each pay £724 to go on a holiday in the USA. How much do the 64 people pay in total?

17 On average, a person in the UK laughs 15 times each day. How many times will a person laugh in one year (52 weeks)?

18 A person sheds 18 kg of skin in his or her lifetime. How much skin would be shed by 500 people over their lifetimes?

19 In 2014, single men in the UK spent an average of £186 on a first date. How much in total would 73 single men have spent on their first dates?

20

TV	£527
DVD player	£218

How much will 34 televisions and 19 DVD players cost in total?

11

21 Gianna is planning a theatre trip.
The costs are given below:

Coach (53 seats)	£410 per coach
Food	£13 per person
Theatre ticket	£34 per person
Extra costs	£45

A ticket for the theatre trip costs £58.
Eighty-seven people buy a ticket. Is this enough
money for Gianna to pay for the coaches, food,
theatre tickets and extra costs? Show all your
working out to explain your answer.

22 Armaan throws 9 darts. He scores
19 three times, a double 17, a treble 18,
a treble 16 as well as scores of
11, 20 and 5.
How far short is he of a total
score of 501?

Short division

(a) $625 \div 5$

$$5 \overline{)6^12^25}$$
$$1\,2\,5$$

(b) $936 \div 4$

$$4 \overline{)9^13^16}$$
$$2\,3\,4$$

(c) $3073 \div 7$

$$7 \overline{)3^30^27^63}$$
$$0\,4\,3\,9$$

M1.10

Copy and complete the following division problems.

1 $6 \div 3 = ?$ **2** $8 \div 4 = ?$ **3** $48 \div 8 = ?$ **4** $88 \div 11 = ?$

5 $20 \div 5 = ?$ **6** $99 \div 11 = ?$ **7** $50 \div 5 = ?$ **8** $96 \div 12 = ?$

9 $24 \div 6 = ?$ **10** $14 \div 7 = ?$ **11** $54 \div 6 = ?$ **12** $100 \div 10 = ?$

13 $28 \div 4 = ?$ **14** $15 \div 3 = ?$ **15** $0 \div 7 = ?$ **16** $5\frac{1}{2} \div 5\frac{1}{2} = ?$

Work out

17	$3\overline{)729}$	**18**	$5\overline{)725}$	**19**	$4\overline{)1028}$	**20**	$8\overline{)1856}$
21	$6\overline{)1296}$	**22**	$7\overline{)343}$	**23**	$9\overline{)6561}$	**24**	$6\overline{)2796}$
25	$8\overline{)2056}$	**26**	$5\overline{)1025}$	**27**	$6\overline{)7776}$	**28**	$7\overline{)5082}$
29	$3050 \div 10$	**30**	$1387 \div 1$	**31**	$38\,199 \div 7$	**32**	$14\,032 \div 8$
33	$31\,386 \div 6$	**34**	$3490 \div 5$	**35**	$28\,926 \div 9$	**36**	$15\,638 \div 7$

(a)   How many teams of 5 can you make from 113 people?

Work out $113 \div 5$ $5\overline{)1^11^13}$ remainder 3 $\begin{smallmatrix}0\ 2\ 2\end{smallmatrix}$

Here we round *down*. You can make 22 teams and there will be 3 people left over.

(b)   An egg box holds 6 eggs. How many boxes do you need for 231 eggs?

Work out $231 \div 6$ $6\overline{)23^51}$ remainder 3 $\begin{smallmatrix}3\ 8\end{smallmatrix}$

Here we round *up* because you must use complete boxes. You need 39 boxes altogether.

M1.11

1	$8\overline{)514}$	**2**	$9\overline{)375}$	**3**	$5\overline{)2642}$	**4**	$2\overline{)7141}$
5	$1079 \div 7$	**6**	$2132 \div 5$	**7**	$4014 \div 8$	**8**	$235 \div 6$

9   There are 27 children in a class. How many teams of 4 can be made?

10   Tickets cost £7 each. I have £100. How many tickets can I buy?

11   Tins of spaghetti are packed 8 to a box. How many boxes are needed for 943 tins?

12   Five people can travel in one car. 83 people are to be transported. How many cars are needed?

13   A tennis coach has 52 tennis balls. A box holds 4 tennis balls. How many boxes does the tennis coach have?

Long division

You can divide large numbers in the same way as you do short division.

$962 \div 26$

Write out the 26 times table by adding on 26 each time.

The most you will need are 9 numbers.

Write out the division leaving a space between each digit in 962.

26
52
78
104
130
156
182
208
234

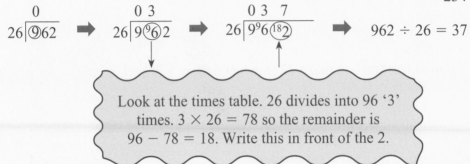

Look at the times table. 26 divides into 96 '3' times. $3 \times 26 = 78$ so the remainder is $96 - 78 = 18$. Write this in front of the 2.

M1.12

1 $504 \div 14$

2 $513 \div 19$

3 $400 \div 16$

4 $552 \div 24$

5 $559 \div 13$

6 $408 \div 17$

7 $704 \div 22$

8 $625 \div 25$

9 $798 \div 21$

10 $812 \div 28$

11 $884 \div 34$

12 $851 \div 37$

13 $630 \div 35$

14 $972 \div 27$

15 $702 \div 39$

16 Find the age of each person in years.

Elaine   384 months

Carl   420 months

Maisy   132 months

Dan   108 months

17 840 packets of crisps are packed into 24 boxes. How many packets of crisps are there in each box?

1. There are 380 children in a school. How many classes of 31 children can be made? How many children would be left over?

2. Tom has to put 1000 bottles into crates. One crate will take 24 bottles. How many crates will Tom need?

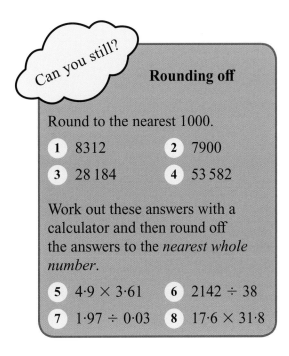

Can you still?

Rounding off

Round to the nearest 1000.

1. 8312   2. 7900

3. 28 184   4. 53 582

Work out these answers with a calculator and then round off the answers to the *nearest whole number*.

5. $4 \cdot 9 \times 3 \cdot 61$ 6. $2142 \div 38$

7. $1 \cdot 97 \div 0 \cdot 03$ 8. $17 \cdot 6 \times 31 \cdot 8$

3. How many 27p stamps can I buy with a £20 note?

4. A party of 17 people are going on holiday to Greece. The total holiday bill is £7191. How much does each person have to pay?

5. In a warehouse Isaac can pack 15 boxes in one hour. Lexa can pack 20 boxes in one hour. How much quicker is it for Lexa to pack 90 boxes than for Isaac?

6. Copy and complete the crossnumber using the clues.

Clues across	Clues down
1 874 ÷ 23	**1** 5372 ÷ 17
2 9504 ÷ 18	**2** 7436 ÷ 13
4 1598 ÷ 34	**3** 9493 ÷ 11
5 3536 ÷ 52	**6** 9828 ÷ 12
7 3888 ÷ 16	**8** 5978 ÷ 14
9 1152 ÷ 64	**10** 6540 ÷ 15
10 2058 ÷ 42	**11** 2871 ÷ 87
11 4836 ÷ 13	**12** 6318 ÷ 26
13 2117 ÷ 29	**13** 4788 ÷ 63
14 8764 ÷ 14	
15 3818 ÷ 46	

M1.14

1

$$-10\ -9\ -8\ -7\ -6\ -5\ -4\ -3\ -2\ -1\ \ 0\ \ 1\ \ 2\ \ 3\ \ 4\ \ 5\ \ 6\ \ 7\ \ 8\ \ 9\ \ 10$$

A   B   C   D   E   F

The *difference* in temperature between C and D is 3°C. Give the difference in temperature between:

(a) E and F   (b) B and C   (c) D and E

(d) A and B   (e) A and C   (f) B and E

In questions **2** to **4** put the numbers in order, smallest first:

2

7   −3
0   9
−1   −2

3

1   −5
−8   −4
4   −10

4

−3   2
6   0
−5   −6

5 The temperature in Birmingham at midday is 15° C.
During the night it falls by 16°C.
What is the new temperature?

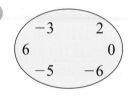

6 Copy and complete the table below by moving up or down the thermometer to find the new temperature.

Temperature °C	Change °C	New temperature °C
4	falls by 5	
1	falls by 6	
−3	rises by 2	
−6	falls by 3	
−4	rises by 7	
−9	rises by 6	
5	rises by 3	
0	falls by 7	
−2	falls by 3	
6	falls by 10	

7 One night the temperature in Plymouth is 1°C and the temperature in Newcastle is −3°C. How much colder is Newcastle than Plymouth?

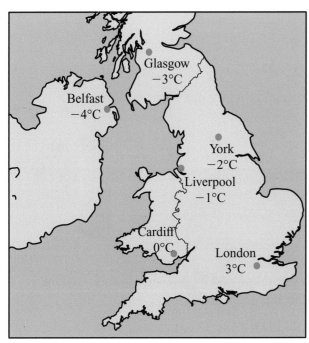

8 Which city has the highest temperature?

9 Which city has the lowest temperature?

10 What is the difference in temperature between York and London?

11 What is the difference in temperature between Belfast and Liverpool?

12 During the day, the temperature in Glasgow rises by 10°C. What is the new temperature?

13 During the day, the temperature in Liverpool rises by 15°C and the temperature in Belfast rises by 17°C. Which city now has the higher temperature, Liverpool or Belfast?

14 Work out

(a) $3 - 6$ (b) $-5 - 1$ (c) $-5 + 1$ (d) $-3 + 3$

(e) $-8 + 5$ (f) $3 - 9$ (g) $2 - 10$ (h) $-4 - 5$

(i) $-8 + 6$ (j) $-10 + 6$ (k) $-7 - 2$ (l) $-6 + 5$

15 Copy and complete the table below:–

Old temperature °C	Change °C	New temperature °C
−2	rises by 7	
	rises by 3	2
	falls by 6	−4
−8	falls by 2	
	rises by 7	0
−6		−2
−12	rises by 8	
	rises by 3	−1
	falls by 5	−7
−10		−14

Key Facts

Two signs together

$8 - -5$ can be read as '8 take away negative 5'. This is sometimes written as $8 - (-5)$.

It is possible to replace two signs next to each other by one sign as follows:

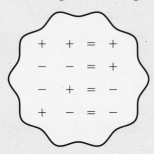

```
+   +  =  +
-   -  =  +
-   +  =  -
+   -  =  -
```

'same signs: +'

'different signs: −'

When two signs next to each other have been replaced by one sign in this way, the calculation is completed using the number line as before.

Examples

(a) $-6 + -2$
$= -6 - 2$
$= -8$

(b) $3 - -4$
$= 3 + 4$
$= 7$

(c) $-4 + -2$
$= -4 - 2$
$= -6$

M1.15

1 Work out

(a) $3 + -1$ (b) $8 - -5$ (c) $-4 - 2$ (d) $-2 + -3$

(e) $8 + -3$ (f) $4 - -2$ (g) $-3 + -4$ (h) $-2 - -1$

(i) $7 - 10$ (j) $4 + -6$ (k) $-6 - 3$ (l) $-8 - -4$

(m) $7 - -1$ (n) $5 - -4$ (o) $-1 + -6$ (p) $-12 + 5$

2 Cassie is overdrawn at the bank by £63. How much money will she have in the bank if she:

(a) pays in £100   (b) pays in £75   (c) pays in £142?

3 Lola has £12 in her bank account. The bank will allow her to go up to £50 overdrawn. She wants to buy a £22 scarf for her dog and a £39 jumper for herself. Can she use her bankcard to buy the scarf and jumper? Give reasons for your answer.

4 Todd has £36 in his bank account. His grandmother has £550 in her bank account.
Todd buys some clothes for £148 with his bank card. His grandmother then pays off the amount he is overdrawn using her bank card.
How much money has his grandmother now got in her bank account?

5 Work out

(a) $-4 + 3$ (b) $-9 - 1$ (c) $4 - -7$ (d) $-8 - -2$

(e) $6 + -4$ (f) $-3 + -8$ (g) $7 - 13$ (h) $-9 + 5$

(i) $-9 - 5$ (j) $-9 - -5$ (k) $-4 - -10$ (l) $-5 - 6$

(m) $3 + -10$ (n) $-6 + -2$ (o) $-3 - -4$ (p) $-8 + 4 - 3$

(q) $-7 - 2 + 10$ (r) $-5 - -1 - 6$ (s) $4 - 7 + -2$ (t) $-8 + -5 - -5$

6 Which question below gives a different answer to the other two?

A $\boxed{-6 - -4}$ B $\boxed{-6 - 4}$ C $\boxed{-3 + 1}$

Copy and complete the boxes below:

7
$-6 + 4 = -2$
$\square - 2 = -3$
$-8 - -7 = \square$
$-6 + 1 = \square$
$\square - -2 = 7$

8
$7 + -3 = \square$
$\square + -4 = -2$
$\square - 7 = -8$
$6 - \square = -1$
$-3 + \square = 1 - 10$

Can you still?

Adding and subtracting

Work out

1 $6834 - 458$ **2** $6134 - 816$

Copy and fill in the missing numbers below.

3 $371 + \square = 518$ **4** $523 + \square = 741$

5 $681 - \square = 251$ **6** $\square + 334 = 620$

7 $1369 - \square = 817$ **8** $\square - 265 = 306$

9 Check your answers to questions **5** to **8** by *using a calculator*.
Make sure your teacher shows you the correct button for negative numbers.

19

Key Facts

> When a positive number is multiplied by a negative number the answer is negative.

> When two negative numbers are multiplied together the answer is positive.

> For division, the rules are the same as for multiplication.

Examples

$-3 \times (-7) = 21$ $5 \times (-3) = -15$ $-12 \div 3 = -4$

$20 \div (-2) = -10$ $-40 \div (-20) = 2$ $-1 \times (-2) \times (-3) = -6$

M1.16

Work out

1 (a) 3×-5 (b) 6×-3 (c) -4×-6 (d) -3×-7

2 (a) -8×-4 (b) -7×6 (c) -2×-6 (d) 4×-9

3 (a) 5×-6 (b) 3×-1 (c) -9×-5 (d) -4×-4

4 (a) $-10 \div 5$ (b) $-28 \div 4$ (c) $-25 \div -5$ (d) $30 \div -6$

5 (a) $-60 \div -10$ (b) $-42 \div 7$ (c) $21 \div -7$ (d) $-18 \div -3$

6 (a) $48 \div -8$ (b) $-24 \div -4$ (c) $-35 \div -7$ (d) $-49 \div 7$

Copy and complete the squares below:

7

×	−3	−6	8	−2
7	−21			
−5				
−4				
9				

8

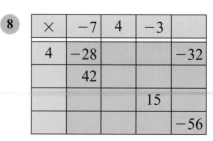

×	−7	4	−3	
4	−28			−32
	42			
			15	
				−56

Work out

9 (a) $45 \div -9$ (b) $-120 \div -10$ (c) $-81 \div -9$ (d) $-63 \div 7$

10 (a) 12×-13 (b) -24×-16 (c) -17×14 (d) -23×-34

11 (a) -2×-2 (b) $-2 \times -2 \times -2$ (c) $-2 \times -2 \times -2 \times -2$

12 (a) $-3 \times -3 \times -3$ (b) $-4 \times 2 \times -4$ (c) $-10 \times -1 \times 3 \times -2$

13 **Check** your answers to questions 7 and 8 by *using a calculator*. Make
   sure your teacher shows you the correct button to use for negative numbers.

M1.17

Each empty square contains either a number or an operation ($+$, $-$, $\times$, $\div$). Copy
each square and fill in the missing details. The arrows are equals signs.

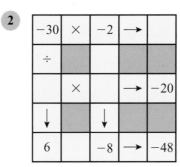
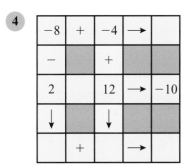
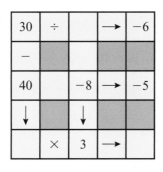

21

Key Facts

Everyone has agreed to work out problems in the same order so that there is only one correct answer.

The table below shows the order.

Brackets	( )	do first	'B'
O			'O'
Division	÷	do this pair next	'D'
Multiplication	×		'M'
Addition	+	do this pair next	'A'
Subtraction	−		'S'

Remember the word
'BODMAS'
(The 'O' is just used
to make a word)

(a) $14 - 6 \div 2$
  $= 14 - 3$
  $= 11$

(b) $(14 - 6) \div 2$
  $= 8 \div 2$
  $= 4$

(c) $14 \times 2 + 3 \times 5$
  $= 28 + 15$
  $= 43$

M1.18

Work out the following: Show every step in your working.

1. $5 + 3 \times 2$
2. $7 + 4 \times 4$
3. $28 \div 7 + 6$
4. $20 \div 4 + 5$
5. $(5 + 3) \times 3$
6. $(6 + 2) \times 5$
7. $36 \div (5 + 1)$
8. $40 \div (4 + 4)$
9. $24 \div 4 + 8$
10. $42 \div 7 + 3$
11. $8 \times (3 + 4)$
12. $3 \times 10 + 4$
13. $40 \div (7 + 3)$
14. $3 \times 8 + 9$
15. $5 \times (8 + 3)$
16. $6 + 2 \times 4 + 3$
17. $(6 + 2) \times (4 + 3)$
18. $(6 + 2) \times 4 + 3$
19. $(7 + 13) \div 5 + 4$
20. $10 + 24 \div (6 + 2)$
21. $(8 + 7) \div (2 + 1)$
22. $35 - 3 \times 5$
23. $8 + 9 + 10 \div 2$
24. $(3 + 8 + 9) \div 4$
25. $5 + 3 \times 4 \div 2$
26. $5 + 21 \div 3 + 6$
27. $8 + 4 \times 7 + 2$

Work out the following, showing every step in your working.

1 $8 + 2 \times 4$

2 $12 - 2 \times 3$

3 $(8 - 3) \times 4$

4 $15 \div 3 - 1$

5 $17 + 9 \div 3$

6 $4 + 39 \div 13$

7 $15 + 4 \times 10$

8 $50 - 11 \times 3$

9 $48 \div (20 - 8)$

10 $(14 + 3) \times 2$

11 $7 + 7 \times 7$

12 $32 - 5 - 11$

13 $9 + 3 \times 3 - 4$

14 $16 - (8 \times 1) + 3$

15 $3 + 15 \div (9 - 6)$

16 $(6 \times 5) - (12 \div 3)$

17 $100 - (88 \div 4)$

18 $(100 + 3) - (104 - 101)$

19 $8 + 32 \div 4 - 5$

20 $40 \div 8 - 24 \div 8$

21 $3 \times (4 \times 5 - 1)$

22 Which calculations below give the same answer?

A $8 + 2 \times 4$

B $(8 + 2) \times 4$

C $\dfrac{8 + 2}{4 - 2}$

D $2 + (8 - 4) - 1$

E $\dfrac{8 + 4}{4 + 2}$

F $8 - 6 \div 2$

Copy each question and write brackets so that each calculation gives the correct answer.

23 $3 + 2 \times 5 = 25$

24 $7 + 4 \times 4 = 44$

25 $5 \times 2 + 3 = 25$

26 $8 + 3 \times 6 = 26$

27 $5 \times 9 - 4 = 25$

28 $6 \times 15 - 6 = 54$

29 $40 - 25 \times 3 = 45$

30 $63 - 7 \div 8 = 7$

31 $42 \div 6 + 1 = 6$

32 $18 - 12 \div 12 \div 4 = 2$

33 $16 + 14 \div 2 = 15$

34 $7 + 25 \div 4 = 8$

35 $7 + 3 \times 8 - 5 = 30$

36 $13 + 2 \times 4 = 60$

37 $3 + 8 + 19 \div 3 = 10$

38 $5 + 6 \times 10 - 4 = 66$

39 Use all the cards below once only to make the largest number possible.

Key Facts

$3 \times 3 = 9$ We write this as 3^2 (3 squared)

9 is a *square number*

The square root of a number n is the number which is multiplied by itself to give that number n.

The square root of 36 is **6** because $6 \times 6 = 36$

The symbol for square root is $\sqrt{}$ so $\sqrt{36} = 6$

$\sqrt{49} = 7$ because $7 \times 7 = 49$

A calculator has a button for finding square roots $\boxed{\sqrt{}}$ or $\boxed{\sqrt{x}}$. Use this button with your teacher to make sure you know how to use it correctly.

M1.20

1 $1(1 \times 1)$ and $4(2 \times 2)$ are the first two square numbers. Write down the first 12 square numbers.

Work out

2 $10^2 + 7^2$

3 $8^2 - 5^2$

4 $8^2 - 6^2$

5 $7^2 + 4^2$

6 $3^2 + 5^2$

7 $(7 - 3)^2$

8 $10^2 - 4^2$

9 $(20 - 11)^2$

10 $1^2 + 2^2 + 3^2 + 4^2$

11   What is the length of one side of this square frame if the area is 100 cm²?

12   Write down the square root of 64.

13   What is the length of one side of a square if the area is 49 cm²?

14 Work out

(a) $\sqrt{1}$ (b) $\sqrt{25}$ (c) $\sqrt{81} + \sqrt{49}$ (d) $\sqrt{(47 - 11)}$

You may **use a calculator** for the rest of the questions.

15 Work out

(a) 17^2 (b) 28^2 (c) 114^2 (d) 0.4^2 (e) 3.8^2 (f) 0.1^2

16 Work out

(a) $\sqrt{289}$ (b) $\sqrt{576}$ (c) $\sqrt{2500}$ (d) $\sqrt{1681}$ (e) $\sqrt{8.41}$ (f) $\sqrt{0.09}$

17 Peyton says that 169 is a square number.
Carlos disagrees. Who is correct? Explain your answer.

18 The area of this chessboard
is 1024 cm².

(a) What is the length of one
side of a small square on
the chessboard?

(b) What is the perimeter of
the whole chessboard?

19 Find a pair of square numbers which give a total of:

(a) 65   (b) 10   (c) 29   (d) 73   (e) 61

Cubes and cube roots

🔑 Key Facts

$2 \times 2 \times 2 = \boxed{8}$ We write this as 2^3 (2 cubed)

$\boxed{8}$ is a *cube number*

The cube root of a number n is the number which is multiplied by itself
3 times to give that number n.

The cube root of 8 is **2** because $\mathbf{2 \times 2 \times 2 = 8}$ so $\sqrt[3]{8} = 2$

25

1 $1^3 = 1 \times 1 \times 1 = 1$
$2^3 = 2 \times 2 \times 2 = 8$
$3^3 = 3 \times 3 \times 3 = ...$
$4^3 = ... = ...$

Copy and complete this list of
cube numbers down to 10^3.

2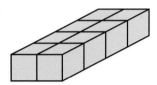

Can all these small cubes be used
to make one large cube? If yes,
draw the large cube made from
the small cubes.

3 Can all these small cubes be used
to make one large cube? If yes,
draw the large cube made from
the small cubes.

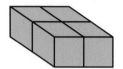

4 What number multiplied
by itself 3 times will
give an answer of 27?

Can you still?

5 Work out

(a) $\sqrt[3]{27}$ (b) $\sqrt[3]{125}$

(c) $\sqrt[3]{64}$ (d) $\sqrt[3]{216}$

A calculator has a button for
finding cube roots $\boxed{\sqrt[3]{\ }}$ or $\boxed{\sqrt[3]{x}}$.
The power button $\boxed{x^y}$ or root
button $\boxed{\sqrt[y]{x}}$ can also be used. You
may **use a calculator** for the rest
of the questions.

+/− negative numbers

1 The temperature in Oslo is −8°C.
The temperature in Athens is 23°C.
What is the difference in temperature?

2 Work out
(a) $-2 - 5$ (b) $-3 + 5$ (c) $-6 + 1$
(d) $3 - 6$ (e) $2 - -4$ (f) $2 - 4$
(g) $-4 - -2$ (h) $-6 - -1$ (i) $-4 - 3$

3 Copy and complete the boxes below:
(a) $\boxed{} - 4 = -6$ (b) $3 - \boxed{} = 5$

6 Work out

(a) 14^3 (b) 21^3 (c) $1{\cdot}5^3$ (d) $0{\cdot}2^3$

7 Evaluate (this means 'work out the value of')

(a) $\sqrt[3]{3375}$ (b) $\sqrt[3]{13\,824}$ (c) $\sqrt[3]{64\,000}$ (d) $\sqrt[3]{0{\cdot}027}$ (e) $\sqrt[3]{0{\cdot}064}$

8 Evaluate

(a) $\sqrt{(5^2 + 3^2 + 2)}$ (b) $(\sqrt{25} - \sqrt{9})^3$ (c) $(\sqrt[3]{343} - \sqrt{4})^3$

Key Facts

3×3 is written as 3^2 ← power 2

$3 \times 3 \times 3$ is written as 3^3 ← power 3

$3 \times 3 \times 3 \times 3$ is written as 3^4

the power 4 means multiply 4 lots of 3 together

Numbers written using powers are said to be in index form.

81 written in *index form* is 3^4

(because $3 \times 3 \times 3 \times 3 = 81$)

'3 to the power 5' is 3^5 which means $3 \times 3 \times 3 \times 3 \times 3$

M1.22

2^4 means $2 \times 2 \times 2 \times 2$

Copy and complete the following:

1 8^4 means _ _ _ _ _ _ _

2 6^5 means _ _ _ _ _ _ _

3 10^4 means _ _ _ _ _ _ _

4 12^2 means _ _ _ _ _ _ _

5 7^5 means _ _ _ _ _ _ _

6 3^7 means _ _ _ _ _ _ _

7 8^6 means _ _ _ _ _ _ _

8 2^8 means _ _ _ _ _ _ _

Write the following in index form

9 $4 \times 4 \times 4 \times 4 \times 4$

10 $2 \times 2 \times 2 \times 2 \times 2 \times 2$

11 $5 \times 5 \times 5$

12 $3 \times 3 \times 3 \times 3 \times 3 \times 3 \times 3 \times 3$

13 $10 \times 10 \times 10 \times 10 \times 10$

14 $6 \times 6 \times 6 \times 6$

15 The volumes of the boxes shown opposite are $125\,000 \text{ cm}^3$, $27\,000 \text{ cm}^3$ and $15\,625 \text{ cm}^3$.

(a) Find the length of one side of each box.

(b) How high will the stack of boxes be when they are placed on the floor?

16 Which is larger? 2^4 or 3^3

17 Which is larger? 4^3 or 2^6

Work out the value of the following:

18 $2^3 \times 3$ **19** $2^4 \times 3$ **20** $5^2 \times 2^2$ **21** $4^2 \times 2^3$

22 Copy and complete this table, *using a calculator* when needed.

We say	We write	We work out	Answer
3 to the power 4	3^4	$3 \times 3 \times 3 \times 3$	81
2 to the power 5		$2 \times 2 \times 2 \times 2 \times 2$	
7 to the power 3	7^3		
8 to the power 4			
	4^7		
9 to the power 5			
10 to the power 6			

23 Zoe invests £2 and each month her money doubles in size. How much money will she have after 1 year?

24 There are 5^9 people living in a country. Ten years later there are 5 times as many people living in the country. How many people now live in the country?

25 Work out

$$\sqrt{(3 \times 3 \times 5 \times 5 \times 6 \times 6)}$$

without using a calculator.

Can you still?

Number work

Work out

1 386×47 **2** $2412 \div 36$

3 2000 cartons of milk need to be packed into boxes. How many boxes are needed if one box holds 18 cartons?

4 An adult ticket costs £16 and a child ticket costs £7. Work out the total cost of 23 adult tickets and 14 child tickets.

Key Facts

A *factor* is a number which divides exactly into another number (there will be no remainder).

If 2 divides into a number exactly, that number is an *even* number (2, 4, 6, 8, …).

If 2 does *not* divide into a number exactly, that number is an *odd* number (1, 3, 5, 7, …).

A prime number has exactly two different factors (these are the numbers 1 and itself). The first four prime numbers are 2, 3, 5, 7, …

M1.23

Reminder: All the factors of 10 are ⌐1, 10⌐ ⌐2, 5⌐ so the factors of 10 are 1, 2, 5, 10.

Write down all the factors of the following numbers:

1 8 (4 factors) **2** 16 (5 factors) **3** 11 (2 factors) **4** 15 (4 factors)

5 24 (8 factors) **6** 19 **7** 35 **8** 28

9 40 **10** 23 **11** 30 **12** 42

13 17 **14** 26 **15** 50

16 Write down the numbers given in questions **1** to **15** which are *odd* numbers.

17 Write down the numbers given in questions **1** to **15** which are *even* numbers.

18 Write down the numbers given in questions **1** to **15** which are *prime* numbers (remember: this means they have 2 factors only).

19 Harry picks his National Lottery numbers by choosing the first six prime numbers. The winning numbers are drawn as below.

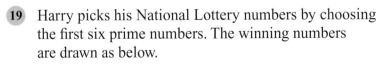

5   **42**   **1**   **13**   **40**   **6**

Does Harry win a small prize for picking 3 correct numbers?

29

20 1, 2, 4, 5, 10 and 20 are all the factors of which number?

21 1, 2, 11 and 22 are all the factors of which number?

22 Which numbers between 20 and 30 have 7 as a factor?

23 Write down the next 4 odd numbers after 49.

24 Add together all the prime numbers less than 20.

25 32 people want to do a
tug of war. All the people are
divided into teams of equal
size (at least 2 people in
a team).
Write down all the sizes
of the teams that could
be used.

26 Which numbers between 80 and 100 have 9 as a factor?

27 Hannah says that there are 3 numbers between 110 and 210 that have 25 as a factor.
Is she correct? Explain your answer.

Multiples and the Lowest Common Multiple

 # Key Facts

Multiples are the numbers in a multiplication table. 6, 12, 18, 24, 30, … are multiples of 6.

The *Lowest Common Multiple* (LCM) of two or more numbers is the smallest number which each of these numbers will divide into.

Here, for example, we find the LCM of 4 and 10.

The multiples of 4 are 4, 8, 12, 16, ⟨20⟩, 24, …

The multiples of 10 are 10, ⟨20⟩, 30, …

The *lowest* number in both lists is 20

The LCM of 4 and 10 is 20.

Copy and complete the first 10 multiples of the number in the first box:

1

2

3 30

Copy and draw a circle around the numbers which are *not* multiples of:

4 5 11 25 35 54   **5** 9 36 22 38 91   **6** 6 23 18 54 42

7 An unknown number is a multiple of 8 which is greater than 50.
70 is subtracted from this unknown number to make the smallest possible prime number.
Write down the unknown number.

8 Here are the first six multiples of 6 and 10

6:	6	12	18	24	30	36
10:	10	20	30	40	50	60

Write down the Lowest Common Multiple (LCM) of 6 and 10 (ie the lowest number which is in both lists).

9 Find the Lowest Common Multiple of each of these pairs of numbers:

(a) 3 and 10   (b) 3 and 7

(c) 5 and 9   (d) 10 and 7

(e) 3 and 6   (f) 8 and 20

(g) 12 and 15   (h) 12 and 20

(i) 6, 10 and 12

Can you still?

×/÷ negative numbers

1 Work out

(a) 2×-3 (b) 4×-5

(c) -6×-2 (d) -5×6

(e) $-8 \div 2$ (f) $15 \div -3$

2 Copy and complete the boxes below:

(a) $-3 \times \boxed{} = 12$

(b) $5 \times \boxed{} = -45$

(c) $10 \div \boxed{} = -5$

3 Work out

(a) $(-3)^2$ (b) $(-9)^2$

(c) $-1 \times -1 \times -1$

(d) $-5 \times 6 \times -2$

10 In the game of 'Fizzbuzz', people take it in turns to count up one number at a time. When a multiple of 3 is reached, the person must say 'Fizz'. When a multiple of 5 is reached, the person must say 'Buzz'. If a multiple of both 3 and 5 is reached, the person says 'Fizzbuzz'.

Write down the first 2 numbers when the person would have to say 'Fizzbuzz'.

11 Party hats are sold in packets of 10.
Balloons are sold in bags of 15.
Party poppers are sold in packs of 12.
Brianna wants to buy the same number of party hats, balloons and party poppers.

(a) What is the smallest number of each item she could buy?

(b) How many bags of balloons would she buy?

Highest Common Factor

All the factors of 21 are 1, 3, (7), 21

All the factors of 28 are 1, 2, 4, (7), 14, 28

The highest factor in both lists is 7

This is called the Highest Common Factor (HCF)

M1.25

1 Copy and complete the sentences below:

(a) All the factors of 15 are 1, 3, ☐, ☐

(b) All the factors of 18 are 1, 2, 3, ☐, ☐, ☐

(c) The Highest Common Factor of 15 and 18 is ☐.

2 Copy and complete the sentences below:

    (a) All the factors of 20 are 1, 2, ☐, ☐, ☐, ☐

    (b) All the factors of 30 are 1, 2, ☐, ☐, ☐, ☐, ☐, ☐

    (c) The HCF of 20 and 30 is ☐.

3 (a) List all the factors of 32

    (b) List all the factors of 40

    (c) Write down the HCF of 32 and 40

4 (a) List all the factors of 24

    (b) List all the factors of 36

    (c) Write down the HCF of 24 and 36

5 Find the Highest Common Factor of

    (a) 8 and 10   (b) 10 and 40   (c) 15 and 35   (d) 15 and 40

    (e) 12 and 20   (f) 16 and 40   (g) 11 and 13   (h) 16 and 48

6 Find the HCF of

    (a) 4, 6 and 12   (b) 10, 20 and 45   (c) 24, 48 and 60

Prime factors

Key Facts

Factors of a number which are also prime numbers are called prime factors.

Find the prime factors of 36.

Factor Tree

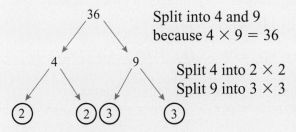

Split into 4 and 9
because $4 \times 9 = 36$

Split 4 into 2×2
Split 9 into 3×3

Stop splitting when all numbers are prime.
These are the prime factors.

We can say $36 = \underbrace{2 \times 2 \times 3 \times 3}_{\text{prime factors}}$

$2 \times 2 \times 3 \times 3$ is the *product of its prime factors*.

Dividing by prime numbers

Divide by any
prime number

```
2) 36
2) 18  ← 36 ÷ 2 = 18
3)  9  ← 18 ÷ 2 = 9
3)  3  ← 9 ÷ 3 = 3
    1  ← 3 ÷ 3 = 1
```
Stop when you get to 1

These are the prime factors.

1 Work out these products

(a) $2 \times 2 \times 5$ (b) $2 \times 3 \times 5$ (c) $3 \times 3 \times 5$

(d) $2 \times 3 \times 7$ (e) $3 \times 5 \times 11$ (f) $2 \times 2 \times 5 \times 5$

2 Copy and complete these factor trees:

(a)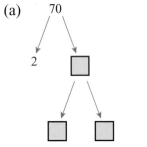

$70 = 2 \times \square \times \square$

(b)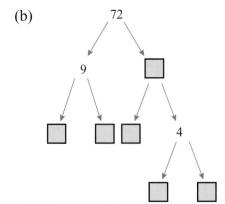

$72 = \square \times \square \times \square \times \square \times \square$

3 Copy and complete the boxes below:

(a)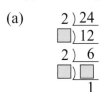

$24 = \square \times \square \times \square \times \square$

(b)
```
□ ) 84
□ ) 42
3 ) 21
□ ) □
    1
```

$84 = \square \times \square \times \square \times \square$

4 Using any method, write the following numbers as products of prime factors:

(a) 18   (b) 28   (c) 22   (d) 32   (e) 48   (f) 50

(g) 81   (h) 96   (i) 200   (j) 120   (k) 196   (l) 392

5 Copy the numbers below and put a circle round all the common factors for each pair of numbers.

(a) $180 = 2 \times 2 \times 3 \times 3 \times 5$

$120 = 2 \times 2 \times 2 \times 3 \times 5$ Write down the HCF of 180 and 120.

(b) $720 = 2 \times 2 \times 2 \times 2 \times 3 \times 3 \times 5$

$600 = 2 \times 2 \times 2 \times 3 \times 5 \times 5$ Write down the HCF of 720 and 600.

(c) $3850 = 2 \times 5 \times 5 \times 7 \times 11$

$140 = 2 \times 2 \times 5 \times 7$ Write down the HCF of 3850 and 140.

Key Facts

A number written in standard form will have the form

A is a number between
1 and 10, actually $1 \leqslant A < 10$ $\longrightarrow A \times 10^n \longleftarrow$ n is an integer
(a whole number)

Change ordinary numbers into standard form

$1980 = 1.98 \times 1000 = 1.98 \times 10^3$ $5\,300\,000 = 5.3 \times 1\,000\,000 = 5.3 \times 10^6$

Numbers between 0 and 1

Quick method

$0.0082 = 8.2 \times 10^{-3}$ ﹨the decimal point moves to the right 3 places from A to B.
  ↑ ↑
  A B

---

1 Copy each statement below and fill in the empty boxes.

(a) $70\,000 = 7 \times 10^{\square}$ (b) $64\,000 = 6.4 \times 10^{\square}$ (c) $3500 = 3.5 \times 10^{\square}$

(d) $984\,000 = 9.84 \times 10^{\square}$ (e) $0.04 = 4 \times 10^{\square}$ (f) $0.036 = 3.6 \times 10^{\square}$

(g) $0.000\,87 = 8.7 \times 10^{\square}$ (h) $590\,000 = 5.9 \times 10^{\square}$ (i) $0.0093 = 9.3 \times 10^{\square}$

2 The average distance of the moon
   from Earth is 384 000 km. Write
   this number in standard form.

3 150 000 tonnes of tea are
   consumed by people in the UK
   each year. Write this number
   in standard form.

4 Write the numbers below in standard form.

(a) 800 000   (b) 700   (c) 3900   (d) 48 200

(e) 79 000   (f) 0·0092   (g) 0·68   (h) 0·000 016

(i) 0·683   (j) 54 000 000   (k) 0·0087   (l) 0·0596

5 Angling is the most popular participant sport in Britain. There are 3 500 000 anglers in Britain. Write this number in standard form.

6 The hairs on the knee of the common flea are of length 0·000 007 m. Write this in standard form.

7 Write down which numbers below are *not* written in standard form.

(a) $7·1 \times 10^{-2}$ (b) $0·32 \times 10^{8}$ (c) 48×10^{3}

(d) 59×10^{-3} (e) $5·6 \times 10^{-3}$ (f) $0·02 \times 10^{7}$

8 Write each number below as an ordinary number.

(a) 6×10^{3} (b) $5·9 \times 10^{2}$

(c) $4·7 \times 10^{4}$ (d) 3×10^{-3}

(e) $7·15 \times 10^{3}$ (f) $2·6 \times 10^{-4}$

(g) $3·5 \times 10^{-2}$ (h) $5·68 \times 10^{-1}$

(i) $1·93 \times 10^{5}$ (j) $8·46 \times 10^{-4}$

9 Write the numbers below in standard form.

(a) 0·009   (b) 516

(c) 52 800   (d) 614 000

(e) 0·076   (f) 0·0008

(g) 0·000 07   (h) 5280

(i) 16 700 000   (j) 0·012

Can you still?

Powers and roots

Do not use a calculator

1 Write down true or false for each statement below:

(a) $4^{2} > 2^{3}$ (b) $2^{4} < 6^{2}$

(c) $4^{3} = 8^{2}$ (d) $3^{3} - 10 > 4^{2}$

2 Work out

(a) $2^{5} \times 3^{2}$ (b) 4×5^{2}

(c) $2^{2} \times 4 \times 5$ (d) $3^{2} \times 2^{3}$

3 Find the value of

(a) $\sqrt{(13^{2} - 12^{2})}$ (b) $\sqrt[3]{64}$

(c) $\sqrt[3]{(10^{2} + 5^{2})}$ (d) $\sqrt[3]{(2^{2} + 2^{2})}$

36

Key Facts

$7{\cdot}2 \times 10^{14}$ is typed in as $\boxed{7}\,\boxed{\cdot}\,\boxed{2}\,\boxed{\times 10^x}\,\boxed{1}\,\boxed{4}$

Example

Work out $(5{\cdot}1 \times 10^{12}) \times (2{\cdot}8 \times 10^{-38})$ leaving the answer in standard form.

$\boxed{5}\,\boxed{\cdot}\,\boxed{1}\,\boxed{\times 10^x}\,\boxed{1}\,\boxed{2}\,\boxed{\times}\,\boxed{2}\,\boxed{\cdot}\,\boxed{8}\,\boxed{\times 10^x}\,\boxed{(-)}\,\boxed{3}\,\boxed{8}\,\boxed{=}$

The answer is $1{\cdot}428 \times 10^{-25}$

E1.2

1 Use a calculator to work out the following and write each answer in standard form.

(a) $(3 \times 10^{16}) \times (5 \times 10^{-9})$ (b) $(1{\cdot}8 \times 10^{6}) \times (2{\cdot}3 \times 10^{14})$

(c) $(5{\cdot}1 \times 10^{-8}) \div (1{\cdot}7 \times 10^{-19})$ (d) $(4{\cdot}9 \times 10^{-11}) + (2{\cdot}6 \times 10^{-10})$

(e) $(4 \times 10^{14}) \times (3 \times 10^{11})$ (f) $(1{\cdot}5 \times 10^{10}) + (3{\cdot}4 \times 10^{9})$

2 The table below shows the populations of some cities in the UK.

City	Population
Norwich	$1{\cdot}25 \times 10^{5}$
Wells	1×10^{4}
Swansea	$2{\cdot}25 \times 10^{5}$
Aberdeen	$2{\cdot}15 \times 10^{5}$
London	$7{\cdot}2 \times 10^{6}$
St. Davids	2×10^{3}
Liverpool	$4{\cdot}4 \times 10^{5}$
Chester	$1{\cdot}18 \times 10^{5}$

(a) How many more people live in Aberdeen than in Wells?

(b) Which city is the smallest?

(c) How many times larger is London than St. Davids?

(d) Write out the cities in order of size, starting with the smallest.

3 Use a calculator to work out the following and write each answer in standard form.

(a) $\dfrac{6 \times 10^{14}}{3 \times 10^3}$

(b) $(8 \times 10^{21}) - (6 \times 10^{20})$

(c) $(4{\cdot}5 \times 10^{-6}) \times (2 \times 10^{-11})$

(d) $(5{\cdot}2 \times 10^{-17}) + (2{\cdot}9 \times 10^{-18})$

(e) $\dfrac{(6 \times 10^{22}) + (5 \times 10^{21})}{2 \times 10^{14}}$

(f) $\dfrac{(5 \times 10^{-8})^2}{4 \times 10^9}$

4 The distance of the Earth from the Sun is about $1{\cdot}5 \times 10^{11}$ m.
The distance of the Earth from the Moon is about 4×10^8 m.
How many times further away from the Earth is the Sun compared to the Moon?

5 The table opposite shows earnings (in dollars) on the USA golf tour in 2013.

Player	Earnings ($)
Woods	$8{\cdot}53 \times 10^6$
Stenson	$6{\cdot}41 \times 10^6$
Kuchar	$5{\cdot}67 \times 10^6$
Hadden	$8{\cdot}92 \times 10^5$
Jackson	$7{\cdot}11 \times 10^5$
Jones	$6{\cdot}36 \times 10^4$

(a) How much more money did Woods earn than Jones?

(b) Which player earned approximately eight times more money than Jackson? Justify your answer.

(c) Work out the total earnings of the six players.

USE YOUR MATHS! – Win the Premiership

Team	Games played P	Games won W	Games drawn D	Games lost L	Goals scored for the team F	Goals scored against the team A	Points total Pts
Chelsea	31	20	8	3	70	23	68
Manchester United	30	20	5	5	72	26	65
Liverpool	31	19	7	5	61	27	64
Arsenal	32	18	10	4	58	25	64

This table shows the positions of the top four football teams in the premiership during one season.

> goal difference = 'goals for' − 'goals against'

If teams are level on points, the team with the higher goal difference is placed above the other team.
Liverpool goal difference = 61 − 27 = 34
Arsenal goal difference = 58 − 25 = 33
So Liverpool are above Arsenal.

> Points scored
> 3 points for a win
> 1 point for a draw
> 0 points for a loss

Task A

The season ends when each team has played 38 games.

Each team's final results are shown below:
Liverpool: 5 wins, 0 draws, 2 losses, 14 goals for, 8 goals against.
Manchester United: 7 wins, 0 draws, 1 loss, 18 goals for, 6 goals against.
Arsenal: 5 wins, 1 draw, 0 losses, 10 goals for, 5 goals against.
Chelsea: 5 wins, 2 draws, 0 losses, 15 goals for, 7 goals against.
Draw a final full table to show the positions of these four teams.

Task B

Draw a full table to show the positions of these four teams at the end if their final results are as shown below:

Manchester United	Arsenal	Chelsea	Liverpool
Man Utd 3v1 Sunderland	Arsenal 3v2 West Ham	Chelsea 3v2 Man City	Liverpool 2v1 Leicester
Man Utd 2v0 Spurs	Arsenal 3v0 Leicester	Chelsea 1v0 Everton	Liverpool 2v1 Southampton
Man Utd 1v1 Chelsea	Arsenal 2v1 Hull	Chelsea 1v1 Man Utd	Liverpool 0v0 Aston Villa
Man Utd 2v0 Stoke City	Arsenal 1v0 Spurs	Chelsea 4v2 Sunderland	Liverpool 1v1 West Ham
Man Utd 2v1 Aston Villa	Arsenal 1v2 Chelsea	Chelsea 2v1 Arsenal	Liverpool 4v3 Everton
Man Utd 4v0 Swansea	Arsenal 3v1 WBA	Chelsea 3v0 Hull	Liverpool 2v1 Spurs
Man Utd 2v2 Liverpool		Chelsea 2v1 Aston Villa	Liverpool 2v2 Man Utd
Man Utd 1v0 Leicester			

39

TEST YOURSELF ON UNIT 1

1. Understanding place value

What is the value of the underlined digit in each number below?

(a) 4<u>1</u>9   (b) 46<u>2</u>1   (c) 0·7<u>9</u>   (d) 12·<u>6</u>8   (e) 31·82<u>7</u>

2. Rounding off numbers

(a) Round off 3·5 to the nearest whole number.

(b) Round off 7·82 to the nearest whole number.

(c) Which numbers below give 8000 when rounded off to the nearest 1000?

8510   8390   7865   8601   7396   7950

3. Adding and subtracting whole numbers

Work out   (a) 67 + 248   (b) 263 − 146   (c) 5126 − 3811

(d) Find the difference between 824 and 578.

4. Multiplying and dividing whole numbers

Work out

(a) 70 × 80   (b) 384 × 6   (c) 984 ÷ 3   (d) 2282 ÷ 7

(e) 39 × 78   (f) 362 × 53   (g) 1608 ÷ 24   (h) 3286 ÷ 62

(i) 289 children are going on an ice-skating trip. One coach holds 48 children. How many coaches are needed for this trip?

(j) Gary sells slippers at £9 a pair and hats at £12 each. One day he sells at a market stall which costs £26 for the day. How much money will he have at the end of the day if he sells 14 pairs of slippers and 13 hats?

5. Using negative numbers

(a) The temperature in Sydney is 34°C. The temperature in Moscow is −12°C. What is the difference in the temperatures?

(b) The temperature in Moscow in part (a) rises by 9°C. What is the new temperature in Moscow?

Work out

(c) $7 - 10$ (d) $-8 + 4$ (e) $-6 - -2$ (f) $7 + -3$

(g) 8×-3 (h) $-63 \div -9$ (i) $-48 \div 6$ (j) $-8 - 4$

6. Doing calculations in the correct order

Work out

(a) $5 + 2 \times 4$ (b) $20 - (7 + 4)$

(c) $(9 + 7) \div 4$ (d) $(6 + 10) \div (10 - 2)$

(e) $12 + 8 \div 2$ (f) $(7 - 2) \times 9$

> **Remember:**
>
> 'BODMAS'

Copy the questions for parts (g) and (h) then write brackets so that each calculation gives the correct answer.

(g) $7 \times 4 + 5 = 63$ (h) $10 - 7 \times 8 + 2 = 30$

7. Using powers

(a) (i) Which of these are square numbers?

    (ii) Which of these are cube numbers?

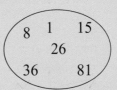

Work out

(b) 2^3 (c) $\sqrt[3]{64}$ (d) $\sqrt{16}$ (e) $4^2 - 3^2$ (f) 5^3

(g) 2^5 (h) $5 \times 5 \times 5 \times 5$ (i) 10^4 (j) $\sqrt{(3^3 - 18)}$

8. Finding factors and prime numbers

Write down all the factors of   (a) 18   (b) 32

(c) Which of these are prime numbers?

6   3   10   12   5   17   7

9. Finding HCF and LCM

(a) Write down two multiples of 7 which lie between 40 and 50.

Find the Lowest Common Multiple of each of these groups of numbers:

(b) 8 and 12   (c) 3, 4 and 8

Find the Highest Common Factor of:

(d) 21 and 35   (e) 8, 12 and 20

10. Breaking down numbers into prime factors

Write the following numbers as products of prime factors:

(a) 12   (b) 36   (c) 54   (d) 100   (e) 144

11. Using standard form

Write the numbers below in standard form.

(a) 7000   (b) 58 400   (c) 0·093   (d) 0·004

Write the numbers below as ordinary numbers.

(e) 5×10^4 (f) $2·6 \times 10^4$ (g) $4·8 \times 10^{-3}$ (h) $3·5 \times 10^2$

(i) Write the following numbers in order of size, starting with the smallest.

P	$3·9 \times 10^6$	Q	$2·4 \times 10^4$	R	$8·6 \times 10^4$
S	$1·8 \times 10^7$	T	$2·7 \times 10^6$	U	$4·3 \times 10^6$

Use a calculator to work out the following and write each answer in standard form.

(j) $(7·2 \times 10^{14}) \times (3 \times 10^{19})$ (k) $(4·6 \times 10^{18}) - (2·9 \times 10^{17})$

(l) $\dfrac{5·6 \times 10^{10}}{4 \times 10^{-4}}$ (m) $\dfrac{(3·4 \times 10^{16}) + (2·8 \times 10^{15})}{2 \times 10^{-8}}$

Mixed examination questions

1   (a)   Write down the value of 9^2

      (b)   Calculate the value of $\sqrt{2 \cdot 56}$

      (c)   Calculate the value of $3 \cdot 2^2$ (CEA)

2   Work out the **two** missing values in this shopping bill.

4 doughnuts at 60p each	£2·40
3 coffees at .... each	....
Total	£6·00

                                                                        (AQA)

3   Peter says,

"When you add any two prime numbers together you **always** get an even number as the answer."

Show, using an example, that Peter is not correct.   (CEA)

4   (a)   One afternoon the temperature was 2°C.
            By evening the temperature had fallen by 5 degrees.

            What was the temperature in the evening.

      (b)   What temperature is 4 degrees warmer than -1°C?   (OCR)

5   Find the missing numbers.

      (a) $7 \times \blacklozenge = 21$ (b) $6 + \spadesuit = 12$

      (c) $29 - \heartsuit = 11$ (d) $42 \div \clubsuit = 6$ (OCR)

6 Buses to Acton leave a bus station every 24 minutes.
Buses to Barton leave the same bus station every 20 minutes.

A bus to Acton and a bus to Barton both leave the bus station
at 9.00 am.

When will a bus to Acton and a bus to Barton next leave the bus
station at the same time? (EDEXCEL)

7 (a) Here is a list of numbers.

$$3 \qquad 7 \qquad 8 \qquad 16 \qquad 33 \qquad 42 \qquad 70$$

From this list write down a number which is

(i) a multiple of 11,

(ii) a cube,

(iii) a common factor of 21 and 35.

(b) Hannah and David are playing a game.

(i) Hannah thinks of a number.
She tells David that it is:

- less than 50
- a square
- a multiple of 2 **and** a multiple of 3.

What is the number that Hannah is thinking of?

(ii) David thinks of a number.
He tells Hannah that it is:

- an odd number
- a prime number
- a factor of 52.

What is the number that David is thinking of? (OCR)

8 (a) Write down the value of 10^0

(b) Write $6 \cdot 7 \times 10^{-5}$ as an ordinary number.

(c) Work out the value of $(3 \times 10^7) \times (9 \times 10^6)$
Give your answer in standard form. (EDEXCEL)

9 The sum of two consecutive cube numbers is 341.

Work out the two numbers. (AQA)

10 (a) Put brackets in these calculations to make them correct.

   (i) $4 + 3 \times 8 - 13 = 43$ (ii) $5 + 3^2 \times 2 \div 8 = 16$

(b) Calculate.

   (i) $18 \cdot 4^2$ (ii) $\sqrt{3136}$ (OCR)

11 The diagram shows distances between some towns.

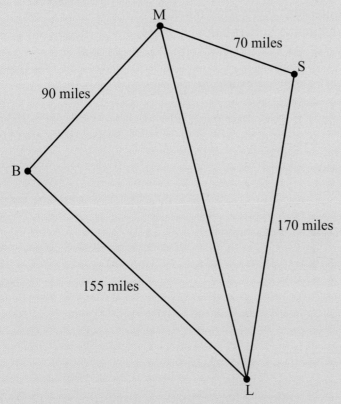

A van travels from M to S and then from S to L.

(a) Work out the total distance the van travels.

(b) The **direct** distance from M to L is three times the distance from M to S.
   How much further does the van travel by **not** going directly
   from M to L?   (AQA)

12 (a) Calculate $3^2 \times 8^3$

(b) Calculate $3 \cdot 6^2 + \sqrt{2 \cdot 89}$ (CEA)

13 (i) Two numbers multiply together to equal -21.
   They add together to equal -4.
   What are the two numbers?

(ii) Two numbers multiply together to equal 10.
   They add together to equal -7.
   What are the two numbers?   (OCR)

14 Text messages cost 11p each.

How many do you get for £15?   (AQA)

15 (a) Write 600 as a product of its prime factors.

(b) At Rumblestone Station northbound trains stop every 20 minutes
and southbound trains stop every 16 minutes.
Two trains stopped together at the station at 15 00.
Work out the next time when two trains will stop together at
this station.   (OCR)

16 Each small shaded square has an area of 4 cm².

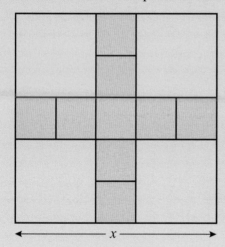

Area = 4 cm²

Work out the length x.   (AQA)

17 (a) Write down the value of $\dfrac{1}{2 \times 10^{-6}}$ in standard form.

(b) Find, in standard form, the value of $(2 \cdot 3 \times 10^{-5}) + (7 \cdot 8 \times 10^{-6})$,
giving your answer correct to two significant figures.   (WJEC)

18 Jalin has a £10 note to spend on stickers.
A packet of stickers costs 79p.

He buys as many packets of stickers as possible.

Work out how much change Jalin should get.   (EDEXCEL)

In this unit you will learn how to:

- use letters and symbols in algebra
- substitute numbers for letters
- collect and simplify terms
- use rules for indices
- multiply out brackets
- take out common factors
- solve equations with unknown on one side
- ⟨ USE YOUR MATHS! ⟩ – wages, overtime

Forming expressions

🔑 **Key Facts**

Letters can be used in place of numbers to solve problems:

Example – shoes cost £40

shoes cost £x

$a + b$ is an algebraic *expression*

$3a$ means $3 \times a$	ab means $a \times b$
a^2 means $a \times a$	$7a + 2$ means '$7 \times a$ then add 2'
$\dfrac{a}{b}$ means $a \div b$	$7(a + 2)$ means '$a + 2$ then multiply by 7'
a^3 means $a \times a \times a$	$4a^2$ means '$a \times a$ then multiply by 4'

$(4a)^2$ means '$4 \times a$ then square the answer'

A magazine costs £8 so n magazines cost £$8n$.

A newspaper costs 70p so x newspapers cost $70x$ pence.

Annie in n years old. Carol is 5 years older than Annie so Carol is $(n + 5)$ years old.

Simon has £A and shares it equally between n people so each person gets £$\left(\dfrac{A}{n}\right)$.

M2.1

1 Getting a basket in basketball scores 2 points. During one game Maurice gets n baskets. How many points does Maurice score (give the answer in terms of n)?

2 Victoria is 4 years younger than Dylan. Dylan is 7 years older than Ryan. Ryan is x years old. Write down an expression, in terms of x, for

(a) Dylan's age

(b) Victoria's age

(c) the total age of the 3 people

(d) Dylan's age in 7 years time.

3 A pen costs £5. A ruler costs £2. Write down an expression for the cost of

(a) x pens

(b) y rulers

(c) the total cost of x pens and y rulers.

4 A group of photographers each have p lenses. Write down an expression for how many lenses eleven photographers have in total.

5 Connor earns £3 for each window he cleans. He is also paid a basic wage of £20 each day as well as the money for each window. The table below shows how many windows he cleaned on each day of the week.

Mon	Tue	Wed	Thu	Fri
65	m	n	50	n

How much did Connor earn

(a) on Monday?

(b) on Tuesday?

(c) on Wednesday?

(d) for the whole week?

6 Lillian has £n. Sheila has three times as much money as Lillian. Lillian gives £8 to Pavel. Sheila gives £y to Jim.

(a) Write down expressions for exactly how much money each person now has.

(b) How much money have the 4 people got in total?

7 Colton has £x and gives £y to his grandmother. He shares the remaining money equally between his 3 children. Write down an expression for how much money each child gets.

Substitution

Find the value of each expression when $a = 3$, $b = 2$ and $c = 5$

$ab = 3 \times 2 = 6$

$5a - 1 = 5 \times 5 - 1 = 24$

$c^2 = 5 \times 5 = 25$

$4(b + 3) = 4 \times (2 + 3) = 4 \times 5 = 20$

$\dfrac{c}{b} = 5 \div 2 = 2 \cdot 5$

$3b^2 = 3 \times b \times b = 3 \times 2 \times 2 = 12$

Key Facts

Remember: BODMAS. The order of operations is Brackets then $\div \times + -$

M2.2

In questions ① to ⑳ find the value of each expression when $a = 6$
$b = 2$
$c = 4$

1 $\quad 4a$	**2** $\quad a + b + c$	**3** $\quad 2a - b$	**4** $\quad a + b - c$
5 $\quad bc$	**6** $\quad 3c - 5$	**7** $\quad ab$	**8** $\quad 7b + 2c$
9 $\quad c^2$	**10** $\quad a^2$	**11** $\quad a^2 + b^2$	**12** $\quad 4(b + c)$
13 $\quad 3(a - c)$	**14** $\quad b(a + c)$	**15** $\quad \dfrac{a - c}{b}$	**16** $\quad a(c - b)$
17 $\quad a(b + c)$	**18** $\quad b(2a - c)$	**19** $\quad \dfrac{3b + a}{c}$	**20** $\quad \dfrac{6c}{a}$

In questions ㉑ to ㉜ find the value of each expression when
$x = 3$, $y = 0$ and $z = 8$

21 $\quad 14 + 2z$	**22** $\quad 3x - 2y$	**23** $\quad x^2$	**24** $\quad y^2 + x^2$
25 $\quad xy$	**26** $\quad yz$	**27** $\quad xyz$	**28** $\quad x^2 + y^2 + z^2$
29 $\quad 3(2x + z)$	**30** $\quad x(z - y)$	**31** $\quad 4(x^2 + z^2)$	**32** $\quad \dfrac{10x}{5x}$

In questions ㉝ to ㊵ find the
value of each expression.

33 $\quad 3x + 2$ if $x = 4$	**34** $\quad 5x - 7$ if $x = 6$
35 $\quad 2a + 9$ if $a = 5$	**36** $\quad b^2 + 4$ if $b = 6$
37 $\quad 6(a - 3)$ if $a = 5$	**38** $\quad x^2 - 6$ if $x = 5$
39 $\quad 8 + 2b$ if $b = 4$	**40** $\quad 9(x^2 - 3)$ if $x = 2$

In questions **1** to **20** find the value of each expression when
$x = 5$
$y = 4$
$z = 7$

1 $y^2 + z^2$

2 x^2

3 $4x^2$

4 $(4x)^2$

5 $(2y)^2$

6 $2z^2$

7 $3y^2$

8 xyz

9 $2(x^2 + y^2)$

10 $2y + 3x$

11 $x^2 + y^2 + z^2$

12 $2x^2 - y^2$

13 $y(3z - 2x)$

14 $z(4x + 2y)$

15 $\dfrac{21(x - y)}{z}$

16 $6(x^2 - y^2)$

17 $y(2z + 3y)$

18 $(2x)^2 - 2x^2$

19 $6(3x + y^2)$

20 $\dfrac{5z + x}{y}$

In questions **21** to **28** find the value of each expression.

21 $x^2 - 3$, if $x = 7$

22 $2b^2$, if $b = 3$

23 $3a^2$, if $a = 1$

24 $7(p - 2)$, if $p = 2$

25 $(4a)^2$, if $a = 1$

26 $3x$, if $x = -2$

27 $20 + b$, if $b = -6$

28 $3 - 6x$, if $x = 2$

In questions **29** to **44** find the value of each expression when
$a = 4$
$b = -2$
$c = -3$

29 bc

30 $5a + 3b$

31 $3c - 2$

32 $2b + 4c$

33 b^2

34 $a^2 + b^2$

35 $2c^2$

36 $3(4b - 2)$

37 $b(a + c)$

38 abc

39 $9c$

40 $(3b)^2$

41 $8(a - b)$

42 $24 - c$

43 $5c + 10$

44 $3a + 2b - c$

Using formulas

If base = 9 cm and height = 6 cm

then $b = 9$ and $h = 6$

Area A $= \dfrac{bh}{2}$

so A $= \dfrac{9 \times 6}{2} = 27$

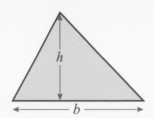

M2.3

In questions **1** to **12** you are given a formula. Find the value of the letter required in each case.

1 $a = 5b + 2$
Find a when $b = 3$

2 $x = 7y - 6$
Find x when $y = 3$

3 $a = \dfrac{b}{4} + 5$
Find a when $b = 20$

4 $c = \dfrac{d}{3} - 2$
Find c when $d = 15$

5 $g = 4h + 9$
Find g when $h = 6$

6 $p = 2(q + 8)$
Find p when $q = 3$

7 $m = n + 3p$
Find m when $n = 8$ and $p = 6$

8 $p = 6q + 2r$
Find p when $q = 4$ and $r = 5$

9 $v = 2(3w + 2y)$
Find v when $w = 4$ and $y = 5$

10 $a = \dfrac{4b + 7c}{5}$
Find a when $b = 4$ and $c = 2$

11 $x = 3y + 6z - 8$
Find x when $y = 4$ and $z = 2$

12 $e = \dfrac{f}{3} + \dfrac{d}{4}$
Find e when $f = 15$ and $d = 28$

In questions **13** and **14** use the formula
$s = ut$ to find the value of s
(s means distance, u means speed
and t means time taken).

13 $u = 7, t = 8$ **14** $u = 47, t = 16$

In questions **15** to **16** use the formula $v = at + u$ to find the value of v when:

15 $a = 7, t = 6$, and $u = 43$

16 $a = 17, t = 32$, and $u = 217$

17

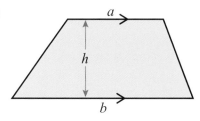

The area A of a trapezium can be found using the formula

$A = \dfrac{1}{2}h(a + b)$

$\left(\dfrac{1}{2}h \text{ means } \dfrac{1}{2} \text{ of } h\right)$

Find the area of a trapezium when $h = 8, a = 8{\cdot}9$ and $b = 6{\cdot}1$

18

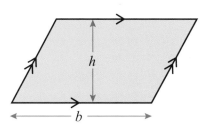

The area A of a parallelogram can be found using the formula

$A = bh$

Find the area of a parallelogram when $b = 6{\cdot}2$ and $h = 4{\cdot}9$

 **Can you still?**

Do calculations in the correct order

Work out

1 $3 + 8 \times 2$

2 $28 \div (3 + 4)$

3 $9 \times (6 - 4)$

4 $30 \div 5 + 4$

5 $(5 - 1) \times 5 + 7$

6 $25 - 3 \times 4$

7 $(8 + 4) \div (5 - 2)$

8 $22 + 8 \div 2$

9 $36 \div (4 + 8)$

10 $20 - 20 \div 4$

11 $(8 - 3) \times 3$

12 $6 + 8 \div 2 + 4$

Copy each question below and write brackets so that each calculation gives the correct answer.

13 $7 + 4 \times 3 = 33$

14 $25 - 20 \times 4 = 20$

15 $7 - 2 \times 5 + 1 = 30$

19 $a = \dfrac{v - u}{t}$ Use the formula to find the value of a when $v = 11, u = 4$ and $t = 0{\cdot}5$

20 c, d and e are connected by the formula

$c = \sqrt{(d^2 + e^2)}$

Find c when $d = 3$ and $e = 4$

1 Below are several different formulas for z in terms of x. Find the value of z in each case.

(a) $z = 10x - 6$ when $x = 3 \cdot 5$

(b) $z = \dfrac{5x + 3}{2}$ when $x = 3$

(c) $z = 4(3x + 7)$ when $x = 2$

2 Using the formula $a = 100 + 2b$, find the value of a when

(a) $b = 6$ (b) $b = 100$ (c) $b = \dfrac{1}{2}$

3 The relationship between temperature and volume for a gas is given by the formula $V_1 = \dfrac{V_2 T_1}{T_2}$. Find the value of V, when

(a) $V_2 = 20$, $T_1 = 4$ and $T_2 = 16$

(b) $V_2 = 0 \cdot 5$, $T_1 = 17$ and $T_2 = 0 \cdot 25$

(c) $V_2 = 0 \cdot 1$, $T_1 = 60$ and $T_2 = 0 \cdot 5$

4 Here are some polygons.

Number of sides:	3	4	5
Sum of angles:	180°	360°	540°

The sum of the angles in a polygon with n sides is given by the formula

sum of angles $= (n - 2) \times 180°$

(a) Find the sum of angles in a hexagon (6 sides)

(b) Find the sum of angles in a polygon with 102 sides

(c) Show that the formula gives the correct answer for the sum of the angles in a pentagon (5 sides)

5 Here is a formula $h = t^2 - 7$.
Find the value of h when

(a) $t = 6$ (b) $t = 1$

(c) $t = -3$

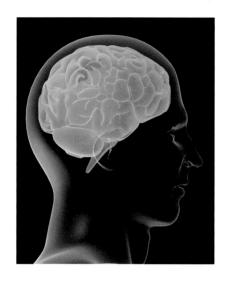

6 Using the formula $C = N^2 - P^2$
find the value of C when

(a) $N = 8$ and $P = 5$

(b) $N = 4$ and $P = 7$

(c) $N = -3$ and $P = -6$

7 Using the formula $V = 3B^2$ find the value of V when

(a) $B = 5$ (b) $B = 10$ (c) $B = -2$ (d) $B = -8$

8 An estimate for the volume of a cylinder of radius r and
height h is given by the formula $V = 3r^2h$

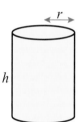

(a) Find the value of V when $r = 10$ and $h = 2$

(b) Find the value of V when $r = 5$ and $h = 4$

9 The kinetic energy of a moving object is given by the formula $\frac{1}{2}mv^2$ where
m is its mass and v is its velocity.

Find the kinetic energy when

(a) $m = 16$ and $v = 3$ (b) $m = 38$ and $v = 7$

10 If $T = a^2 + 3a - 5$, find the values of T when

(a) $a = 3$ (b) $a = 10$ (c) $a = 1$

11 The total surface area A of the solid cuboid shown
is given by the formula

$$A = 2bc + 2ab + 2ac$$

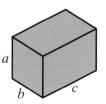

Find the value of A when $a = 2$, $b = 3$, $c = 4$

12 Using the formula $P = QR + S$, find the value of P when

(a) $Q = -2, R = -4, S = -5$ (b) $Q = -3, R = 5, S = 10$

Key Facts

$a + b$ cannot be added together because the *term a* is not like the term b

$a + 3a = 4a$ because the *term a* is like the term $3a$

a and $3a$ are *like terms*

Examples

(a) $6a + 4b + 2a + 3b = 8a + 7b$ (b) $5p + p + 3p = 9p$

(c) $ab + 3b + 2b = ab + 5b$ (d) $4x^2 + 3x + 2x^2 + 6x = 6x^2 + 9x$

        (*ab* is *not* like 3*b*)

(e) $7a + 3 + 2a = 9a + 3$ (f) $6m + 4n - 2m + n = 4m + 5n$

M2.4

Collect like terms

1 $3a + 4b + 2a$ **2** $5a + 6a + a$ **3** $3a + 4a + 4b$

4 $4p + 8q + 3p$ **5** $9p + 2p + 5q$ **6** $3p + 4q + 5q + 4p$

7 $8p + 5p + 6q + 2q$ **8** $7x + 5y - 3x$ **9** $7x + 3y - 7x$

10 $5x + 7y - 4y$ **11** $5a + 6a - 2a$ **12** $6x + 9x + 4y$

13 $8x - 3x + 4x$ **14** $9x - 5x + 2y$ **15** $6a + 3 + 5a - 2$

16 $9x - 3 + 3x - 5x$ **17** $8p + 4q + 4q - 3p$ **18** $6c + 3c - 2 + 5c$

19 $8a + 3a + 7a + 4$ **20** $6x + 4y + 5y - 2x$ **21** $6c + 3 + 6 - 3c$

Find the perimeter of each shape in questions **22** to **25**. Simplify each answer.

22

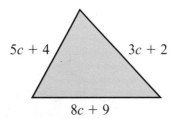

23

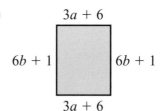

24

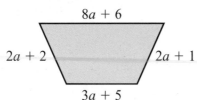

25

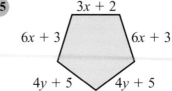

Simplify questions **26** to **33**.

26 $8m - 3m + 2n$

27 $a + 6b - a - 3b$

28 $9a + 3a + 10 - 4a$

29 $4p + 6q + 3q - 8q - 2p$

30 $6a + 9a - 10a + 3b - 2$

31 $8a - 3a + 6b + 2b$

32 $8x + 7y + 3x + 6x$

33 $5x - 2x + 8x + 6 - 2$

> **Can you still?**

Squares, cubes and roots

Work out

1 8^2 **2** $\sqrt{81}$ **3** $\sqrt{400}$ **4** $\sqrt[3]{8}$ **5** $\sqrt[3]{1}$

6 4^3 **7** $9^2 - 3^2$ **8** $\sqrt{64} + \sqrt{16}$ **9** $(4 + 2)^2$

10 Write down the first 3 cube numbers.

11 Which is larger, 2^2 or $\sqrt{100}$?

12 Find two square numbers which add up to 41

M2.5

Simplify

1 $8a + a$ **2** $-5c + 7c$ **3** $-7a + a$

4 $-b + 6b$ **5** $-a + a$ **6** $8a - 3b + 2a + 6b$

7 $8p + 3q - p + 4q$ **8** $4m - 2n + 6m$ **9** $3a + 2b - 5a - b$

10 $a + 4b - a - 3b$ **11** $4a + b - 3b - 2a$ **12** $6x + 2x - 8x - 3x$

13 $6p - 2 + 8 - 2p$ **14** $5p - 3p - 6p - 2$ **15** $5a - 1 - 1 - a$

16 $6x - 3y + 2y - x$ **17** $3a + 6a + 8 - 10$ **18** $5c - 2c - c - 7$

19

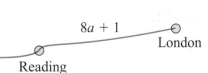

$5a + 2$ — Swindon — $6b - 9$ — Reading — $8a + 1$ — London

Bristol

Write down an expression for how far it is between:

(a) Bristol and London

(b) Bristol and Reading

(c) Swindon and London

57

20 Which of the expressions below are identical (ie. the same as each other)?

$$5m + 3n - n + 2m$$ $$3m + 2n + 4m + 2n$$ $$m + 6n - 5n + 6m + n$$

21 Gabriella travels $(m^2 + 3n + 2)$ miles on Tuesday and $(3m^2 - n + 6)$ miles on Wednesday. How far does she travel in total?

22 Luke says that $4a^2 + 3a - 2a^2 - a$ is identical to $2a^2 + 2a$. Explain whether Luke is correct or not.

23

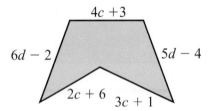

Find the perimeter of this shape. Simplify your answer.

Simplify questions **24** to **33**.

24 $3ab + a + 2ab$

25 $6ab + 3a + 2a + 2ab$

26 $4xy + 2xy - 3xy$

27 $5xy - 2 - 3 - 2xy$

28 $9ab + 3ab + 6 + 5ab$

29 $6xy - 3xy + 5xy - 2xy$

30 $7ab + 3ab - 2a + 4b$

31 $5xy - 2xy + 3x - 6x$

32 $4a^2 + a^2 + 9 - 2$

33 $7a^2 - 3a + 5a^2 - 2a$

Simplifying terms

(a) $4a \times 2 = 8a$ $\qquad$ $c \times c = c^2$

(b) $3a \times 2a = 6a^2$ $\qquad$ multiply numbers first then the letters

(c) $3m \times 2n = 6mn$ $\qquad$ $5y \times y = 5y^2$

(d) $6a \div 2 = 3a$ $\qquad$ $28n \div 7 = 4n$

Do the following multiplications and divisions.

1. $4x \times 2$
2. $3x \times 5$
3. $8x \times 2$
4. $4y \times 2$
5. $5y \times 4$
6. $7a \times 6$
7. $8x \times 10$
8. $4a \times 9$
9. $3d \times 6$
10. $6 \times 4c$
11. $9 \times 4p$
12. $5 \times 9x$
13. $7 \times 2c$
14. $9 \times 3d$
15. $6 \times 8x$
16. $8x \div 4$
17. $24x \div 4$
18. $4p \div 2$
19. $20x \div 4$
20. $21A \div 3$
21. $27Q \div 9$
22. $42n \div 6$
23. $9A \div 3$
24. $36N \div 4$
25. $16r \div 4$
26. $90t \div 9$
27. $48T \div 4$
28. $35a \div 5$
29. $80R \div 10$
30. $12b \div 3$
31. $a \times a$
32. $c \times c$
33. $Q \times Q$
34. $3c \times c$
35. $4p \times p$
36. $5d \times d$
37. $r \times 2r$
38. $B \times B$
39. $c \times 5c$
40. $a \times 6a$
41. $2a \times 4b$
42. $3y \times 6y$
43. $7a \times 2a$
44. $5t \times 5t$

Can you still?

Factors and multiples

1. Write down all the factors of:
   (a) 10   (b) 25   (c) 24
2. Which numbers below have 4 factors only?
   15   7   16   22
3. Which of the numbers below are multiples of 6?
   17   12   22   30   19   42
4. Find the Lowest Common Multiple of each of these pairs of numbers:
   (a) 4 and 7   (b) 6 and 9   (c) 8 and 6

Do the following multiplications and divisions.

1. $3a \times 2b$
2. $6x \times 3y$
3. $5p \times 2q$
4. $7e \times 3e$
5. $8m \times 3n$
6. $6c \times 9c$
7. $3x \times 8x$
8. $2B \times 8B$
9. $5P \times 9Q$
10. $3v \times 12u$
11. $8c \div 2$
12. $15A \div 3$

13 $64p \div 8$ **14** $72x \div 9$ **15** $a \times b \times c$ **16** $3a \times 2b \times 2c$

17 $4x \times 3y \times 5z$ **18** $2a \times 6b \times 3c \times 2d$

In questions **19** to **33** answer 'true' or 'false'.

19 $c \times d = cd$ **20** $n \times n = n^2$

21 $2n \times 3n = 5n^2$ **22** $a \times 3a = 3a^2$

23 $p + p = p^2$ **24** $3 \times a = a \times 3$

25 $8n \times 4n = 32n^2$ **26** $10a \div 2 = 5a$

27 $3c \times 12d = 36cd$ **28** $12p \div 3 = 9p$

29 $3a - a = 3$ **30** $4n + 4n = 8n^2$

31 $n \times n \times n = n^3$ **32** $a + a^2 = a^3$

33 $m \times 3 \times n = 3mn$

Simplify

34 $m \times -m$ **35** $2a \times -3b$ **36** $-4c \times 5d$ **37** $-2x \times -4y$

38 $-9y \div 3$ **39** $-6a \div -2$ **40** $-8P \div 4$ **41** $-6c \times -3d$

42 $8x \times -5y$ **43** $28q \times -4$ **44** $-9y \times 6$ **45** $3a \times -7a$

46 $-14x \div -2$ **47** $18a \times -3b$ **48** $-9P \times -6P$

Rules for indices

Key Facts

$3^4 \Leftarrow$ the 'power' 4 is also called the 'index' ('indices' for more than one index)
⇧
this number is called the 'base'

$$a^m \times a^n = a^{m+n}$$ $$a^m \div a^n = a^{m-n}$$

Base numbers must be the same.
To multiply numbers with indices, add the indices.
To divide numbers with indices, subtract the indices.

1 Copy and complete. Write the answer as a number in index form.

(a) $3^3 \times 3^4 =$ (b) $5^2 \times 5^4 =$ (c) $8^3 \times 8^3 =$

(d) $7^2 \times 7^3 =$ (e) $4^6 \times 4 =$ (f) $6^5 \times 6^2 =$

2 Copy and complete. Write the answer as a number in index form.

(a) $7^6 \div 7^2$ (b) $4^7 \div 4^4$ (c) $3^9 \div 3$

(d) $5^8 \div 5^5$ (e) $6^{10} \div 6^7$ (f) $4^6 \div 4^5$

3 Work out and write each answer as a number in index form.

(a) $8^6 \times 8^2$ (b) $4^7 \times 4^3$ (c) $9^8 \div 9^5$

(d) $6^4 \times 6^4$ (e) $8^7 \div 8$ (f) $5^5 \div 5^2$

(g) $3^3 \times 3^2 \times 3^4$ (h) $2^6 \times 2 \times 2^3$ (i) $(4^3)^2$

4

← 2^6 cm →

2^3 cm

Write down the area of this rectangle in index form.

5 Copy and complete.

(a) $3^4 \times 3^2 = \square$ (b) $\square \times 6^4 = 6^6$ (c) $\square \times 9^4 = 9^7$

(d) $4^6 \times \square = 4^8$ (e) $9^3 \times \square = 9^4$ (f) $4^8 \div 4^2 = \square$

(g) $3^8 \div \square = 3^2$ (h) $8^{10} \div \square = 8^5$ (i) $\square \div 4^5 = 4^7$

6 Write down the area of this square in index form.

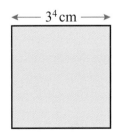

← 3^4 cm →

7 Work out and write each answer as a number in index form.

(a) $5^3 \times 5^9 \times 5^2$ (b) $8^7 \times 8^2 \times 8^4$ (c) $\dfrac{4^8 \times 4^3}{4^7}$

(d) $\dfrac{7^6 \times 7^8}{7^4}$ (e) $\dfrac{8^9}{8^2 \times 8^3}$ (f) $\dfrac{6^8}{6^3 \times 6^3}$

8 The volume of this cube is 5^9 cm³. How long is one side of the cube. Give the answer in index form.

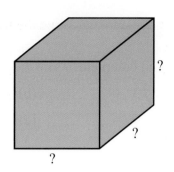

9 Which statements below are true?

(a) $4^3 \times 4^2 = 4^5$ (b) $7^9 \div 7^3 = 7^6$ (c) $2^8 \times 2 = 2^9$

(d) $3^6 \times 3 = 3^6$ (e) $5^6 \div 5^3 = 5^2$ (f) $8^7 \div 8 = 8^6$

 Key Facts

To raise an index number to another power, multiply the indices.

$$(a^m)^n = a^{mn}$$

(a) $\dfrac{a^2 \times a^7}{(a^2)^2} = \dfrac{a^9}{a^4} = a^5$

(b) $\dfrac{n^4 \times n^6}{(n^4)^2} = \dfrac{n^{10}}{n^8} = n^2$

$4^2 \div 4^2 = 4^{2-2} = 4^0$
$4^2 \div 4^2 = 16 \div 16 = 1$
so $4^0 = 1$

LEARN! $a^0 = 1$ for any number a (apart from a = 0)

E2.3

1 Copy and complete. Write the number in index form.

(a) $(3^2)^4$ (b) $(5^3)^2$

(c) $(6^3)^4$ (d) $(7^4)^2$

(e) $(5^6)^3$ (f) $(8^2)^5$

(g) $(3^5)^3$ (h) $(6^3)^5$

2 Which is larger? $\boxed{10^0}$ or $\boxed{3^0}$

3 Copy and complete. Write the number in index form.

(a) $(3^4)^2 \times 3^3$

(b) $(2^3)^4 \times 2^6$

(c) $6^5 \times (6^2)^2$

(d) $\dfrac{7^3}{7^0}$

(e) $\dfrac{(5^2)^4}{(5^3)^2}$

(f) $\dfrac{9 \times (9^3)^3}{9^7}$

(g) $\dfrac{8^2 \times 8^6}{(8^2)^3}$

(h) $\dfrac{4^3 \times (4^5)^2}{4^7}$

(i) $\dfrac{(2^3)^2 \times (2^3)^2}{2^4 \times 2^3}$

4 What is the value of $(4^0)^6$?

5 Simplify the expressions below.

(a) $a^4 \times a^3$

(b) $x^7 \times x^4$

(c) $x^9 \div x^4$

(d) $(n^3)^2$

(e) $a^{10} \div a^6$

(f) $(x^3)^3$

(g) n^0

(h) $p^8 \times p$

(i) $m^{14} \div m^8$

(j) $(x^2)^0$

(k) $(a^2)^4 \times a^5$

(l) $x^p \div x^p$

6 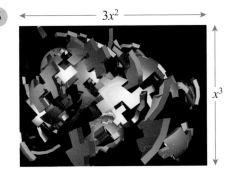 Write down the area of this picture in index form.

$3x^2$

x^3

7 Simplify the expressions below.

(a) $5x^3 \times x^6$

(b) $4x^2 \times 4x^2$

(c) $5p^3 \times 2p^2$

(d) $8a^2 \times 3a^4$

(e) $\dfrac{8a^5}{a^2}$

(f) $\dfrac{10x^6}{2x^4}$

8 Which is larger? $\boxed{\dfrac{(3^3)^2 \times 3^2}{3^3 \times (3^2)^2}}$ or $\boxed{\dfrac{(3^2)^3 \times 3^3}{3^5 \times 3^2}}$

A   B

9 Simplify the expressions below.

(a) $\dfrac{x^5 \times x^3}{x^6}$

(b) $\dfrac{a^2 \times a^6}{(a^2)^2}$

(c) $\dfrac{(m^3)^2 \times m^4}{(m^3)^3}$

(d) $\dfrac{a^8}{a^3 \times a}$

(e) $\dfrac{n^9 \times (n^2)^4}{(n^3)^5}$

(f) $\dfrac{x^8 \times x^4}{(x^3)^2 \times x^2}$

(g) $\dfrac{(x^3)^6}{x^2 \times (x^2)^5}$

(h) $\dfrac{a^{20}}{(a^3)^4 \times (a^2)^2}$

(i) $\dfrac{n^2 \times (n^4)^2}{(n^2)^3 \times n}$

63

Multiplying out brackets

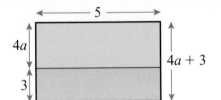

total area $= 5(4a + 3)$
total area $= 5 \times 4a + 5 \times 3$
$5(4a + 3) = 20a + 15$

(a) Multiply out $2(3 + 5)$ means 2×3 add $2 \times 5 = 6 + 10 = 16$

(b) Multiply out $2(a + b)$ means $2 \times a$ add $2 \times b = 2a + 2b$

(c) Expand $a(b + c)$ means $a \times b$ add $a \times c = ab + ac$

(d) Multiply out $p(2q - 3)$ means $p \times 2q$ subtract $p \times 3 = 2pq - 3p$

(e) Expand $5n(2n + 3)$ means $5n \times 2n$ add $5n \times 3 = 10n^2 + 15n$

M2.9

Multiply out

1 $2(a + 3)$	**2** $8(2y - 1)$	**3** $6(4x - 2)$	**4** $5(3x + 4)$
5 $7(3x - 5)$	**6** $4(7y + 2)$	**7** $5(a - b)$	**8** $2(2a + b)$
9 $7(3x + y)$	**10** $3(x + 2y)$	**11** $6(3x + 2)$	**12** $4(p + q)$
13 $4(p + 2q)$	**14** $6(3a - 5b)$	**15** $9(4c + 8d)$	**16** $x(x + y)$
17 $x(2x + y)$	**18** $a(b - c)$	**19** $a(b + a)$	**20** $p(p - q)$
21 $c(2c + d)$	**22** $p(p + 3)$	**23** $a(a - 7)$	**24** $3a(a + 1)$
25 $5x(y + 2)$	**26** $3b(c + 2d)$	**27** $4a(a + 2b)$	**28** $3m(2m - 5n)$
29 $6a(4b - 8c)$	**30** $3x(2x + 3y)$		

(a) Multiply out $-4(x - 2)$ means $-4 \times x$ and $-4 \times -2 = -4x + 8$

(b) Expand $-3(2a + 4)$ means $-3 \times 2a$ and $-3 \times 4 = -6a - 12$

(c) Expand $-a(a + b)$ means $-a \times a$ and $-a \times b = -a^2 - ab$

(d) Multiply out $-b(b - c)$ means $-b \times b$ and $-b \times -c = -b^2 + bc$

Expand

1 $-2(x + 6)$ **2** $-5(y - 3)$ **3** $-3(a - 2)$ **4** $-2(x + 4)$

5 $-5(c + 10)$ **6** $-2(3x - y)$ **7** $-4(3p - 5)$ **8** $-5(2a + 1)$

9 $-4(8b - 2)$ **10** $-3(2c + 4)$

11 $-3(5a + 2)$ **12** $-6(3x - 3)$

13 $-4(5a - 6)$ **14** $3(3b - 7)$

15 $7(1 - 2x)$ **16** $-a(b + c)$

17 $-e(f - g)$ **18** $-x(x - y)$

19 $-p(2p + q)$ **20** $-y(3y + z)$

21 $-x(2x - y)$ **22** $-a(a + b)$

23 $-m(m - n)$ **24** $-(3x - y)$

25 $-(2p + 5q)$ **26** $-3a(a + b)$

27 $2b(3a - 2b)$ **28** $5x(3x - 2y)$

Can you still?

Negative numbers

Work out

1 $-3 + 1$ **2** $-8 - 2$ **3** $-6 + 7$

4 $-9 + 3$ **5** $2 - 10$ **6** $-5 - -1$

7 $-10 - 3$ **8** $-9 - -4$

Copy and fill in each empty box

9 $\square - 6 = -9$ **10** $\square - -2 = -5$

11 $-4 - \square = -3$ **12** $-8 - \square = -9$

Work out

13 -6×4 **14** -8×-3

15 -6×-5 **16** -6×3

17 8×-2 **18** $-8 \div 2$

19 $-24 \div -3$ **20** $-36 \div 9$

Simplify $3(2a + 2) + 4(a + 1)$

   $= 6a + 6 + 4a + 4$ (multiply out brackets first)

Answer $= 10a + 10$ (now collect like terms)

Simplify

1 $2(x + 3) + 5$ **2** $5(2x + 1) + 3$ **3** $4(3x + 2) + 2x$

4 $5(3x + 4) + 7x$ **5** $9(2x + 3) - 14$ **6** $3(2a + 4) - 2a$

7 $6(4a + 3) - 8a$

8 $9(3y + 2) - 6$

9 $5(a + 2) + 2(2a + 1)$

10 $3(x + 4) + 6(x + 2)$

11 $6(x + 1) + 3(2x + 4)$

12 $5(2a + 3) + 4(a - 2)$

13 $3(4a + 8) + 2(a - 3)$

14 $7(2x + 3) + 4(3x + 1)$

Write down an expression for each area shown below.
Expand and simplify the answer where possible.

15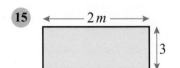

16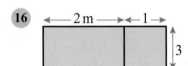

17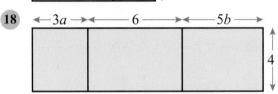

18

19

20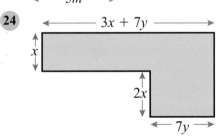

21

22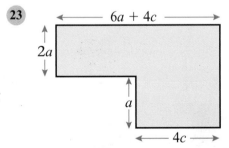

23

24

Expand and simplify

25 $4(2d + 2) + 6(3d + 4)$

26 $6x + 9 + 3(4x + 2)$

25 $3a + 2(4a + 7) - 10$

26 $8(2x + 1) + 3(4x - 1)$

25 $6a + 3(2a + 4) + 2(5a + 4)$

26 $3x + 2(3x + 4) + 5(2x - 1)$

66

Key Facts

We know that $3(a + b)$ is the same as $3a + 3b$ so $3a + 3b = 3(a + b)$

Consider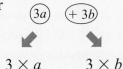

3 is *a factor* of both $3a$ and $3b$

so 3 is the *common factor* of $3a$ and $3b$

$3 \times a \qquad 3 \times b$

Common factors can be extracted from algebraic expressions.

Take out common factor 3.

$3a + 3b$ ➡ Write remaining terms in a bracket ➡ $3(a + b)$

⬇

Multiply out bracket to check
you have the same expression
you started with

This is called *'factorising'* $3a + 3b$

Factorise $7x - 7y$

$7x$ and $7y$ have common factor 7

so $7x - 7y = 7(x - y)$

Factorise $5a + 10b$

5 divides into $5a$ and $10b$

so $5a$ and $10b$ have common factor 5

so $5a + 10b = 5(a + 2b)$

M2.11

Copy and complete

1. $6a + 15 = 3(2a + \boxed{})$

2. $9c + 6 = 3(3c + \boxed{})$

3. $5x - 15 = 5(x - \boxed{})$

4. $12a + 18 = 6(\boxed{} + 3)$

5. $15m + 20 = 5(\boxed{} + \boxed{})$

6. $7n - 35 = 7(\boxed{} - \boxed{})$

7. $8x + 32 = \boxed{}(x + \boxed{})$

8. $9x + 36 = 9(\boxed{} + \boxed{})$

9. $14a - 35 = 7(2a - \boxed{})$

10. $16n - 24 = 8(2n - \boxed{})$

11. $45x + 36 = \boxed{}(\boxed{} + \boxed{})$

12. $48a - 40 = \boxed{}(\boxed{} - \boxed{})$

67

Factorise the expressions below:

13 $8a + 10$

14 $6x + 27$

15 $5x - 20$

16 $6m + 42$

17 $25a - 35$

18 $16x - 4$

19 $27p - 18$

20 $18a + 24b$

21 $16x + 40y$

22 $14a - 21b$

23 $24m - 20n$

24 $21x + 28y$

25 $56a + 32b$

26 $20x - 10y$

27 $36x - 27y$

28 $72c + 40d$

29 $10a + 15b + 25c$

30 $6p + 9q + 3r$

31 $7x + 14y - 7z$

32 $9a - 9b - 21c$

33 $24m + 12n + 16p$

34 $42a + 35b - 14$

35 $18a - 27b + 36c$

36 $28x - 36y + 16$

Letters as well as numbers can be the common factors.

(a) Factorise $ab + ac$

ab and ac have common factor a

So $ab + ac = a(b + c)$ **multiply out to check the answer is correct**

(b) Factorise $5ac + 15bc$ Factorise $4x^2 - 6x$

$5ac$ and $15bc$ have common factor $5c$ $4x^2$ and $6x$ have common factor $2x$

so $5ac + 15bc = 5c(a + 3b)$ so $4x^2 - 6x = 2x(2x - 3)$

M2.12

Copy and complete

1 $xy + xz = x(y + \boxed{})$

2 $ab - ac = a(\boxed{} - \boxed{})$

3 $x^2 + 6x = x(x + \boxed{})$

4 $5a + a^2 = a(5 + \boxed{})$

5 $3b^2 - 12b = 3b(\boxed{} - \boxed{})$

6 $cd + c^2 = c(\boxed{} + \boxed{})$

7 $3xy + 15xz = 3x(y + \boxed{})$

8 $8ab - 24bc = 8b(\boxed{} - \boxed{})$

9 $12x^2 - 8x = \boxed{}(3x - \boxed{})$

10 $6m^2 - m = \boxed{}(6m - \boxed{})$

Factorise the expressions below:

11 $ef + fg$

12 $p^2 + 3p$

13 $7a - a^2$

14 $x^2 - 8x$

15 $a^2 + 5a$

16 $2pq + 4pr$

17 $8ab - 12bc$

18 $6xy - 9yz$

19 $5x^2 - 15x$

20 $5st + 35s$

21 $8pr - 40pq$

22 $6ab + 4b$

23 $3a^2 + 8a$

24 $12x - 16x^2$

25 $x^2 + xy$

26 $3x^2 + 21xy$

27 $20ab - 50b$

28 $a^2b - a^2c$

29 $a^2 + abc$

30 $5x^2 - 6xy$

31 $20p^2 - 30pq$

32 $36abc - 16b^2$

33 $49x^2 + 42xy$

34 $63a^2 - 35ab$

35 Darryl says that
$6a^2 + 2ab + 2 = 2(3a^2 + ab)$
Darryl has made a mistake.
Explain what is wrong with
Darryl's answer.

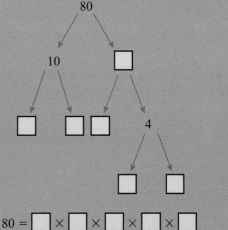

Can you still?

Prime factors and HCF

1 Copy and complete this factor tree.

80 = ☐ × ☐ × ☐ × ☐ × ☐

2 Write the following numbers as
products of prime factors:
(a) 30   (b) 36   (c) 50   (d) 144

3 Find the Highest Common Factor of:
(a) 24 and 60   (b) 45 and 75
(c) 135 and 81

Solving equations with the unknown on one side

🔑 Key Facts

An 'equation' contains an ' = ' sign.

(a) Solve $n - 4 = 2$
    $n = 6$ because $\boxed{6} - 4 = 2$

(b) Solve $\dfrac{n}{3} = 2$
    $\dfrac{n}{3}$ means '$n \div 3$'
    $n = 6$ because $\dfrac{\boxed{6}}{3} = 2$

(c) Solve $3n = 18$
    $3n$ means '$3 \times n$'
    $n = 6$ because $3 \times \boxed{6} = 18$

1 Work out the missing numbers:

(a) $n + 6 = 10$ (b) $n + 2 = 5$ (c) $n + 6 = 9$ (d) $n - 4 = 1$

(e) $n - 8 = 3$ (f) $n - 20 = 7$ (g) $n - 5 = 12$ (h) $n + 10 = 32$

(i) $n - 1 = 9$ (j) $n + 7 = 14$ (k) $n + 9 = 12$ (l) $n - 7 = 9$

2 Solve these equations:

(a) $x - 15 = 8$ (b) $x - 17 = 12$ (c) $x + 28 = 40$ (d) $x + 16 = 30$

(e) $x + 31 = 52$ (f) $x + 43 = 75$ (g) $x - 24 = 20$ (h) $x - 30 = 27$

3 Solve these equations:

(a) $3 \times n = 21$ (b) $5 \times n = 30$ (c) $3 \times n = 12$ (d) $4n = 24$

(e) $10n = 70$ (f) $8n = 48$ (g) $3n = 27$ (h) $n \div 2 = 3$

(i) $n \div 4 = 3$ (j) $\dfrac{n}{5} = 6$ (k) $\dfrac{n}{4} = 8$ (l) $\dfrac{n}{10} = 7$

(m) $6n = 42$ (n) $\dfrac{n}{6} = 6$ (o) $7n = 56$

4 Jan has some marbles. She buys 12 more marbles and now has 21. How many marbles did she have to start with?

5 Jim thinks of a number and then adds 7. If the answer is 15, what number did Jim think of?

6 Teresa thinks of a number and then subtracts 8. If the answer is 9, what number did Teresa think of?

7 Ed thinks of a number and then subtracts 14. If the answer is 13, what number did Ed think of?

8 Candice has some sweets. Her sister has 6 times as many sweets. If her sister has 54 sweets, how many sweets does Candice have?

9 Gemma has some money. Her brother has 8 times as much money. If her brother has £32, how much money does Gemma have?

10 Solve:

(a) $x + 8 = 20$ (b) $x + 17 = 31$ (c) $3x = 15$ (d) $9x = 63$

(e) $x + 43 = 61$ (f) $23 = x - 16$ (g) $7 = \dfrac{x}{4}$ (h) $21 = x - 32$

(i) $\dfrac{x}{7} = 5$ (j) $6x = 30$ (k) $110 = x + 88$ (l) $\dfrac{x}{3} = 12$

Sometimes the missing number may be a *negative number*.

(a) Solve $n + 6 = 2$

$n = -4$ because $\boxed{-4} + 6 = 2$

(b) Solve $n - 3 = -8$

$n = -5$ because

$\boxed{-5} - 3 = -8$

(c) $3n = -12$

$n = -4$ because

$3 \times \boxed{-4} = -12$

E2.5

1 Solve these equations:

(a) $n + 4 = 3$ (b) $n + 6 = 1$ (c) $n + 9 = 4$ (d) $n + 7 = 2$

(e) $n - 2 = -1$ (f) $n - 8 = -13$ (g) $n - 4 = -8$ (h) $n - 4 = -9$

(i) $n - 6 = -3$ (j) $n + 7 = 0$ (k) $n + 12 = 4$ (l) $n - 12 = -20$

2 Solve:

(a) $4n = -20$ (b) $7n = -21$ (c) $5n = -35$

(d) $9n = -18$ (e) $6n = -36$ (f) $-5n = 30$

(g) $-9n = 27$ (h) $-3n = 24$ (i) $-7n = -28$

(j) $-6n = -42$ (k) $-3n = 18$ (l) $-10n = -60$

3 Solve:

(a) $n \div 3 = -6$ (b) $n \div 2 = -8$ (c) $n \div 3 = -2$ (d) $\dfrac{n}{5} = -3$

(e) $\dfrac{n}{2} = -4$ (f) $\dfrac{n}{-3} = 7$ (g) $3 = \dfrac{n}{-2}$ (h) $-6 = \dfrac{n}{-1}$

(i) $4 = \dfrac{n}{-5}$ (j) $\dfrac{n}{2} = -9$ (k) $\dfrac{n}{-2} = -2$ (l) $-2 = \dfrac{n}{7}$

4 If $2n = 1$ then $n = \frac{1}{2}$ because $2 \times \boxed{\frac{1}{2}} = 1$

This answer could also be written as $n = 0\cdot5$
Solve these equations:

(a) $2n = 3$ (b) $2n = 7$ (c) $2n = -1$ (d) $2n = -5$

(e) $1 = 3n$ (f) $6 = 4n$ (g) $10n = -3$ (h) $2n = -9$

(i) $2 = 8n$ (j) $5n = -4$ (k) $-1 = 7n$ (l) $-2 = 9n$

71

Solving longer equations

(a) Solve $5n + 2 = 17$ OR

$\boxed{5n} + 2 = 17$

↑

This box = 15 because $\boxed{15} + 2 = 17$

So $\boxed{5n} = 15$

↓

$5n$ means $5 \times n$

So $5 \times n = 15$

So $n = 3$ because $5 \times \boxed{3} = 15$

Solve $5n + 2 = 17$

Take off 2 from each pan

Each $\boxed{n}$ must equal 3 because 5 $\boxed{n}$ boxes are equal to 15

So $n = 3$

M2.14

Find the value of n in questions **1** to **4**

1

2

3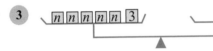

4

Solve these equations:

5 $5n + 6 = 21$ **6** $5n + 7 = 17$

7 $4n + 7 = 19$ **8** $5n + 4 = 34$

9 $3n - 2 = 10$ **10** $6n - 1 = 29$

11 $7n + 6 = 34$ **12** $4n + 10 = 26$

13 $23 = 4n + 3$ **14** $9 = 3n - 6$

15 $21 = 8n - 3$ **16** $5n - 5 = 45$

17 $10n - 2 = 38$ **18** $23 = 4n - 9$

19 $9 = 7n - 12$ **20** $22 = 9n - 5$

21 $22 = 3n - 8$ **22** $6n + 8 = 26$

23 $5n + 12 = 32$ **24** $10n + 13 = 73$

Can you still?

Number work
Do not use a calculator

Work out

1 527×48 **2** $1222 \div 26$

3   190 footballers are to be split into teams of 11. How many complete teams can be formed?

4   Write the numbers below in standard form:

(a) 49 800   (b) 0·09   (c) 0·85

5   Which number is larger?
$5·6 \times 10^{14}$ or $7·9 \times 10^{13}$

Equations with 'trickier' numbers

(a) Solve $5n + 13 = 3$
Subtract 13 from
each side of equation $5n = -10$

divide each side of
equation by 5 $n = -2$

(b) Solve $2 - 3n = 14$
Subtract 2 from
each side of equation $-3n = 12$

divide each side of
equation by -3 $n = -4$

E2.6

Solve these equations:

1 $2n + 1 = 4$ **2** $10n + 7 = 14$ **3** $4n + 11 = 8$

4 $5 - 2n = 11$ **5** $-4 - 3n = -10$ **6** $30 = 40 + 2n$

7 $3x + 4 = 6$ **8** $5x + 8 = 12$ **9** $2x + 9 = 8$

10 $4x + 9 = 5$ **11** $3x + 8 = 7$ **12** $8x + 5 = 2$

13 $6x + 10 = 5$ **14** $6x + 19 = 16$ **15** $4x + 3 = 17$

In questions **16** to **21** below, I am thinking of
a number. Write down an equation then solve it
to find the number.

16   If we multiply the number by 4 and then add 2, the answer is 3.
Let the number be n so $4n + 2 = 3$.
Now solve the equation to find n.

17   If we multiply the number by 7 and then add 5, the answer is 8.

18   If we multiply the number by 5 and then add 11, the answer is 6.

19   If we double the number and add 7, the answer is 1.

20   If we multiply the number by 8 and subtract 4, the answer is -20.

21   If we treble the number and add 8, the answer is -7.

Solve these equations:

22 $7x + 8 = -6$ **23** $4x - 6 = -22$ **24** $6x - 2 = -20$

25 $9x + 4 = -32$ **26** $14 = 20 + 2x$ **27** $31 = 39 + 4x$

28 $8 = 33 + 5x$ **29** $9 - 2x = 17$ **30** $16 - 5x = 31$

31 $13 - 7x = -22$ **32** $-6 = 9 + 3x$ **33** $20 = 48 - 7x$

Overtime is money paid for working more than the agreed number of hours each week.

Overtime is often paid at a different rate such as 'time and a half' or 'double time' (for example, evening work is often paid at 'time and a half' and weekend work is often 'double time').

> Jess the mechanic is paid £8 per hour and overtime at 'time and a half'.
>
> One week, Jess works for 40 hours plus 5 hours overtime. How much will Jess earn that week?
>
> pay for 40 hours is $40 \times £8 = £320$
>
> ('time and a half' pay rate) $= £8 \times 1.5 = £12$)
>
> pay for 5 hours overtime $= 5 \times £12 = £60$
>
> total pay $= £320 + £60 = £380$

Task

1 Andy is paid £10 per hour for a 40 hour week.

   Overtime is paid at time and a half.

   How much will he be paid for a full week plus two hours overtime?

2 Jane is paid £9 per hour for a 40 hour week.

   Overtime is paid at time and a half.

   How much will she be paid for a full week plus 5 hours overtime?

3

Work out how much the following people are paid for one week's work at Alf's Cheese Factory.

(a) Emma: 30 hours plus 4 hours overtime.

(b) Billy: 35 hours plus 6 hours overtime.

(c) Jack: 32 hours plus 7 hours overtime.

(d) Sarah: 40 hours plus 10 hours overtime.

(e) Ashley: 40 hours plus 8 hours overtime.

Pay Rate:
£8 per hour
Overtime paid at time and a half

4 Sophie is paid £7·30 per hour for 40 hours plus 4 hours overtime at *double time*. How much was she paid?

5 Max is paid £8·40 per hour for 35 hours plus 4 hours overtime at time and a half. How much was he paid?

6 Work out the amount of pay for each part below:

(a) £8·80 per hour. 30 hours plus 6 hours overtime at time and a half.

(b) £7·70 per hour. 40 hours plus 5 hours overtime at double time.

(c) £9·60 per hour. 32 hours plus 6 hours overtime at time and a half.

(d) £8·90 per hour. 38 hours plus 4 hours overtime at time and a half.

7

> ## BRIDGE MOTORS
>
> **Pay Rate: £9·50 per hour**
>
> **Saturday overtime: time and a half**
>
> **Sunday overtime: double time**

Jake works at Bridge Motors. He works for 40 hours then does 4 hours on Saturday and 3 hours on Sunday. How much money does Jake earn?

8 Tamsin works at Bridge Motors. She works for 36 hours then does 3 hours on Saturday and 6 hours on Sunday. How much money does Tamsin earn?

9 Jenny earns £8·40 per hour.

Simon earns £8·20 per hour.

Jenny works for 35 hours plus 6 hours overtime at time and a half.

Simon works for 35 hours plus 7 hours overtime at time and a half.

Who earns the most money and by how much?

10 Harry works for 35 hours plus some overtime at time and a half.
He earns £9 per hour.
One week he earns £423.
How many hours of overtime did he work for?

1. Using letters and symbols in algebra

(a) Henry is twice as old as Shreya. Write down an expression for Henry's age if Shreya is n years old.

(b) Natalie has £m. Ashley has three times more money than Natalie. Gavin has £8 less than Ashley. Write down an expression for the amount of money Gavin has.

(c) What is the total cost of 3 bikes at £x each and 4 skateboards at £y each.

2. Substituting numbers for letters

Find the value of each expression below:

(a) p^2 if $p = 9$ 　　　　　　　　(b) $a(3b + 4)$ if $a = 5$, $b = 3$

(c) $3b^2$ if $b = 2$ 　　　　　　　　(d) $5 + 7a$ if $a = -2$

(e) $a = \dfrac{b}{4} + 6$ 　　　Find the value of a when $b = 20$

(f) $V = IR$ 　　　Find the value of V when $I = 6{\cdot}2$, $R = 20{\cdot}1$

(g) $v = u + at$ 　　　Find the value of v when $u = 10$, $a = 5$, $t = 7$

3. Collecting and simplifying terms

Simplify

(a) $3x + 7y + 3x$ 　　　(b) $9a + 6b - 4a$ 　　　(c) $4p + 2 + 3p$

(d) $8m - 2m + 3n + n$ 　(e) $5 + 2x - 2 + 3x$ 　(f) $x^2 + x^2 + x^2$

(g) $4a + 2ab + 3ab$ 　　(h) $5a \times 3$ 　　　　(i) $3b \times 2b$

(j) $6p \div 2$ 　　　　　　(k) $45b \div 5$ 　　　　(l) $6m \times 4n$

4. Using rules for indices

Write each answer in index form.

(a) $6^7 \div 6^5$ 　　(b) $5^3 \times 5^4$ 　　(c) 4^0 　　　(d) $(3^2)^3$

(e) $\dfrac{4^2 \times 4^6}{(4^3)^2}$ 　　(f) $\dfrac{x^4 \times x^5}{x^7}$ 　　(g) $(x^4)^5$ 　　(h) $\dfrac{x^3 \times (x^2)^4}{(x^3)^3}$

5. Multiplying out brackets

Expand (this means 'multiply out')

(a) $3(x + 7)$ (b) $6(2a - b)$ (c) $5(x + 5y)$ (d) $p(q + 6)$

(e) $a(2a - 5)$ (f) $b(2b + 3c)$ (g) $3x(y - 2x)$ (h) $-4(2a - b)$

Multiply out and simplify

(i) $3(x + 2) + 5(x + 6)$ (j) $4(2m + 3) + 5(3m + 1)$

6. Taking out common factors

Factorise

(a) $5x + 15$ (b) $8a - 24$ (c) $35p - 21$ (d) $4a + 10b - 8c$

(e) $cd + ce$ (f) $x^2 - 4xy$ (g) $6pq - 10qr$ (h) $5a^2 + 30ab$

7. Solving equations with the unknown on one side

Solve these equations:

(a) $n + 4 = 11$ (b) $n - 3 = 12$ (c) $5n = 40$

(d) $\dfrac{n}{3} = 8$ (e) $6n = -18$ (f) $30 = 7n + 2$

(g) $23 = 4n - 9$ (h) $10n + 8 = 58$ (i) $38 = 9n - 7$

(j) Tom thinks of a number and then subtracts 8. The answer is 19.
Let the number be n. Make an equation using n then solve it to find
the number n.

Mixed examination questions

1 Write each expression in its simplest form.

(i) $6r + 5r - 4r$ (ii) $9s + 8t + 4s - 10t$ (OCR)

2 $a = 4b$

(a) Work out the value of a when $b = 3$

$P = 4d - 3$

(b) Work out the value of P when $d = 2$ (EDEXCEL)

3 (i) Copy and complete by filling in the box.

$$4 \times 4 \times 4 \times 4 \times 4 = 4^{\square}$$

(ii) Work out the value of x.

$$6^x = 6^4 \times 6^3$$ (OCR)

4 (a) Simplify $3a + 2a - a$

(b) Simplify $2b \times 3b$

(c) Multiply out $3(2c + 1)$ (AQA)

5 (a) Solve $3x = 12$

(b) Solve $y - 7 = 5$

(c) Solve $2t + 8 = 3$ (EDEXCEL)

6

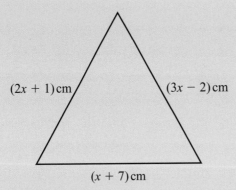

$(2x + 1)\,\text{cm}$ $(3x - 2)\,\text{cm}$

$(x + 7)\,\text{cm}$

Work out the length of the longest side of the triangle when $x = 5$.   (AQA)

7 (a) Multiply out.

$$a(3 + a)$$

(b) Factorise.

$$4b - 12$$ (OCR)

8 (a) Solve $b - 7 = 12$

(b) Solve $5e = 40$

(c) Solve $4m + 6 = 15$ (EDEXCEL)

9 Write in index form

(a) $2^6 \times 2^2$ (b) $3^4 \div 3^2$ (c) $\dfrac{5^4 \times 5^5}{5^3 \times 5^2}$

10 (a) Write down an expression for the perimeter of each triangle.
Write each answer as simply as possible.

(i)   (ii)

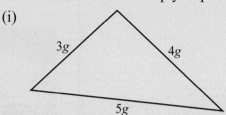

(b) Simplify.
$$3c - d - 2c - 4d$$

(c) A regular pentagon has a perimeter of length $10y$.

What is the length of one side of the pentagon?   (OCR)

11 (a) Factorise $4x + 10y$

(b) Factorise $x^2 + 7x$ (EDEXCEL)

12 (i) A sweet weighs w grams. Write down, in terms of w,
the weight of 10 sweets.

(ii) A boy is 6 years older than his brother. One of the boys
is x years old.

Write down, in terms of x, the 2 possible ages of his brother.   (WJEC)

13

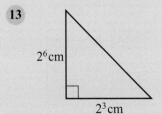

Work out the area of this
triangle, giving the answer
in index form.

14 Expand $4(3t - 1)$ (CEA)

15 (a) Solve $\dfrac{y}{4} = 8$

(b) Solve $3p - 2 = 16$ (CEA)

NUMBER 2

3

In this unit you will learn how to:

– use basic fractions

– find a fraction of a number

– find equivalent fractions

– put fractions in order of size

– convert between fractions and decimals

– order decimals

– convert improper fractions and mixed numbers

– add and subtract fractions

– multiply fractions

– divide fractions

– use reciprocals

– (USE YOUR MATHS!) – pitch the tent

Using basic fractions

M3.1

1 Which of these squares are split into quarters?

(a)   (b)   (c)   (d)

2 What fraction of each of these shapes is red?

(a)   (b)   (c)   (d)

(e)   (f)   (g)   (h)

3 In a class of 33 students, 18 are girls.

    (a) What fraction of the class are girls?

    (b) What fraction of the class are boys?

4 What fraction of these people have spiky hair?

5 In a class of 30 students, 25 are right-handed. What fraction are left-handed?

6 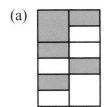 What fraction of these shapes are squares?

7 2, 3 and 5 are prime numbers.

    What fraction of these numbers are prime?

8	2	5	6	4	5	2
6	8	4	4	2	9	3
9	8	9	3	6	4	8

8 What fraction of £1 is:

    (a) 10p   (b) 25p   (c) 40p   (d) 3p   (e) 65p   (f) 48p

9 What fraction of the numbers from zero to ninety-nine contain the number 8?

10 What fraction of each shape below is red?

    (a)   (b)   (c)

Finding fractions of a number

M3.2

1 Find   (a) $\frac{1}{4}$ of 12   (b) $\frac{1}{4}$ of 28

2 Find   (a) $\frac{1}{3}$ of 24   (b) $\frac{1}{3}$ of 60

3 Find   (a) $\frac{2}{3}$ of 24   (b) $\frac{2}{3}$ of 60

4 $\frac{2}{3}$ of these sheep are sold.

How many sheep are sold?

Work out

5 $\frac{1}{10}$ of £70   **6** $\frac{1}{7}$ of £49   **7** $\frac{1}{8}$ of 48 g   **8** $\frac{1}{5}$ of 40

9 $\frac{3}{5}$ of 40   **10** $\frac{4}{7}$ of £49   **11** $\frac{7}{10}$ of 50   **12** $\frac{5}{8}$ of 48 g

13 The petrol tank of a car holds 60 litres. How much petrol is in the tank when it is $\frac{3}{5}$ full?

14 Work these out. You may use a calculator if you need to:

(a) $\frac{3}{4}$ of £64   (b) $\frac{2}{9}$ of £378   (c) $\frac{2}{3}$ of 1275 m   (d) $\frac{3}{5}$ of 270

(e) $\frac{3}{8}$ of £4976   (f) $\frac{5}{7}$ of 175 kg   (g) $\frac{1}{10}$ of £75   (h) $\frac{5}{8}$ of 112 cm

15 $\frac{9}{10}$ of a human body is made up of water.
Terri weighs 70 kg.
How much of her body is water?

M3.3

1

| Sofa normal price £320 |
| Sale $\frac{3}{8}$ off! |

How much does the sofa cost in the sale?

82

2 Jesse's new jeans are 96 cm long when she buys them. After washing they shrink to $\frac{7}{8}$ of their previous length. What is the new length of the jeans?

3 Dom has £28. He spends $\frac{3}{4}$ of his money on a Christmas present. How much money does he have left?

4 A packet of jelly tots has $\frac{3}{5}$ extra. If a packet normally has 45 g in it, how much does it weigh now?

5 Ollie has £96. He spends $\frac{1}{2}$ of it on clothes and $\frac{3}{8}$ of it on music. How much money does Ollie have left?

6 Here are calculations with letters. Put the answers in order of size, smallest first. Write down the letters to make a word.

C	F	R
$\frac{4}{5}$ of 45	$\frac{5}{9}$ of 45	$\frac{3}{10}$ of 60

E	P	T	E
$\frac{3}{4}$ of 36	$\frac{2}{7}$ of 21	$\frac{7}{8}$ of 48	$\frac{5}{6}$ of 18

7 Jenny earns £54 for her Saturday job. Jenny got $\frac{5}{6}$ extra as a bonus on the Saturday before Christmas. How much money did she get in total?

8 Mariana weighs 64 kg and Rishi weighs 75 kg. Mariana puts on $\frac{1}{8}$ of her body weight and Rishi loses $\frac{1}{15}$ of his body weight. Who weighs more now and by how much?

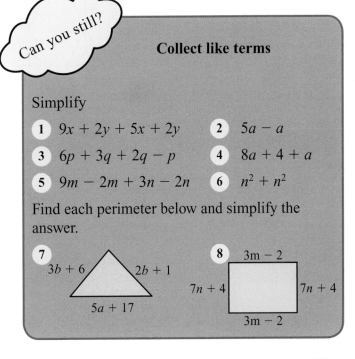

Can you still?

Collect like terms

Simplify

1 $9x + 2y + 5x + 2y$ **2** $5a - a$

3 $6p + 3q + 2q - p$ **4** $8a + 4 + a$

5 $9m - 2m + 3n - 2n$ **6** $n^2 + n^2$

Find each perimeter below and simplify the answer.

7 $3b + 6$ $\quad$ $2b + 1$ $\quad$ $5a + 17$

8 $3m - 2$ $\quad$ $7n + 4$ $\quad$ $7n + 4$ $\quad$ $3m - 2$

83

Cancelling Fractions

We often like to make the numerator (top number) and denominator (bottom number) as small as possible by dividing the numerator and denominator by the same number.

This is called 'cancelling down the fraction'.

$\frac{2}{8}$ is the same as $\frac{1}{4}$ $\frac{2}{8}$ $\frac{2}{8} \overset{\div 2}{\underset{\div 2}{=}} \frac{1}{4}$

M3.4

Write the equivalent fractions shown by the blue areas in each pair of diagrams.

1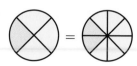

2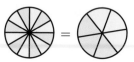

3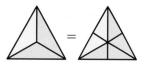

4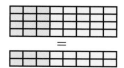

5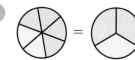

6

7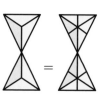

8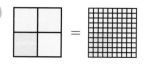

9

Copy and complete these equivalent fractions by filling in the box.

$\left(\text{Example: } \frac{7}{10} = \frac{\Box}{30} \implies \frac{7}{10} \overset{\times 3}{\underset{\times 3}{=}} \frac{21}{30}\right)$

10 $\frac{1}{6} = \frac{\Box}{12}$

11 $\frac{7}{8} = \frac{\Box}{16}$

12 $\frac{1}{2} = \frac{\Box}{8}$

13 $\frac{3}{5} = \frac{\Box}{20}$

14 $\frac{4}{5} = \frac{\Box}{20}$

15 $\frac{5}{6} = \frac{\Box}{12}$

16 $\frac{5}{8} = \frac{\Box}{24}$

17 $\frac{4}{7} = \frac{\Box}{21}$

18 $\frac{3}{4} = \frac{\Box}{20}$

19 $\frac{8}{9} = \frac{\Box}{45}$

20 $\frac{3}{10} = \frac{\Box}{60}$

21 $\frac{2}{5} = \frac{8}{\Box}$

22 $\frac{4}{9} = \frac{12}{\Box}$

23 $\frac{1}{2} = \frac{9}{\Box}$

24 $\frac{3}{8} = \frac{15}{\Box}$

25 $\frac{7}{10} = \frac{\Box}{80}$

84

Copy the questions below and fill in each box.

1 $\dfrac{25}{30} = \dfrac{\square}{6}$

2 $\dfrac{3}{24} = \dfrac{\square}{8}$

3 $\dfrac{8}{10} = \dfrac{\square}{5}$

4 $\dfrac{8}{12} = \dfrac{\square}{3}$

5 $\dfrac{10}{30} = \dfrac{1}{\square}$

6 $\dfrac{6}{18} = \dfrac{1}{\square}$

7 $\dfrac{12}{24} = \dfrac{\square}{2}$

8 $\dfrac{30}{40} = \dfrac{3}{\square}$

9 Cancel each fraction below to its lowest terms.

(a) $\dfrac{8}{20}$ (b) $\dfrac{4}{10}$ (c) $\dfrac{7}{21}$ (d) $\dfrac{4}{18}$ (e) $\dfrac{4}{12}$

(f) $\dfrac{20}{30}$ (g) $\dfrac{12}{18}$ (h) $\dfrac{20}{24}$ (i) $\dfrac{32}{36}$ (j) $\dfrac{6}{15}$

(k) $\dfrac{14}{42}$ (l) $\dfrac{18}{30}$ (m) $\dfrac{27}{45}$ (n) $\dfrac{28}{36}$ (o) $\dfrac{45}{90}$

10 Find the fractions in the tables below which are equivalent to the given fraction. Rearrange the letters to make a word using the clue.

(a) Find fractions $= \frac{1}{10}$

Clue: country

$\frac{8}{80}$	N
$\frac{6}{50}$	P
$\frac{5}{60}$	U
$\frac{4}{20}$	Y
$\frac{2}{20}$	A
$\frac{9}{90}$	I
$\frac{8}{24}$	M
$\frac{3}{30}$	C
$\frac{5}{50}$	H
$\frac{9}{108}$	U

(b) Find fractions $= \frac{3}{4}$

Clue: fruit

$\frac{6}{8}$	R
$\frac{9}{12}$	E
$\frac{7}{14}$	T
$\frac{8}{24}$	I
$\frac{5}{7}$	X
$\frac{5}{12}$	B
$\frac{15}{20}$	P
$\frac{9}{15}$	M
$\frac{25}{50}$	C
$\frac{75}{100}$	A

(c) Find fractions $= \frac{1}{4}$

Clue: school subject

$\frac{8}{20}$	T
$\frac{2}{8}$	G
$\frac{5}{20}$	E
$\frac{6}{25}$	F
$\frac{3}{12}$	H
$\frac{4}{16}$	N
$\frac{4}{7}$	A
$\frac{25}{100}$	L
$\frac{20}{80}$	I
$\frac{12}{48}$	S

(d) Find fractions $= \frac{2}{3}$

Clue: sport

$\frac{14}{22}$	N
$\frac{18}{21}$	A
$\frac{20}{30}$	O
$\frac{4}{6}$	Y
$\frac{32}{49}$	B
$\frac{60}{90}$	K
$\frac{16}{24}$	E
$\frac{12}{18}$	C
$\frac{16}{25}$	R
$\frac{14}{21}$	H

Key Facts

Get the denominator the same for each fraction so that you can easily compare the fractions.

Place $\frac{3}{4}$, $\frac{5}{8}$ and $\frac{4}{5}$ in order, smallest first.

Get the denominators the same for each fraction. 4, 8, and 5 all divide exactly into 40.

$$\frac{3}{4} \overset{\times 10}{\underset{\times 10}{=}} \frac{30}{40} \qquad \frac{5}{8} \overset{\times 5}{\underset{\times 5}{=}} \frac{25}{40} \qquad \frac{4}{5} \overset{\times 8}{\underset{\times 8}{=}} \frac{32}{40} \qquad \Rightarrow \qquad \begin{array}{ccc} \frac{25}{40} & \frac{30}{40} & \frac{32}{40} \\ \downarrow & \downarrow & \downarrow \\ \frac{5}{8} & \frac{3}{4} & \frac{4}{5} \end{array}$$

so the answer is

M3.6

1 Write down the larger fraction.

(a)

$\dfrac{3}{8}$ or $\dfrac{1}{2}$

(b)

$\dfrac{2}{5}$ or $\dfrac{3}{10}$

2 $\dfrac{1}{2} = \dfrac{\square}{6}$ $\qquad$ $\dfrac{1}{3} = \dfrac{\square}{6}$

Which is larger, $\dfrac{1}{2}$ or $\dfrac{1}{3}$?

3 $\dfrac{3}{4} = \dfrac{\square}{8}$

Which is larger, $\dfrac{3}{4}$ or $\dfrac{7}{8}$?

Can you still?

Expanding brackets

Expand (multiply out)

1 $5(x - 3)$ $\qquad$ **2** $4(2x + 5)$ $\qquad$ **3** $5(7m - 2)$

4 $7(4a + 2b)$ $\qquad$ **5** $a(b + c)$ $\qquad$ **6** $m(m - 6)$

7 $3(a + 3)$ $\qquad$ **8** $4n(n - 7)$ $\qquad$ **9** $5a(3a + 8)$

4 Write down the *larger* fraction, explaining your reasons clearly.

(a) $\frac{1}{4}$ or $\frac{1}{3}$

(b) $\frac{1}{10}$ or $\frac{1}{5}$

(c) $\frac{3}{8}$ or $\frac{3}{4}$

(d) $\frac{3}{4}$ or $\frac{2}{3}$

(e) $\frac{2}{5}$ or $\frac{7}{20}$

(f) $\frac{4}{7}$ or $\frac{3}{5}$

5 Place in order, *smallest first*:

(a) $\frac{1}{3}, \frac{1}{2}, \frac{1}{6}$

(b) $\frac{1}{2}, \frac{3}{8}, \frac{3}{4}$

(c) $\frac{1}{6}, \frac{2}{3}, \frac{7}{12}$

(d) $\frac{3}{10}, \frac{1}{2}, \frac{2}{5}$

(e) $\frac{7}{10}, \frac{4}{5}, \frac{13}{20}$

(f) $\frac{3}{4}, \frac{11}{16}, \frac{5}{8}$

6 Write down the *smaller* fraction, explaining your reasons clearly.

(a) $\frac{3}{5}$ or $\frac{11}{20}$

(b) $\frac{7}{10}$ or $\frac{13}{20}$

(c) $\frac{3}{4}$ or $\frac{13}{16}$

(d) $\frac{8}{9}$ or $\frac{9}{10}$

(e) $\frac{5}{6}$ or $\frac{4}{7}$

(f) $\frac{7}{40}$ or $\frac{1}{5}$

Decimals and fractions

 # Key Facts

If you change a decimal into a fraction, *cancel* the fraction if you can.

$$0{\cdot}2 = \frac{2}{10} \overset{\div 2}{\underset{\div 2}{=}} \frac{1}{5} \qquad\qquad 0{\cdot}34 = \frac{34}{100} \overset{\div 2}{\underset{\div 2}{=}} \frac{17}{50}$$

Changing fractions into decimals.

If you can find an equivalent fraction with the denominator (bottom part) equal to 10, 100 or 1000, it will be easier to find the decimal value.

$$\frac{3}{5} \overset{\times 2}{\underset{\times 2}{=}} \frac{6}{10} = 0{\cdot}6 \qquad \frac{7}{20} \overset{\times 5}{\underset{\times 5}{=}} \frac{35}{100} = 0{\cdot}35 \qquad \frac{101}{200} \overset{\times 5}{\underset{\times 5}{=}} \frac{505}{1000} = 0{\cdot}505$$

Note.

If you cannot easily change the denominator into 10, 100 or 1000, divide the numerator (top part) by the denominator (bottom part).

Write True or False for each of the following statements.

1 $0.3 = \dfrac{3}{10}$

2 $0.07 = \dfrac{7}{100}$

3 $0.08 = \dfrac{1}{8}$

4 $0.5 = \dfrac{1}{2}$

5 $0.049 = \dfrac{49}{100}$

6 $0.079 = \dfrac{79}{1000}$

7 $0.4 = \dfrac{2}{5}$

8 $0.25 = \dfrac{1}{4}$

9 $0.217 = \dfrac{217}{1000}$

10 $0.7 = \dfrac{1}{7}$

11 $0.75 = \dfrac{3}{4}$

12 $0.81 = \dfrac{81}{100}$

13 Aiden thinks that 0.43 is larger than $\dfrac{41}{100}$. Explain fully whether he is correct or not.

14 Elena thinks that 0.7 is larger than $\dfrac{3}{5}$. Explain fully whether she is correct or not.

Change the following decimals to fractions in their most simple form.

15 0.04

16 0.002

17 0.37

18 0.012

19 0.35

20 0.015

21 0.36

22 0.375

Copy questions **23** to **26** and fill in the boxes.

23 $\dfrac{4}{5} = \dfrac{\square}{10} = 0.\square$

24 $\dfrac{3}{20} = \dfrac{\square}{100} = 0.\square\square$

25 $\dfrac{9}{25} = \dfrac{\square}{100} = \square$

26 $\dfrac{11}{200} = \dfrac{\square}{1000} = \square$

Convert the fractions below to decimals.

27 $\dfrac{1}{20}$

28 $\dfrac{21}{25}$

29 $\dfrac{9}{20}$

30 $\dfrac{3}{200}$

31 $\dfrac{1}{8}$

32 $\dfrac{17}{20}$

33 $\dfrac{119}{1000}$

34 $\dfrac{21}{200}$

Change the following fractions to decimals by dividing the numerator by the denominator.

35 $\frac{2}{3}$ **36** $\frac{5}{11}$ **37** $\frac{2}{9}$

38 $\frac{7}{9}$ **39** $\frac{1}{6}$ **40** $\frac{5}{6}$

To change $\frac{3}{11}$ to a decimal we work out $3 \div 11$

$$\begin{array}{r} 0.\ 2\ 7\ 2\ 7\ 2\ 7... \\ 11\overline{)\ 3.\ ^30\ ^80\ ^30\ ^80\ ^30\ ^80...} \end{array}$$

$\frac{3}{11} = 0\cdot\dot{2}\dot{7}$

Ordering decimals

Key Facts

Write the set of decimals in a line with the decimal points in a column.

Fill in any empty spaces with zeros. This makes it easier to compare the decimals.

Arrange 0·29, 0·209, 0·09 and 0·2 in order, starting with the smallest.

Write in column	Put in zeros	Arrange in order
0·29	0·290	0·09
0·209	0·209	0·2
0·09	0·090	0·209
0·2	0·200	0·29

M3.8

1 Alexis takes 43·09 seconds to do a ski run. Christian takes 43·1 seconds to do the same ski run. Who was quicker?

2 Chen says that 7·2 is less than 7·02. Explain clearly whether he is correct or not.

$$\boxed{> \text{ means 'more than'} \qquad < \text{ means 'less than'}}$$

Copy and complete questions **3** to **10** by writing >, < or = in the box.

3 0·7 ▢ 0·73 **4** 0·18 ▢ 0·2 **5** 0·81 ▢ 0·82 **6** 0·6 ▢ 0·60

7 0·09 ▢ 0·83 **8** 3·1 ▢ 3·06 **9** 5·17 ▢ 5·2 **10** 0·187 ▢ 0·3

11 Nathan says that 0·83 is less than 0·847. Explain clearly whether he is correct or not.

12 Chloe says that 0·2 is less than 0·028. Explain clearly whether she is correct or not.

In questions **13** to **21**, arrange the numbers in order of size, smallest first.

13 0·014, 0·017, 0·1, 0·107 **14** 0·03, 0·303, 0·31, 0·32, 0·034

15 0·81, 0·806, 0·812, 0·087, 0·82 **16** 0·061, 0·06, 0·064, 0·603, 0·61

17 0·107, 0·11, 0·121, 0·13, 0·015 **18** 3·6, 3·16, 3·04, 3·2, 3·18

19 8·1, 8·13, 8·021, 8·14, 8·019 **20** 0·51, 5·02, 0·53, 5·1, 5·17

21 1·72, 1·07, 1·16, 1·03, 0·19

22 Here are numbers with letters

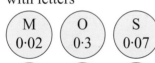

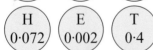

(M 0·02) (O 0·3) (S 0·07)

(Y 0·029) (S 0·402) (T 0·019)

(H 0·072) (E 0·002) (T 0·4)

(A 0·018) (R 0·31)

Put the numbers in order, smallest first. Write down just the letters. Write out the sentence clearly.

Can you still?

Substitute numbers for letters

Find the value of each expression when $x = 6$, $y = 2$ and $z = 4$

1 x^2 **2** yz **3** $3x + 2z$

4 $5(x - z)$ **5** $\dfrac{x}{y}$ **6** $y(x + z)$

7 xyz **8** $3y^2$ **9** z^3

10 $a = b + 9c$ Find a when $b = 4$ and $c = 3$

11 $f = \dfrac{m}{4} - 6$ Find f when $m = 32$

23

O 0·031 D 0·05 G 0·17 U 0·038

O 0·061 Y 0·03 H 0·006 N 0·108

W 0·01 O 0·007 I 0·1

Here are numbers with letters

Put the numbers in order, smallest first. Write down just the letters. Write out the sentence clearly.

24 Four people finish a kayak race with the following times:

Addison   3 minutes 12·38 seconds
Edward   3 minutes 12·6 seconds
Jaden   3 minutes 12·4 seconds
Kaitlyn   3 minutes 12·09 seconds

Write the names out in order starting with the quickest.

25 Max has three suitcases weighing 28·7 kg, 27·93 kg and 28·59 kg. He wants to put the heaviest suitcase into the boot of his car first. Which suitcase goes into his boot first?

26 Here we have fractions and decimals.

Write the numbers in order to find a word.

P $\frac{3}{4}$ S 0·01   N $\frac{5}{6}$

H $\frac{1}{50}$ E 0·81   A 0·035   R $\frac{3}{10}$

Improper fractions and mixed numbers

M3.9

Change the following improper fractions to mixed numbers.

1 $\frac{7}{2}$

2 $\frac{13}{6}$

3 $\frac{11}{4}$

4 $\frac{11}{3}$

Copy and complete the boxes in questions **5** to **8**.

5 $\dfrac{9}{4} = 2\dfrac{\square}{4}$ **6** $\dfrac{15}{7} = \square\dfrac{\square}{7}$ **7** $\dfrac{25}{8} = \square\dfrac{\square}{8}$ **8** $\dfrac{7}{4} = \square\dfrac{\square}{4}$

Change the following improper fractions to mixed numbers.

9 $\dfrac{20}{7}$ **10** $\dfrac{19}{9}$ **11** $\dfrac{5}{2}$ **12** $\dfrac{35}{6}$ **13** $\dfrac{23}{3}$ **14** $\dfrac{17}{2}$

15 $\dfrac{41}{8}$ **16** $\dfrac{29}{5}$ **17** $\dfrac{17}{6}$ **18** $\dfrac{29}{9}$ **19** $\dfrac{44}{5}$ **20** $\dfrac{27}{4}$

Change $2\dfrac{3}{8}$ to an improper fraction.

Multiply whole number by denominator $2 \times 8 = 16$

Add the numerator: $16 + 3 = 19$

Put sum over denominator. $\dfrac{19}{8}$

$2\left(= \dfrac{16}{8}\right) + \dfrac{3}{8}$ ➡ $2\dfrac{3}{8} = \dfrac{19}{8}$

M3.10

Change the following mixed numbers to improper fractions.

1 $2\dfrac{1}{3}$ **2**  $3\dfrac{1}{2}$

3 $4\dfrac{3}{4} = \dfrac{19}{\square}$ **4** $5\dfrac{2}{3} = \dfrac{17}{\square}$ **5** $4\dfrac{1}{2} = \dfrac{\square}{2}$ **6** $5\dfrac{3}{4} = \dfrac{\square}{4}$

7 $6\dfrac{1}{3}$ **8** $3\dfrac{7}{8}$ **9** $4\dfrac{2}{3}$ **10** $5\dfrac{3}{5}$ **11** $3\dfrac{2}{9}$ **12** $4\dfrac{3}{7}$

13 $8\dfrac{3}{4}$ **14** $7\dfrac{4}{9}$ **15** $9\dfrac{5}{7}$ **16** $6\dfrac{2}{5}$ **17** $8\dfrac{6}{7}$ **18** $5\dfrac{3}{8}$

19 Olivia says that $3\dfrac{3}{5}$ is smaller than $\dfrac{19}{5}$.

Is she correct?
Explain your answer fully.

Adding and subtracting fractions

(a) $\dfrac{1}{5} + \dfrac{1}{10} = \dfrac{2}{10} + \dfrac{1}{10} = \dfrac{3}{10}$

The denominators must be the same before adding.

(b) $\dfrac{3}{4} - \dfrac{1}{6} = \dfrac{9}{12} - \dfrac{2}{12} = \dfrac{7}{12}$

$\dfrac{3}{4} \overset{\times 3}{\underset{\times 3}{=}} \dfrac{9}{12}$ and $\dfrac{1}{6} \overset{\times 2}{\underset{\times 2}{=}} \dfrac{2}{12}$

M3.11

1 Copy and fill in the boxes.

(a) $\dfrac{1}{4} = \dfrac{\square}{20}$

(b) $\dfrac{2}{5} = \dfrac{\square}{20}$

(c) Work out $\dfrac{1}{4} + \dfrac{2}{5}$

2 Copy and fill in the boxes.

(a) $\dfrac{6}{7} = \dfrac{\square}{35}$

(b) $\dfrac{3}{5} = \dfrac{\square}{35}$

(c) Work out $\dfrac{6}{7} - \dfrac{3}{5}$

Work out

3 $\dfrac{1}{5} + \dfrac{2}{3}$

4 $\dfrac{3}{4} - \dfrac{2}{7}$

5 $\dfrac{3}{8} + \dfrac{3}{10}$

6 $\dfrac{1}{3} + \dfrac{2}{15}$

7 $\dfrac{5}{8} - \dfrac{1}{4}$

8 $\dfrac{4}{5} + \dfrac{1}{10}$

9 $\dfrac{1}{6} + \dfrac{2}{3}$

10 $\dfrac{2}{5} + \dfrac{3}{10}$

11 $\dfrac{5}{8} - \dfrac{1}{2}$

12 $\dfrac{1}{3} - \dfrac{1}{4}$

13 $\dfrac{1}{2} + \dfrac{1}{3}$

14 $\dfrac{2}{3} + \dfrac{1}{4}$

In questions **15** to **17**, which answer is the odd one out?

15 (a) $\dfrac{3}{7} + \dfrac{1}{7}$

(b) $\dfrac{6}{7} - \dfrac{2}{7}$

(c) $\dfrac{2}{7} + \dfrac{1}{7}$

16 (a) $\dfrac{1}{4} + \dfrac{1}{3}$

(b) $\dfrac{1}{6} + \dfrac{1}{2}$

(c) $\dfrac{5}{6} - \dfrac{1}{4}$

17 (a) $\dfrac{3}{5} - \dfrac{1}{20}$

(b) $\dfrac{1}{5} + \dfrac{9}{20}$

(c) $\dfrac{3}{4} - \dfrac{1}{10}$

1 (a) Write $2\frac{1}{4}$ as an improper fraction.

   (b) Work out $2\frac{1}{4} + \frac{2}{3}$, giving the answer as a mixed number.

2 (a) Write $2\frac{1}{5}$ as an improper fraction.

   (b) Write $1\frac{3}{4}$ as an improper fraction.

   (c) Work out $2\frac{1}{5} + 1\frac{3}{4}$, giving the answer as a mixed number.

3 Match each question to the correct answer.

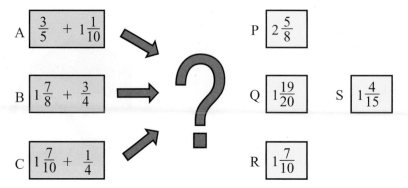

A $\frac{3}{5} + 1\frac{1}{10}$

B $1\frac{7}{8} + \frac{3}{4}$

C $1\frac{7}{10} + \frac{1}{4}$

P $2\frac{5}{8}$

Q $1\frac{19}{20}$ S $1\frac{4}{15}$

R $1\frac{7}{10}$

4 Work out

   (a) $2\frac{1}{3} + \frac{5}{8}$

   (b) $1\frac{7}{8} + \frac{5}{6}$

   (c) $5\frac{1}{2} + \frac{3}{5}$

   (d) $2\frac{1}{3} + 1\frac{1}{2}$

5 Work out

   (a) $2\frac{1}{10} - \frac{2}{3}$

   (b) $3\frac{1}{4} - 1\frac{1}{2}$

   (c) $2\frac{3}{4} - \frac{2}{5}$

Can you still?

Common factors

Factorise

1 $3a + 6b$ **2** $10m - 15n$

3 $ab - ac$ **4** $6ab + 4ac$

5 $a^2 - ab$ **6** $m^2 + 3mn$

7 $4m^2 - 2mn$ **8** $6a^2 + 15ab$

9 $5abc + 6ab$ **10** $4mn + 12m^2$

11 $6m^2n - 18mn$ **12** $6ab + 15a^2$

6

A ● C

? km   B

$3\frac{2}{3}$ km

The total distance along the road from A to C is $8\frac{1}{4}$ km.

What is the distance between A and B along the road?

7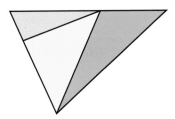

$\frac{2}{5}$ of the large triangle is yellow.
$\frac{1}{3}$ of the large triangle is red.
What fraction of the large
triangle is green?

8 $\frac{5}{6}$ of the people at a carnival
are dancers. $\frac{1}{8}$ of the people
collect money for charity.
What fraction of the people
do not dance or collect money?

Multiplying fractions

The diagram shows that $\frac{1}{2}$ of $\frac{1}{3} = \frac{1}{6}$.
We say $\frac{1}{2} \times \frac{1}{3} = \frac{1}{6}$

> To multiply fractions, multiply the numerators
> and multiply the denominators.

(a) $\frac{1}{3} \times \frac{2}{5} = \frac{2}{15}$

(b) $2\frac{1}{2} \times 3\frac{2}{5} = \frac{1\cancel{5}}{2} \times \frac{17}{\cancel{5}_1} = \frac{17}{2} = 8\frac{1}{2}$

M3.12

Work out

1 (a) $\frac{1}{2}$ of $\frac{1}{4}$ (b) $\frac{1}{3}$ of $\frac{1}{3}$ (c) $\frac{1}{4}$ of $\frac{1}{3}$ (d) $\frac{1}{2}$ of $\frac{1}{6}$

2 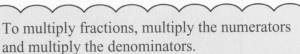 Draw this rectangle and put in more
lines to show that $\frac{1}{4}$ of $\frac{1}{3} = \frac{1}{12}$

3 (a) $\frac{1}{2}$ of $\frac{3}{4}$ (b) $\frac{2}{3}$ of $\frac{3}{4}$ (c) $\frac{1}{4}$ of $\frac{2}{3}$ (d) $\frac{1}{2}$ of $\frac{2}{5}$

Work out

4 (a) $\dfrac{4}{5}$ of $\dfrac{2}{7}$ 　　(b) $\dfrac{1}{5}$ of $\dfrac{5}{6}$ 　　(c) $\dfrac{1}{3}$ of $\dfrac{3}{4}$ 　　(d) $\dfrac{2}{3}$ of $\dfrac{3}{5}$

5 Some people estimate that they will spend 70 minutes rafting down a river. How many minutes are left when they have completed $\dfrac{9}{10}$ of their journey?

Work out the following questions (you must cancel your answers where possible):

6 $\dfrac{2}{3} \times \dfrac{1}{7}$ 　　　　**7** $\dfrac{1}{9} \times \dfrac{1}{10}$ 　　　　**8** $\dfrac{3}{4} \times \dfrac{1}{5}$

9 $\dfrac{5}{7} \times \dfrac{14}{15}$ 　　　**10** $\dfrac{1}{3} \times \dfrac{1}{8}$ 　　　**11** $\dfrac{2}{3} \times \dfrac{1}{8}$

12 $\dfrac{3}{4} \times \dfrac{2}{3}$ 　　　**13** $\dfrac{2}{9} \times \dfrac{3}{8}$ 　　　**14** $\dfrac{1}{9} \times \dfrac{1}{4}$

15 $\dfrac{3}{4} \times \dfrac{1}{9}$ 　　　**16** $\dfrac{3}{5} \times \dfrac{5}{9}$ 　　　**17** $\dfrac{7}{9} \times \dfrac{3}{14}$

18 $\dfrac{1}{10}$ of the children born in a hospital are twins. $\dfrac{3}{4}$ of these are identical twins. What fraction of the children born in the hospital are identical twins?

19 Work out

(a) $\dfrac{3}{8} \times 16$ 　　(b) $\dfrac{2}{5} \times 20$

(c) $\dfrac{3}{4} \times 20$ 　　(d) $\dfrac{1}{8} \times 6$

E3.2

1 Copy and complete

$$\dfrac{3}{4} \times 1\dfrac{2}{5} = \dfrac{3}{4} \times \dfrac{\square}{5} = \dfrac{\square}{20} = \square\dfrac{\square}{20}$$

Work out

2 $3\frac{1}{2} \times \frac{8}{21}$

3 $1\frac{1}{4} \times \frac{3}{5}$

4 $1\frac{2}{3} \times 1\frac{1}{5}$

5 $3\frac{1}{2} \times 1\frac{1}{21}$

6 $2\frac{1}{4} \times 3\frac{1}{5}$

7 $4\frac{1}{2} \times 2\frac{2}{3}$

8 $\frac{1}{20} \times 15$

9 $1\frac{1}{9} \times 5\frac{2}{5}$

10 Match each question to the correct answer.

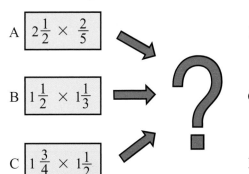

A $\boxed{2\frac{1}{2} \times \frac{2}{5}}$

B $\boxed{1\frac{1}{2} \times 1\frac{1}{3}}$

C $\boxed{1\frac{3}{4} \times 1\frac{1}{2}}$

P $\boxed{2}$

Q $\boxed{2\frac{5}{8}}$

R $\boxed{1}$

11 Work out $\frac{1}{5} + \left(\frac{1}{5} \times \frac{1}{5}\right)$

12

Work out the area
of this triangle.
Cancel your answer.

$\frac{3}{8}$ cm

$\frac{2}{5}$ cm

Dividing fractions

So: $3 \div \frac{1}{2} = 6$

How many halves are there in 3?

Answer: 6

Notice that $3 \times \frac{2}{1} = \frac{6}{1} = 6$

> To divide two fractions, turn the second fraction
> upside-down and then multiply.

(a) $\frac{1}{2} \div \frac{3}{4} = \frac{1}{2} \times \frac{4}{3} = \frac{4}{6} = \frac{2}{3}$

(b) $2\frac{1}{2} \div \frac{2}{3} = \frac{5}{2} \times \frac{3}{2} = \frac{15}{4} = 3\frac{3}{4}$

97

Copy and complete questions **1** to **3** :

1 $\dfrac{1}{4} \div \dfrac{1}{3}$

$= \dfrac{1}{4} \times \dfrac{\Box}{1}$

$= \dfrac{\Box}{4}$

2 $\dfrac{2}{7} \div \dfrac{5}{9}$

$= \dfrac{2}{7} \times \dfrac{\Box}{5}$

$= \dfrac{\Box}{\Box}$

3 $\dfrac{1}{8} \div \dfrac{5}{7}$

$= \dfrac{1}{8} \times \dfrac{\Box}{5}$

$= \dfrac{\Box}{\Box}$

Work out

4 $9 \div \dfrac{1}{3}$

5 $2 \div \dfrac{1}{2}$

6 $8 \div \dfrac{1}{4}$

7 $6 \div \dfrac{1}{5}$

8 $\dfrac{1}{3} \div \dfrac{2}{9}$

9 $\dfrac{2}{5} \div \dfrac{1}{4}$

10 $\dfrac{1}{9} \div \dfrac{3}{5}$

11 $\dfrac{2}{7} \div \dfrac{4}{5}$

12 Match each question to the correct answer:

A $\boxed{\dfrac{1}{6} \div \dfrac{3}{4}}$

B $\boxed{\dfrac{3}{8} \div \dfrac{5}{7}}$

C $\boxed{\dfrac{1}{6} \div \dfrac{3}{8}}$

P $\boxed{\dfrac{21}{40}}$ S $\boxed{\dfrac{21}{13}}$

Q $\boxed{\dfrac{4}{9}}$

R $\boxed{\dfrac{2}{9}}$

13 A recipe for a cake uses $\dfrac{2}{3}$ of a pound of sugar.

How many cakes can be made from 6 pounds of sugar?

14 Brandon has a $\dfrac{3}{4}$ hour driving lesson each week.

How many weeks will it take Brandon to get 24 hours of driving practice?

Work out

1 $1\dfrac{1}{5} \div \dfrac{3}{10}$

2 $4\dfrac{1}{2} \div \dfrac{7}{10}$

3 $2\dfrac{1}{10} \div 3\dfrac{1}{5}$

4 $5\dfrac{3}{8} \div 2\dfrac{1}{2}$

5 $2\frac{5}{8} \div \frac{1}{2}$ **6** $1\frac{2}{5} \div 1\frac{3}{20}$ **7** $1\frac{1}{5} \div 2\frac{1}{10}$ **8** $2\frac{9}{20} \div 5\frac{3}{10}$

9 $3\frac{1}{2} \div \frac{5}{16}$ **10** $3\frac{3}{5} \div 1\frac{7}{10}$ **11** $1\frac{1}{3} \div \frac{5}{6}$ **12** $6\frac{5}{6} \div 2\frac{1}{3}$

13 A farmer has $37\frac{1}{2}$ kg of potatoes. He packs them into $2\frac{1}{2}$ kg bags.

How many bags of potatoes will the farmer have?

14 Jack's two spaniels together eat $\frac{2}{3}$ of a tin of dog meat twice each day.
Jack has a box with 4 layers each of 16 tins of dog meat. How many days will the box provide food for his spaniels?

Using reciprocals

 Key Facts

The *reciprocal* of a number n is $\frac{1}{n}$ where n can never equal zero.

The reciprocal of 3 is $\frac{1}{3}$ (note: $3 \times \frac{1}{3} = 1$)

The reciprocal of 0·25 is $\frac{1}{0·25}$ which equals 4 (note: $0·25 \times 4 = 1$)

E3.4

1 Write down the reciprocal of each number below:

(a) 5   (b) 8   (c) $\frac{1}{2}$ (d) 0·2   (e) $\frac{1}{9}$ (f) 0·1

2 $0·8 \times 1·25 = 1$ and $0·8 \times 1·5 = 1·2$
Write down the reciprocal of 0·8

3 What number needs to be multiplied by $\frac{1}{7}$ to give an answer of 1?

4 What number needs to be multiplied by $\frac{1}{16}$ to give an answer of 1?

5 What is the reciprocal of $\frac{1}{n}$?

6 If $\frac{2}{3} \times \frac{3}{2} = 1$, write down the reciprocal of $\frac{2}{3}$.

7 Write down the reciprocal of:

(a) $\frac{3}{5}$ (b) $\frac{4}{9}$ (c) $\frac{2}{13}$ (d) $2\frac{1}{2}$ (e) 0·05

3 year average temperature in Belston

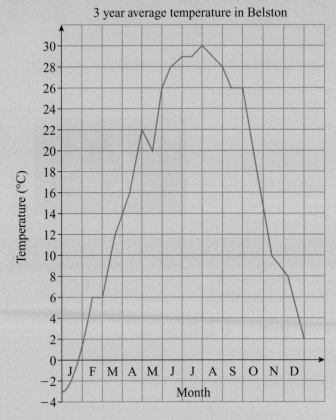

Alisha and her 3 friends are all seventeen years old. They want to camp for 8 nights around Belston.

They want to go camping when the temperature is likely to be between 26°C and 28°C but the amount of rainfall should be less than 4 cm.

They can choose from 4 campsites but want showers to be available.

3 year average rainfall in Belston

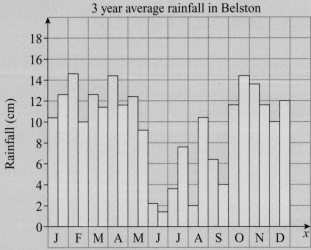

Task A
Use the charts and tables 1 and 2 to find out when and where Alisha and her friends should camp and how much the 8 nights will cost them.

Table 1	Patton Drive	Halby Coombe	Belston Park	Mowley Bush
Under 18s allowed with no adults		✓		✓
Electric hookup	✓		✓	✓
Dogs allowed	✓			✓
Showers available	✓	✓	✓	

Table 2

Campsite costs per night		30th March to 10th May	11th May to 20th June	21st June to 19th July	20th July to 31st August	1st September to 10th October	11th October to 15th November
Patton Drive	Tent	£9·25	£12·50	£13·75	£14·50	£12·50	£8·50
	Electric	£2·60	£2·60	£2·60	£2·60	£2·60	£2·60
	Each dog	£0·50	£0·50	£0·50	£0·50	£0·50	£0·50
Halby Coombe	Tent	£8·25	£9·75	£11·25	£12·75	£9·75	£8·25
Belston Park	Tent	£8·75	£10·50	£12·50	£13·50	£10·50	£8·50
	Electric	£2·85	£2·85	£2·85	£2·85	£2·85	£2·85
Mowley Bush	Tent	£9·50	£11·50	£13·50	£14·75	£11·50	£9·50
	Electric	£2·75	£2·75	£2·75	£2·75	£2·75	£2·75
	Each dog	£0·60	£0·60	£0·60	£0·60	£0·60	£0·60

Trains	Monday to Saturday							Sunday			
Chesham	0747	0832	1015	–	1402	1613	–	0859	1154	1308	1712
Fulton	0812	0857	1040	1253	1427	1638	1809	0924	1219	1333	1737
Denby	0827	0912	1055	1308	1442	1653	1824	0939	1234	1348	1752
Derrington	0850	0935	1118	1331	1505	1716	1847	1002	1257	1411	1815
Canton	0910	0955	1138	1351	1525	1736	1907	1022	1317	1431	1835
Towley	0932	1017	1200	1413	1547	1758	1929	1044	1339	1453	1857
Bisham	0948	1033	1216	1429	1603	1814	1945	1100	1355	1509	1913
Witton	1017	1102	1245	1458	1632	1843	2014	1129	1424	1538	1942
Alton	1032	1117	1300	1513	1647	1858	2029	1144	1439	1553	1957

Task B

Alisha and her friends live in Denby. To go camping they must catch a train to Alton then a bus to Belton. Their campsite will not let new people in after 7 p.m.

At Alton it takes 9 minutes to walk from the train to the bus stop. At Belston it takes 12 minutes to walk from the bus stop to the campsite.

What is the latest train Alisha and her friends can catch in Denby on a Friday and how long does it take to get from Denby to the campsite?

Bus timetable

Henlow	0715	0745	0815	at these	15	until	2115
Rowton	0723	0753	0823	minutes	23		2123
Hanvale	0733	0803	0833	past each hour	33		2133
Corston	0740	0810	0840		40		2140
Alton	0743	0813	0843		43		2143
Parry-le-Hole	0748	0818	0848		48		2148
Barrow Tarn	0750	0820	0850		50		2150
Chinnock	0752	0852	0852		52		2152
Catley	0755	0855	0855		55		2155
Belston	0757	0857	0857		57		2157
Harley	0759	0859	0859		59		2159

1. Using basic fractions

(a)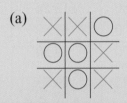

What fraction of these noughts and crosses are the crosses?

(b) What fraction of the days of the week begin with the letter T?

2. Finding a fraction of a number

(a)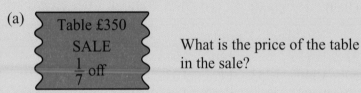

Table £350

SALE

$\frac{1}{7}$ off

What is the price of the table in the sale?

(b) Geena earns £300 each week. One week she gets paid $\frac{3}{10}$ extra for overtime.
How much money does she get paid that week?

3. Finding equivalent fractions

Copy and complete these equivalent fractions by filling in the box.

(a) $\frac{7}{8} = \frac{\square}{24}$ (b) $\frac{2}{7} = \frac{10}{\square}$ (c) $\frac{20}{25} = \frac{\square}{5}$

Cancel each fraction below to its lowest terms.

(d) $\frac{15}{40}$ (e) $\frac{12}{28}$ (f) $\frac{42}{56}$ (g) $\frac{24}{72}$

4. Putting fractions in order of size

Place in order *smallest first*:

(a) $\frac{2}{5}, \frac{1}{4}, \frac{3}{8}$ (b) $\frac{5}{6}, \frac{3}{4}, \frac{2}{3}, \frac{7}{12}$

5. Converting between fractions and decimals

Convert into decimals: (a) $\frac{7}{20}$ (b) $\frac{2}{25}$ (c) $\frac{5}{9}$

Convert to fractions in their most simple form:

(d) 0·37   (e) 0·028   (f) 0·7   (g) 0·42

---

6. Ordering decimals

(a) Which is larger, 0·04 or 0·3?   (b) Which is larger, 0·028 or 0·17?

In the questions below, arrange the numbers in order of size, smallest first:

(c) 0·062, 0·064, 0·63, 0·6   (d) 2·83, 2·183, 2·318, 2·14, 2·714, 2·049

---

7. Converting improper fractions and mixed numbers

Change the following improper fractions to mixed numbers.

(a) $\dfrac{23}{4}$ (b) $\dfrac{9}{2}$ (c) $\dfrac{17}{5}$ (d) $\dfrac{32}{5}$

Change the following mixed numbers to improper fractions.

(e) $2\dfrac{1}{4}$ (f) $5\dfrac{2}{3}$ (g) $3\dfrac{2}{7}$ (h) $4\dfrac{3}{8}$

---

8. Adding and subtracting fractions

Work out

(a) $\dfrac{4}{7} - \dfrac{1}{5}$ (b) $\dfrac{1}{4} + \dfrac{2}{3}$ (c) $2\dfrac{1}{3} + 1\dfrac{3}{4}$ (d) $2\dfrac{1}{4} - \dfrac{5}{6}$

---

9. Multiplying fractions

Work out

(a) $\dfrac{1}{3}$ of $\dfrac{1}{8}$ (b) $\dfrac{2}{7} \times \dfrac{3}{4}$ (c) $3\dfrac{2}{3} \times 1\dfrac{4}{5}$ (d) $\dfrac{8}{9} \times 12$

---

10. Dividing fractions

Work out

(a) $\dfrac{1}{9} \div \dfrac{1}{8}$ (b) $\dfrac{2}{7} \div \dfrac{5}{9}$ (c) $3\dfrac{2}{5} \div 2\dfrac{1}{2}$ (d) $5\dfrac{1}{2} \div 3$

---

11. Using reciprocals

(a) Write down the reciprocal of 10. (b) What is the reciprocal of 0·5?

Mixed examination questions

1 (a) Work out $\frac{2}{3} \times \frac{9}{10}$

Give your answer in its simplest form.

(b) Eric, the cat, eats $\frac{2}{3}$ of a tin of cat food every day.

How much cat food will Eric eat in 7 days   (EDEXCEL)

2 Here is a square grid.

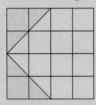

What fraction of the grid is shaded?
Give your answer in its simplest form.   (AQA)

3 Write these decimals in order of size, smallest first.

0·4   0·59   0·16   0·05   (OCR)

4 There are 24 men in a room.

$\frac{1}{2}$ of the men are wearing a red shirt.

$\frac{1}{3}$ of the men are wearing a green shirt.

The rest of the men are wearing a blue shirt.
Work out the number of men wearing a blue shirt.   (EDEXCEL)

5 Copy and circle the **two** fractions that are equivalent to $\frac{4}{5}$

$\frac{2}{10}$ $\frac{6}{8}$ $\frac{8}{10}$ $\frac{20}{25}$ $\frac{8}{9}$ (AQA)

6 (a) Which fraction is bigger, $\frac{1}{3}$ or $\frac{3}{10}$?
Show how you decide.

(b) Work out.

$$3\frac{2}{5} + \frac{2}{3}$$

Give your answer as a mixed number.   (OCR)

7 Write these decimals in order, smallest first.

$$4·17 \qquad 4·079 \qquad 4·712 \qquad 4·072 \qquad 4·7$$

(OCR)

8 Write down the reciprocal of 7

(CEA)

9 Cartons of tomato soup usually cost £1·80 each.
The price is reduced by one third.

Work out how much cheaper the new price is.

(OCR)

10 Work out

(a) $\dfrac{1}{3} \div \dfrac{8}{9}$

(b) $1\dfrac{3}{4} \times 2\dfrac{1}{2}$

11

What fraction of this regular hexagon is shaded?

12 (a) Put these in order starting with the smallest.

$$33·3 \qquad \frac{1}{3} \qquad -0·3 \qquad 3·03$$

(b) Jo thinks the difference between $-0·3$ and $33·3$ is 33.
Is she correct?
Show clearly how you decide.

(AQA)

13 Abigail spends $\dfrac{1}{3}$ of the day sleeping and $\dfrac{3}{8}$ of the day at work.

(a) What fraction of the day is left for other things?

(b) How many hours are left for other things?

GEOMETRY 1

In this unit you will learn how to:

- identify and label angles
- find angles
- use reflection symmetry and rotation symmetry
- recognise common quadrilaterals
- find angles in quadrilaterals
- find angles in polygons
- recognise congruent shapes
- use co-ordinates
- translate shapes
- reflect shapes in mirror lines
- rotate shapes
- enlarge shapes
- USE YOUR MATHS! – mobile phones

Identifying and labelling angles

 Key Facts

An **acute** angle is **less** than a $\frac{1}{4}$ turn (90°)

A **right** angle is a $\frac{1}{4}$ turn (90°)

An **obtuse** angle is **more** than a $\frac{1}{4}$ turn (90°) and **less** than a $\frac{1}{2}$ turn (180°)

A **reflex** angle is **more** than a $\frac{1}{2}$ turn (180°)

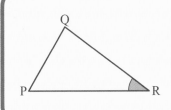

The angle shown is called angle QRP or angle PRQ.

We write this as QR̂P or PR̂Q.

M4.1

1. For each of these angles say whether they are acute, obtuse or reflex:

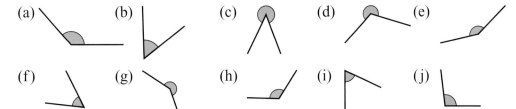

(a)　(b)　(c)　(d)　(e)

(f)　(g)　(h)　(i)　(j)

2. For each shape, say whether the angles marked are acute, obtuse or reflex:

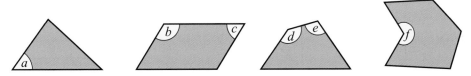

3. (a) Draw a triangle with an obtuse angle. Label this angle as AB̂C.

   (b) Draw a quadrilateral (a shape with 4 sides) with a reflex angle. Label this angle as PQ̂R.

   (c) Can you draw a triangle with a reflex angle inside it?

4.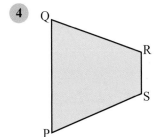

   Is angle PSR acute or obtuse?

5.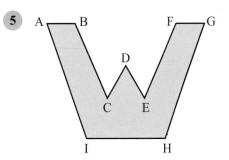

   (a) Name 3 acute angles.

   (b) Name 3 obtuse angles.

   (c) Is GĤI acute or obtuse?

   (d) Is BÂI acute or obtuse?

Key Facts

$x + 50° = 180°$
$x = 130°$

$y + 100° + 120° = 360°$
$y = 140°$

The angles on a straight line add up to 180°.

The angles at a point add up to 360°.

M4.2

Find the angles marked with the letters.

1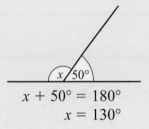

2

3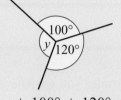

4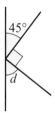

5

6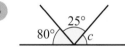

7

8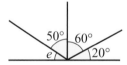

9

10

11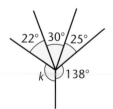

12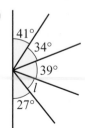

Key Facts

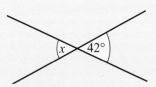

$x = 42°$

When 2 lines intersect the opposite angles are equal.
ie. vertically opposite angles are equal.

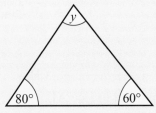

$y + 80° + 60° = 180°$
$y = 40°$
The angles in a triangle add up to 180°.

Lines which cross or meet at right angles are called **perpendicular** lines.

M4.3

Find the angles marked with the letters.

1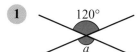

2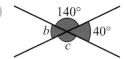

3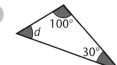

4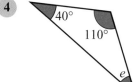

5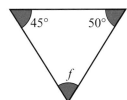

6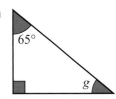

7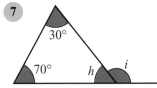

8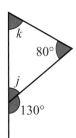

9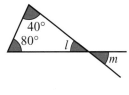

10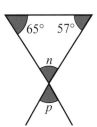

11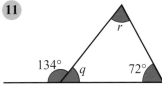

12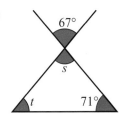

13 Which two lines are perpendicular?

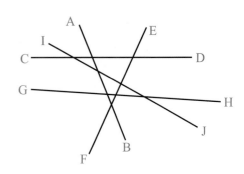

14 (a) Draw a line AB.   A————————B

   (b) Draw a line which is parallel to line AB.

   (c) Draw a line which is perpendicular to line AB.

Isosceles and equilateral triangles

(a)

$a = 73°$ (isosceles triangle)
$b + 73° + 73° = 180°$ (angles in a
$\qquad$ triangle add up to 180°)

$b = 34°$

b)

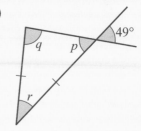

$p = 49°$ (vertically opposite)
$q = p = 49°$ (isosceles triangle)
$r + 49° + 49° = 180°$ (angles in a
$\qquad$ triangle add up to 180°)

$r = 82°$

M4.4

Find the angles marked with the letters.

1

2

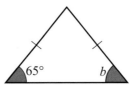

3

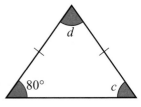

4

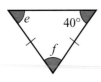

5

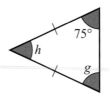

6

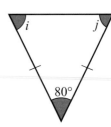

110

7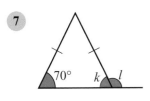

8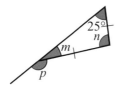

9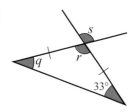

10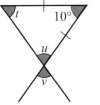

11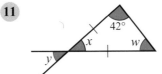

12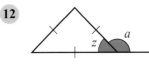

13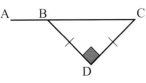

Find the value of
CB̂D and AB̂D.

14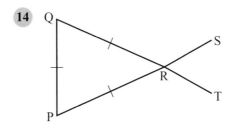

Find the value of
PR̂Q and SR̂T.

15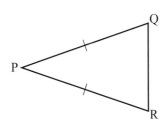

Triangle PQR is isosceles.
QP̂R is acute.
Write down possible values
for QP̂R, PQ̂R and PR̂Q.

Alternate and corresponding angles

 Key Facts

Many people think of
alternate angles as 'Z' angles.

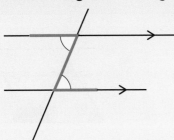

Alternate angles are equal

Many people think of
corresponding angles as 'F' angles.

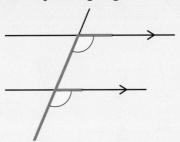

Corresponding angles are equal

1

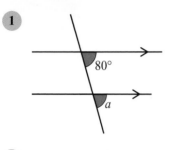

80°

a

2

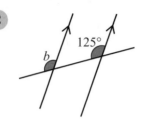

b   125°

3

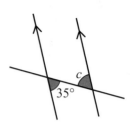

c

35°

4

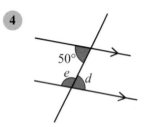

50°

e   d

5

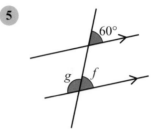

60°

g   f

6

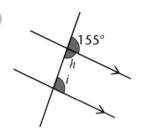

155°

h

i

7

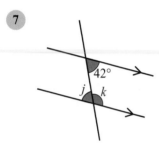

42°

j   k

8

m   n

143°   l

9

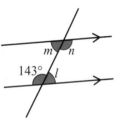

109°

p   80°   s

q   r

Can you still?

Mixed algebra

Simplify

1 $6x \times 7$ **2** $7 \times 4a$ **3** $3y \times 3y$

4 $25n \div 5$ **5** $4m \times 6n$ **6** $n^2 + n^2 + n^2$

Expand

7 $a(a + 2b)$ **8** $3n(n - 2)$

9 $5m(2m - 1)$ **10** $3x(2y + 5x)$

Factorise

11 $4a + 6b$ **12** $mn - my$ **13** $12m + 9mn$

14 $x^2 - 4x$ **15** $a^2 + 6ab$ **15** $15m^2 - 20mn$

10

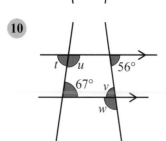

t   u

67°   56°

v

w

11

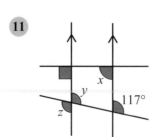

x

y

z   117°

2

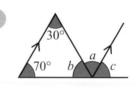

30°

70°   b   a   c

13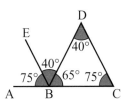

Which lines are parallel?
Give a reason for your answer.

14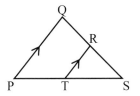

Lines PQ and RT are parallel.
Write down any 2 angles
which are equal.

15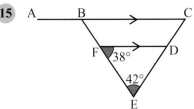

Find the values of

(a) $\hat{CBE}$

(b) $\hat{EDF}$

(c) $\hat{ABE}$

Reflection symmetry and rotational symmetry

M4.6

1 Which of these road signs have one or more lines of symmetry?

 (a) (b) (c) (d) (e) (f)

2 Which of these signs have a line of symmetry?

 (a) (b) (c) (d) (e) (f)

3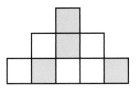

Copy this shape into your book.

Shade two more squares so that it
has a line of symmetry.

4 Sketch these shapes and draw on their line of symmetry using a dotted line.

Hint: Turn them
around to help
see their line
of symmetry

113

5 These shapes have more than one line of symmetry.
Sketch them in your book and draw on all the lines of symmetry.

more than 3   more than 4

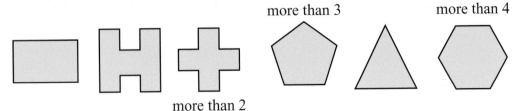

more than 2

6

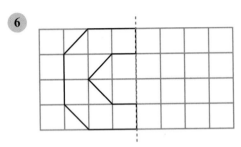

Copy this onto squared paper.

Complete the shapes so that the dotted line is a *line of symmetry*.

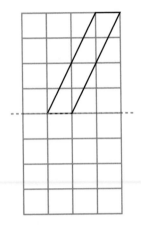

Copy this onto squared paper.

Complete the shape so that the dotted line is a *line of symmetry*.

 **Key Facts**

A shape has **rotational symmetry** if it fits onto itself when rotated (turned) before it gets back to its starting position.

The shape A fits onto itself three times when rotated through a complete turn. It has rotational symmetry of **order three**.

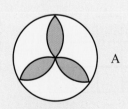

A

If a shape can only fit onto itself in its starting position, it has rotational symmetry of **order one**.

For each shape write down the order of rotational symmetry (use tracing paper if you wish).

1

2

3

4

5

6

7

8

9

10

11

12

13

14

Can you still?

Fractions and decimals

Answer true or false:

1 $\frac{9}{20} > 0.4$ **2** $\frac{4}{7} > \frac{3}{5}$

3 $0.35 < \frac{9}{25}$ **4** $0.06 > 0.059$

5 $\frac{5}{6} = \frac{35}{42}$ **6** $0.18 < \frac{1}{5}$

7 $0.48 = \frac{12}{25}$ **8** $\frac{15}{7} < 1\frac{6}{7}$

Explain each answer fully.

Quadrilaterals – Four sided shapes

You will need some punched strips and tracing paper.

1 Which of these shapes is a quadrilateral?

115

2 The diagram shows a square.

    (a) What is special about its angles?

    (b) What is special about its sides?

3 (a) Draw a square in your book.

    (b) Use dashes to show equal sides and little squares to show right angles.

4 (a) Draw a square in your book and use dotted lines to show all the lines of symmetry.

    (b) Copy and complete: A square has … lines of symmetry.

5 (a) Does the square have rotational symmetry?

    (b) Trace the square. How many times does it fit onto itself when you turn it?

    (c) Copy and complete: A square has rotational symmetry of order …

6

make a square

squash your square to make this shape it is called a rhombus

    (a) What is special about the sides of a rhombus?

    (b) What is special about its opposite angles?

rhombus

7 (a) Draw a rhombus in your book.

    (b) Use dashes to show equal sides and curves to show equal angles.

8 (a) How many lines of symmetry does a rhombus have?

    (b) Draw another rhombus in your book. Show its lines of symmetry using dotted lines.

9 (a) Does the rhombus have rotational symmetry?

    (b) Trace the rhombus. How many times does it fit onto itself when you turn it?

    (c) Copy and complete: A rhombus has rotational symmetry of order …

10 Which of these shapes are rhombuses?

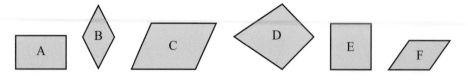

11

(a) Draw a rectangle in your book.

(b) Mark any equal sides using dashes.

(c) Mark any parallel lines using arrows.

(d) Mark any right angles using little squares.

12 (a) Draw a rectangle in your book. Show its lines of symmetry with dotted lines.

(b) Copy and complete: A rectangle has … lines of symmetry.

13 (a) Does the rectangle have rotational symmetry?

(b) Trace the rectangle. How many times does it fit onto itself when you turn it?

(c) Copy and complete: A rectangle has rotational symmetry of order …

14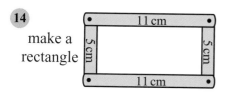

make a rectangle

squash your rectangle to make this shape. It is called a parallelogram.

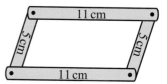

(a) Copy this parallelogram into your book.

(b) Why do you think it is called a parallelogram?

(c) Mark any parallel sides with arrows.

(d) Mark any equal angles with curves.

15 (a) How many lines of symmetry does a parallelogram have?

(b) Trace the parallelogram. Cut it out. Try and fold it onto itself.

(c) Copy and complete: A parallelogram has … lines of symmetry.

16 (a) Does the parallelogram have rotational symmetry?

(b) Trace the parallelogram. How many times does it fit onto itself when you turn it?

(c) Copy and complete: A parallelogram has rotational symmetry of order …

17 Which of these shapes are parallelograms?

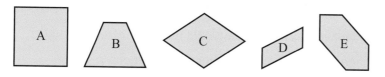

18 Copy and complete each shape below to make a parallelogram.

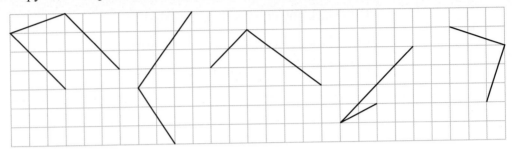

19 Take the parallelogram from question **14** apart.

Take the same four strips.

Make a quadrilateral which is not a parallelogram and not a rectangle.

This shape is called a kite.

20 (a) Draw a kite in your book.

(b) Mark any equal sides with dashes.

(c) Mark any equal angles with curves. (Check with a protractor!)

21 (a) Draw another kite in your book using dotted lines to show any lines of symmetry.

b) Copy and complete: A kite has … line of symmetry.

22   This line across from one corner to another is called a **diagonal**.

diagonal

Copy this **square**.
Draw on both its diagonals. What angle do they meet at?

23 Trace these special **quadrilaterals**.

Draw the diagonals on each shape.

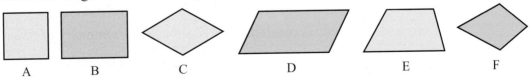

A   B   C   D   E   F

(a) Which of the quadrilaterals have diagonals that meet at right-angles?

(b) Which of the quadrilaterals have diagonals that are the same length?

(c) Which have diagonals which are also lines of symmetry?

Key Facts

A quadrilateral is made from 2 triangles.

Angles in a quadrilateral add up to 360°.

(2 × triangles = 2 × 180° = 360°)

M4.9

Find the angles marked with letters.

1
40° 100°
160°
a

2
120°
100°
b
20°

3
c
70°
165°

4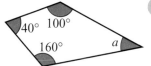
63° d
140° 32°

5
87°
105°
f e
72°

6
g h
75°
153°

7
123°
i
70°
j 118°

8
50°
k

9
82° 61°
126°
l
m

Can you still?

Mixed number work

1 How many factors does 28 have?

2 Express 50 as a product of its prime factors.

3 Which is larger 3^3 or 5^2?

4 Copy and put brackets in to make this calculation correct:

$$4 \times 2 + 3 - 2 = 18$$

5 Using any method, find the Highest Common Factor of 45 and 75.

10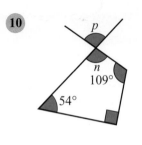

11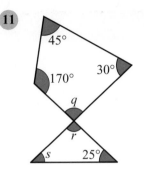

12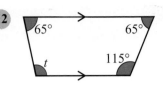

13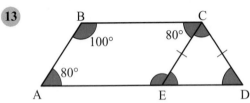

Find the values of

(a) AÊC (b) CÊD

(c) CD̂E (d) DĈE

14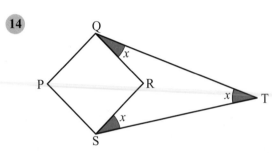

PQRS is a square.

Work out the value of QT̂S.

🔑 # Key Facts

A polygon is a shape with straight sides.

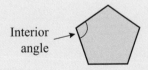

Interior angle →

A polygon with 5 sides is called a pentagon

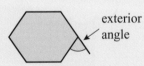

exterior angle

A polygon with 6 sides is called a hexagon

A **regular** polygon has equal sides and equal angles.

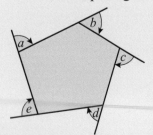

Put all the exterior angles together. We can see that the sum of the angles is 360°. This is true for any polygon.

Exterior angles of a polygon add up to 360°

120

All the exterior angles add up to 360°.

There are 8 sides so 8 equal exterior angles.

One exterior angle $= 360 \div 8 = 45°$

interior angle $+ 45° = 180°$

interior angle $x = 135°$

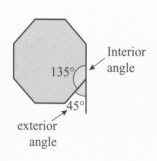

Interior angle

exterior angle

M4.10

1 Each shape below is a *regular* polygon.

Find the angles marked with letters.

  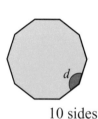

10 sides

2 Find the angles marked with letters.

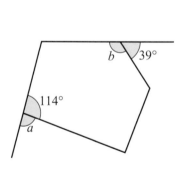 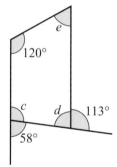 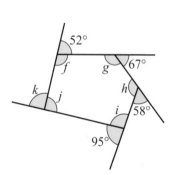

3 A dodecagon has 12 sides.
   (a) Find the size of each exterior angle of a *regular* dodecagon.
   (b) Write down the size of the interior angle for the same shape.

4 (a) Find the size of each exterior angle of a *regular* nonagon (9 sides).
   (b) Write down the size of the interior angle for the same shape.

5 Find the exterior angles of *regular* polygons with
   (a) 15 sides   (b) 20 sides   (c) 60 sides   (d) 90 sides

6 Find the interior angle of each polygon in question **5**.

121

7 Each exterior angle of a *regular* polygon is 8°. How many sides has the polygon?

8 Each exterior angle of a *regular* polygon is 20°. How many sides has the polygon?

9 This diagram shows the interior and exterior angles of a *regular* polygon. How many sides has the polygon?

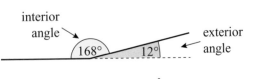

10 Find the size of the interior angle of a *regular* polygon with 24 sides.

11 The diagram shown is formed by joining regular pentagons. Find the angles *x* and *y*.

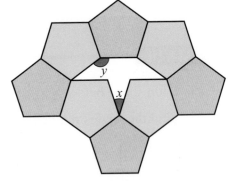

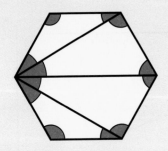

🔑 Key Facts

We can find the sum of the interior angles of any polygon by splitting the polygon into triangles (the triangles must not overlap).

A hexagon can be split into 4 triangles .
The angles in each triangle add up to 180°.
The *sum* of the *interior angles* of a hexagon is
$4 \times 180° = 720°$.

A polygon with 4 sides can be split into 2 triangles so interior angles add up to
$2 \times 180° = 360°$
A polygon with 5 sides can be split into 3 triangles so interior angles add up to
$3 \times 180° = 540°$
A polygon with 6 sides can be split into 4 triangles so interior angles add up to
$4 \times 180° = 720°$
A polygon with *n* sides can be split into $(n - 2)$ triangles so interior angles add up to $(n - 2) \times 180°$

The sum of interior angles of a polygon with *n* sides is $180(n - 2)°$

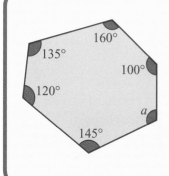

Find the value of angle a.

The polygon has 6 sides

so sum of interior angles = $\underbrace{180 \times (6 - 2)}_{180(n-2)}$ = $180 \times 4 = 720°$

angle a = $720° - (145° + 120° + 135° + 160° + 100°)$
      = $720° - 660° = 60°$

E4.1

1

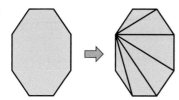

Copy and complete below:

An octagon can be split into ..... triangles.

Sum of interior angles = ... × 180°

      = ... °

2 Find the sum of the interior angles of:

(a) a nonagon (polygon with 9 sides).

(b) a dodecagon (polygon with 12 sides).

3

Copy and complete below:

This polygon can be split into ..... triangles.

Sum of interior angles = ... × 180°

      = ... °

Add up all the given angles:

$95° + 100° + 130° + 135°$ = ... °

angle x = ... °

In questions **4** to **9**, find the angles marked with letters.

4

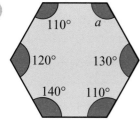

5

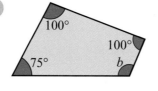

6

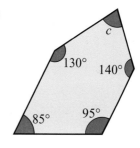

123

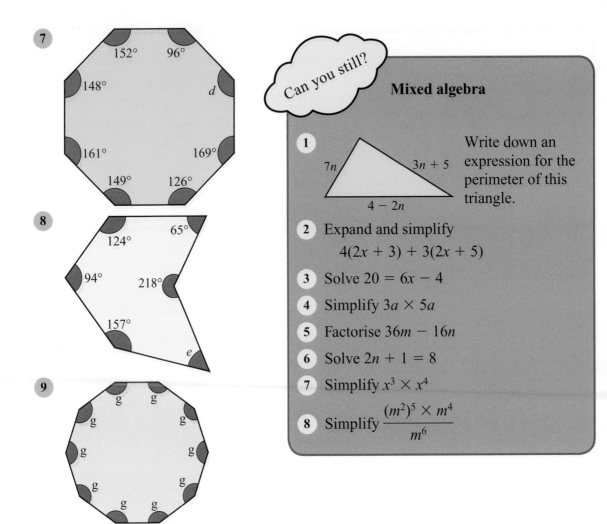

7

152° 96°

148° *d*

161° 169°

149° 126°

Can you still?

Mixed algebra

1

7*n*   3*n* + 5

4 − 2*n*

Write down an expression for the perimeter of this triangle.

2 Expand and simplify
$$4(2x + 3) + 3(2x + 5)$$

3 Solve $20 = 6x - 4$

4 Simplify $3a \times 5a$

5 Factorise $36m - 16n$

6 Solve $2n + 1 = 8$

7 Simplify $x^3 \times x^4$

8 Simplify $\dfrac{(m^2)^5 \times m^4}{m^6}$

8

65°

124°

94°   218°

157°

e

9

g *g*

g   *g*

g   *g*

g   *g*

g *g*

10 Find the sum of the interior angles in a polygon with 23 sides.

11 A polygon has 30 sides. If each interior angle is equal, what is the size of each interior angle?

Congruent shapes

🔑 **Key Facts**

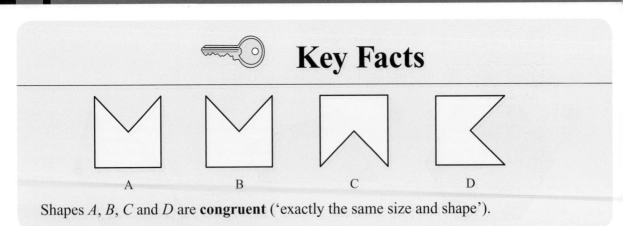

A   B   C   D

Shapes *A*, *B*, *C* and *D* are **congruent** ('exactly the same size and shape').

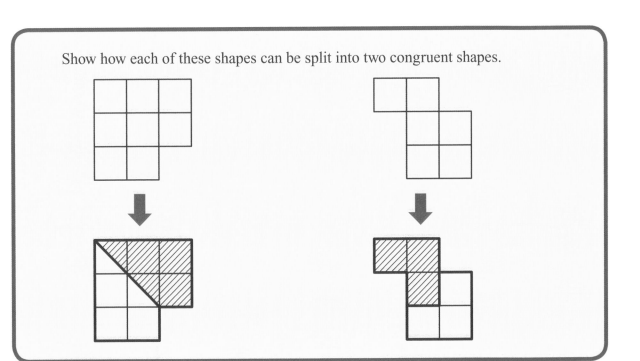

Show how each of these shapes can be split into two congruent shapes.

M4.11

Copy each shape in questions **1** to **12**.

Show how each shape can be split into two congruent shapes.

1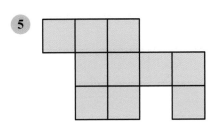

2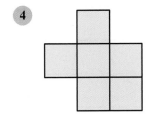

3

4

5

6

125

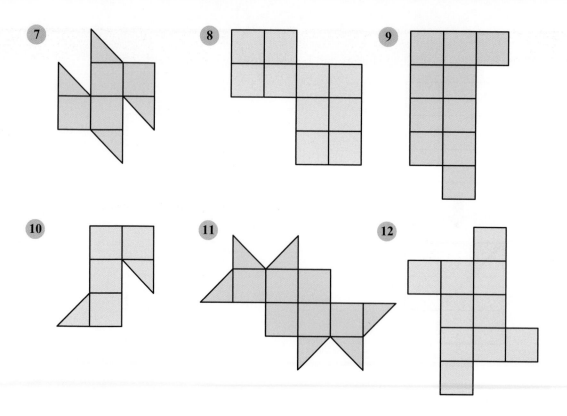

13 Each shape below is congruent to 2 other shapes. Write down the letters of each group of congruent shapes.

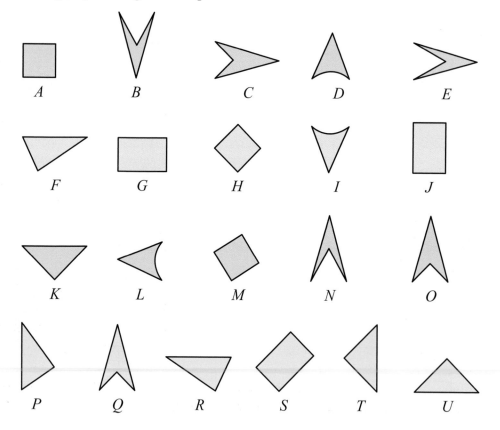

A

B

C

D

E

F

G

H

I

J

K

L

M

N

O

P

Q

R

S

T

U

Key Facts

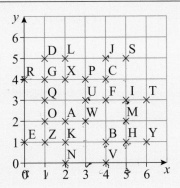

The position of a point on a grid is given by its co-ordinates. The *'across'* co-ordinate always comes first.

Point W is (3, 2)   Point N is (2, 0)

Point H is (5, 1)   Point R is (0, 4)

M4.12

1 Use the grid above to spell out this message.

(5, 3)   (2, 5) (1, 2) (4, 0) (0, 1)   (4, 1) (2, 5) (5, 3) (2, 0) (1, 4)

2 Use co-ordinates to write the word MATHEMATICS.

3 Use the grid above to spell out the joke below. Read across.

(3, 2) (5, 1) (2, 2) (6, 3)

(2, 5) (5, 3) (0, 1) (5, 5)   (2, 2) (6, 3)

(6, 3) (5, 1) (0, 1)

(4, 1) (1, 2) (6, 3) (6, 3) (1, 2) (5, 2)

(1, 2) (4, 3)   (6, 3) (5, 1) (0, 1)

(5, 5) (0, 1) (2, 2)   (2, 2) (2, 0) (1, 5)

(5, 5) (5, 1) (5, 3) (4, 0) (0, 1) (0, 4) (5, 5)?

(2, 2)   (2, 0) (0, 1) (0, 4) (4, 0) (1, 2) (3, 3) (5, 5)

(3, 2) (0, 4) (0, 1) (4, 4) (2, 1).

4 Write a message or joke of your own using co-ordinates. Ask a friend to work out your message.

Fractions

Work out

1 $\dfrac{5}{7} - \dfrac{1}{3}$ **2** $\dfrac{3}{8} \times \dfrac{5}{6}$

3 $3 \div \dfrac{1}{4}$ **4** $1\dfrac{3}{4} + 2\dfrac{1}{3}$

5 $\dfrac{7}{10} \div \dfrac{3}{4}$ **6** $2\dfrac{3}{5} \times 2\dfrac{1}{4}$

7 Brandon takes $\dfrac{3}{5}$ of an hour to mow his lawn and $\dfrac{1}{3}$ of an hour to trim its edges. He starts at 10:25. At what time does he finish?

5

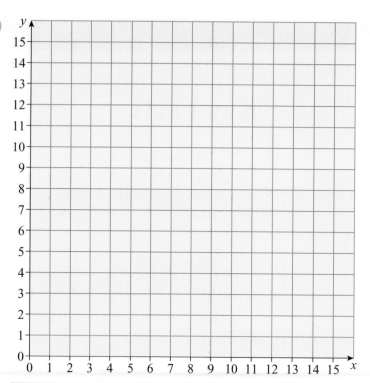

Draw a grid on squared paper as shown.

Label across from 0 to 15 (horizontal axis).

Label up from 0 to 15 (vertical axis).

Plot the points below and join them with a ruler in the order given.

$\left(5, 5\frac{1}{2}\right)$	$\left(4, 5\frac{1}{2}\right)$	$(3, 6)$	$\left(2\frac{1}{2}, 7\right)$	$\left(2\frac{1}{2}, 8\right)$	$\left(3, 9\frac{1}{2}\right)$
$(4, 10)$	$(5, 10)$	$\left(7\frac{1}{2}, 9\frac{1}{2}\right)$	$(8, 10)$	$(9, 10)$	$\left(9\frac{1}{2}, 9\frac{1}{2}\right)$
$\left(13\frac{1}{2}, 10\right)$	$\left(14\frac{1}{2}, 9\frac{1}{2}\right)$				

On the same picture plot the points below and join them up with a ruler in the order given. Do not join the last point in the box above with the first point in the new box.

$(5, 10)$	$\left(5, 10\frac{1}{2}\right)$	$\left(4\frac{1}{2}, 11\right)$	$(4, 11)$	$\left(4\frac{1}{2}, 12\right)$	$\left(7, 12\frac{1}{2}\right)$
$\left(11\frac{1}{2}, 12\right)$	$(11, 11)$	$(10, 10)$	$(10, 8)$	$\left(12, 7\frac{1}{2}\right)$	$(12, 8)$	$\left(13\frac{1}{2}, 9\right)$

$(11, 0)$	$(10, 2)$	$(6, 2)$	$(4, 0)$	$(6, 2)$	$(6, 3)$	$(4, 4)$

$(13, 7)$	$(13, 8)$	$\left(8, 4\frac{1}{2}\right)$	$\left(8, 5\frac{1}{2}\right)$

$(4, 11)$	$\left(3\frac{1}{2}, 11\right)$	$\left(3, 10\frac{1}{2}\right)$	$\left(3, 9\frac{1}{2}\right)$	$(8, 5)$	$(7, 4)$	$(4, 4)$	$\left(3, 4\frac{1}{2}\right)$	$\left(4, 5\frac{1}{2}\right)$

$(10, 2)$	$(12, 6)$	$(13, 6)$	$(14, 7)$	$(14, 8)$	$\left(13\frac{1}{2}, 9\right)$
$\left(13\frac{1}{2}, 13\right)$	$\left(11, 14\frac{1}{2}\right)$	$\left(7, 14\frac{1}{2}\right)$	$(3, 13)$	$(1, 11)$	$\left(4\frac{1}{2}, 12\right)$

$\left(7\frac{1}{2}, 9\frac{1}{2}\right)$	$\left(7\frac{1}{2}, 8\frac{1}{2}\right)$	$(8, 8)$	$(9, 8)$	$\left(9\frac{1}{2}, 8\frac{1}{2}\right)$	$\left(9\frac{1}{2}, 9\frac{1}{2}\right)$

Draw a ● at $(9, 9)$ and a ● at $(4, 10)$

Colour me in.

128

6 The graph shows several incomplete quadrilaterals.
Copy the diagram and complete the shapes.

(a) Write down the co-ordinates of the fourth vertex of each shape.

(b) Write down the co-ordinates of the centre of each shape.

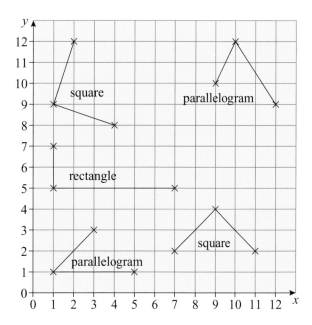

1

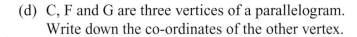

Remember: the 'across' co-ordinate always comes first.

Use the grid to spell out this message.

$(-2, 1)(1, 3)(1, -1)(-3, -2)$

$(1, -1)(-3, -2)$

$(1, -2)(-3, 3)(-3, -2)(0, -1)$

2 Copy the graph shown.

(a) A, B and C are three corners of a square. Write down the co-ordinates of the other corner.

(b) C, A and D are three corners of another square. Write down the co-ordinates of the other corner.

(c) B, D and E are three corners of a rectangle. Write down the co-ordinates of the other corner.

(d) C, F and G are three vertices of a parallelogram. Write down the co-ordinates of the other vertex.

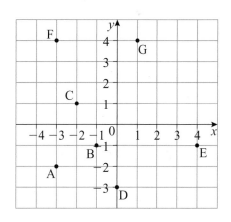

129

3 Draw a horizontal axis from -4 to 8 and a vertical axis from -8 to 11.

Plot the points below and join them up with a ruler in the order given.

$(0, 1)$ $(-2, 1)$ $\left(-2\frac{1}{2}, \frac{1}{2}\right)$ $\left(-2\frac{1}{2}, -\frac{1}{2}\right)$ $\left(2, -\frac{1}{2}\right)$ $\left(4, -1\frac{1}{2}\right)$ $(5, -1)$ $\left(4, -1\frac{1}{2}\right)$

$(4, -3)$ $\left(3, -2\frac{1}{2}\right)$ $\left(-1\frac{1}{2}, -2\frac{1}{2}\right)$ $(0, -5)$ $\left(\frac{1}{2}, -5\frac{1}{2}\right)$ $(1, -7)$ $(6, -5)$ $\left(5\frac{1}{2}, -4\right)$

$\left(4, -4\frac{1}{2}\right)$ $(2, -5)$ $\left(\frac{1}{2}, -5\frac{1}{2}\right)$ $(-1, -7)$ $(0, -5)$

On the same picture plot the points below and join them up with a ruler in the order given. Do not join the last point in the box above with the first point in the new box.

$(6, -1)$ $(6, 1)$ $\left(6\frac{1}{2}, 3\right)$ $\left(6, 3\frac{1}{2}\right)$ $\left(5\frac{1}{2}, 3\right)$ $\left(5\frac{1}{2}, 2\right)$ $(5, 2)$

$(5, 7)$ $(4, 8)$ $(0, 8)$ $\left(-2, 6\frac{1}{2}\right)$ $(-2, 4)$ $\left(-2\frac{1}{2}, 3\right)$

$(6, 2)$ $(6, 3)$

$(4, 3)$ $(4, 2)$ $(3, 1)$ $(2, 1)$ $(1, 2)$ $(1, 3)$ $(2, 4)$ $(3, 4)$ $(4, 3)$ $\left(5\frac{1}{2}, 3\right)$

$\left(-2, 6\frac{1}{2}\right)$ $(-3, 7)$ $(-3, 8)$ $(-1, 10)$ $\left(1, 10\frac{1}{2}\right)$ $\left(5, 10\frac{1}{2}\right)$ $(7, 9)$

$(7, 0)$ $\left(6\frac{1}{2}, -1\right)$ $(6, -1)$ $\left(5\frac{1}{2}, -4\right)$

$\left(-2\frac{1}{2}, -\frac{1}{2}\right)$ $(-3, -1)$ $\left(-3, -2\frac{1}{2}\right)$ $\left(-1\frac{1}{2}, -2\frac{1}{2}\right)$

$(1, -3)$ $\left(\frac{1}{2}, 3\right)$ $\left(\frac{1}{2}, 2\right)$ $\left(-\frac{1}{2}, 1\right)$ $\left(-1\frac{1}{2}, 1\right)$ $\left(-2\frac{1}{2}, 2\right)$ $\left(-2\frac{1}{2}, 3\right)$

$\left(-1\frac{1}{2}, 4\right)$ $\left(-\frac{1}{2}, 4\right)$ $\left(\frac{1}{2}, 3\right)$

$(-2, -1)$ $\left(-2\frac{1}{2}, -2\right)$ $(-1, -1)$ $\left(-1\frac{1}{2}, -2\right)$ $(0, -1)$ $\left(-\frac{1}{2}, -2\right)$

$(1, -1)$ $\left(\frac{1}{2}, -2\right)$ $(2, -1)$ $\left(1\frac{1}{2}, -2\right)$ $(3, -1)$ $\left(2\frac{1}{2}, -2\right)$

Draw a • at $(2, 2)$ and a • at $(-2, 2)$ Colour me in.

Key Facts

A **translation** means movement in a straight line (no turning).

Translation vector

To describe a translation, we do not have to use the words 'left', 'right', 'up', and 'down'. We use a vertical bracket like this:

$\begin{pmatrix} 2 \\ 3 \end{pmatrix}$ The number at the *top* shows 2 units to the *right*.
The number at the *bottom* shows 3 units *up*.

If the number at the top was -2 it would be 2 units to the *left*

If the number at the bottom was -3 it would be 3 units *down*

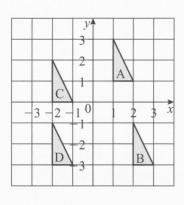

Use translation vectors to describe the following translations.

(a) *A* to *B*   (b) *A* to *C*

(c) *A* to *D*   (d) *B* to *C*

(a) $\begin{pmatrix} 1 \\ -4 \end{pmatrix}$ (b) $\begin{pmatrix} -3 \\ -1 \end{pmatrix}$ (c) $\begin{pmatrix} -3 \\ -4 \end{pmatrix}$ (d) $\begin{pmatrix} -4 \\ 3 \end{pmatrix}$

M4.13

 1

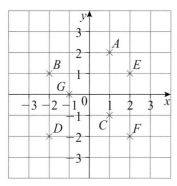

Use translation vectors to describe the following translations.

(a) *A* to *B*   (b) *A* to *F*

(c) *A* to *G*   (d) *B* to *C*

(e) *F* to *G*   (f) *D* to *G*

(g) *E* to *B*   (h) *B* to *F*

2

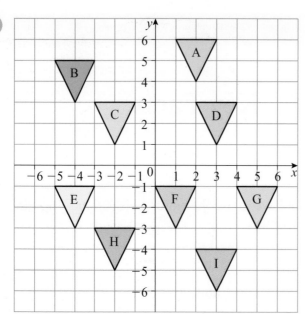

Use translation vectors to describe the following translations.

(a) *A* to *D*   (b) *A* to *G*

(c) *A* to *H*   (d) *A* to *I*

(e) *B* to *E*   (f) *B* to *H*

(g) *C* to *D*   (h) *C* to *A*

(i) *C* to *E*   (j) *D* to *B*

(k) *D* to *H*   (l) *E* to *G*

(m) *E* to *D*   (n) *F* to *C*

(o) *G* to *I*   (p) *G* to *B*

(q) *H* to *D*   (r) *I* to *C*

3

Copy the grid opposite and draw shape *A* as shown.

(a) Translate shape *A* through $\begin{pmatrix}5\\1\end{pmatrix}$
    Label the new shape *B*

(b) Translate shape *B* through $\begin{pmatrix}2\\-3\end{pmatrix}$
    Label the new shape *C*

(c) Translate shape *C* through $\begin{pmatrix}-2\\-5\end{pmatrix}$
    Label the new shape *D*

(d) Translate shape *D* through $\begin{pmatrix}-4\\4\end{pmatrix}$ Label the new shape *E*

(e) Translate shape *E* through $\begin{pmatrix}-3\\-5\end{pmatrix}$ Label the new shape *F*

(f) Use a translation vector to describe the translation that moves shape *E* to shape *B*

(g) Use a translation vector to describe the translation that moves shape *A* to shape *F*

(h) Use a translation vector to describe the translation that moves shape *D* to shape *B*

132

4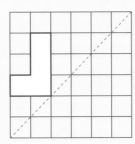

Shape *A* has moved to shape *B*.
Explain why this is *not* a translation.

Mixed algebra

1. Expand $4(2m - 5)$
2. Expand $4n(n + 3)$
3. If $a = \dfrac{v - u}{t}$ then find the value of a if $u = 16 \cdot 2$, $t = 10$ and $v = 23 \cdot 6$
4. Simplify $p^2 + p^2 + 3 + p^2$
5. Simplify $(n^3)^3 \times n^5$
6. $\underset{\longleftarrow 3a + 2 \longrightarrow \longleftarrow y \longrightarrow}{\overline{\longleftarrow\!\!\!-4a + 9\longrightarrow}}$ Express y in terms of a.

Reflections

Reflect this shape in the mirror line.

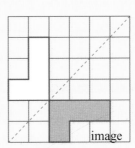

Advice
Turn the paper to make the mirror line vertical then draw the reflection.

image

M4.14

Draw each shape in questions **1** to **12** and reflect in the mirror line.

1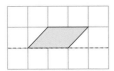

2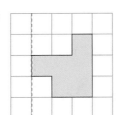

3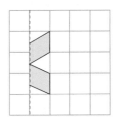

4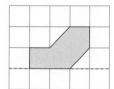

5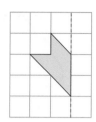

6

7

8

9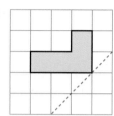

10

11

12

Copy each diagram in questions **13** to **15**. Draw the mirror line for the reflection of each shape.

13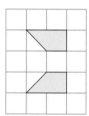

14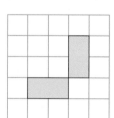

15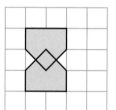

(a) Reflect triangle *A* in the *x*-axis.
Label the image (new triangle) *B*.

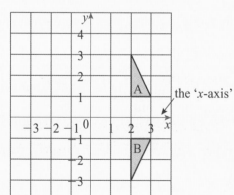

the '*x*-axis'

(b) Reflect triangle *A* in the line $x = 1$.
Label the image (new triangle) *C*.

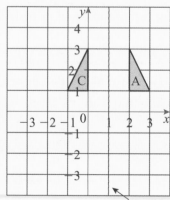

the line '$x = 1$'

1

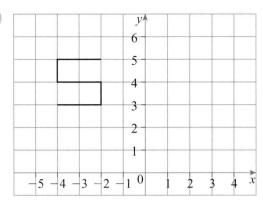

Copy this grid.
Copy the letter then
reflect it in the
y-axis.

2 Copy this grid.
Copy the shape then
reflect it in the
x-axis.

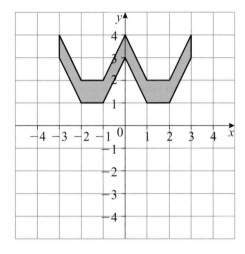

3

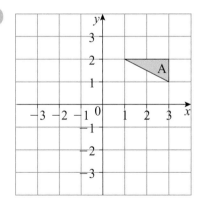

Copy the grid and shape opposite.

(a) Reflect triangle A in the y-axis.
Label the image (new triangle) B.

(b) Reflect triangle A in the x-axis.
Label the image C.

(c) Reflect triangle C in the y-axis.
Label the image D.

(d) Describe how you could *transform*
(change) triangle D into triangle B.

135

4

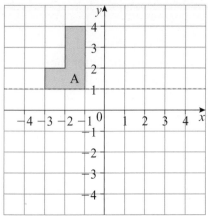

Copy the grid and shape above.

(a) Reflect shape *A* in the *y*-axis. Label the image *B*.

(b) Reflect shape *A* in the line *y* = 1 (the dotted line). Label the image *C*.

(c) Reflect shape *B* in the line *y* = 1. Label the image *D*.

(d) Describe how you could *transform* (change) shape *C* into shape *D*.

1 An orchard has 14 rows each with 7 trees. On average every tree should produce 85 apples each year. How many apples should the orchard produce in one year?

2 Write down a factor of 36 between 10 and 20 whose sum of its digits is a square number.

3 Express 42 800 in standard form.

4 Work out $-6 - -2 - 4$

5 Work out $(3 \times 10^7) \times (2 \times 10^{12})$, leaving the answer in standard form.

5 Shape *A* is reflected onto shape B opposite and shape P is reflected onto shape Q. Copy the diagram and draw the two mirror lines (lines of reflection).

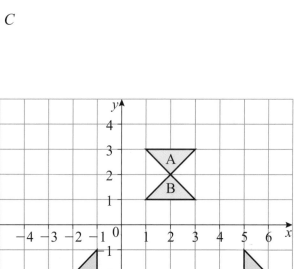

Key Facts

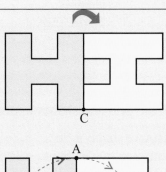

This shape has turned clockwise through a right angle (90° turn).

Remember: clockwise

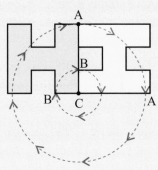

Each point in the shape rotates around a circle with its centre at the dot (C).

The dot (C) is called the **centre of rotation**.

Note

For 90° rotations, horizontal lines become vertical and vice versa.

M4.16

Use tracing paper. In questions **1** to **12**, draw the shape and the centre of rotation (C). Rotate the shape as indicated and draw the image.

1

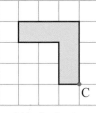

90° clockwise

2

90° anticlockwise

3

90° clockwise

4

180°

5

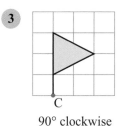

90° anticlockwise

6

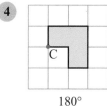

90° clockwise

7

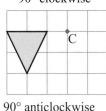

90° clockwise

8

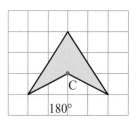

180°

137

9

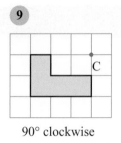

90° clockwise

10

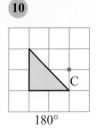

180°

11

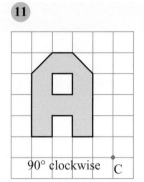

90° clockwise C

12

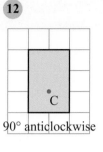

90° anticlockwise

13

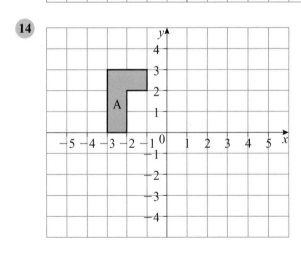

Copy the grid and shapes opposite.

(a) Rotate shape *A* 90° anticlockwise about $(-3, -4)$. Label the image *P*.

(b) Rotate shape *B* 90° clockwise about $(1, 0)$. Label the image *Q*.

(c) Rotate shape *C* 90° clockwise about $(2, 1)$. Label the image *R*.

14

Copy the grid opposite. The *x*-axis goes from -5 to 5. The *y*-axis goes from -4 to 4. Shape *A* has vertices (corners) at $(-1, 2)$, $(-1, 3)$, $(-3, 3)$, $(-3, 0)$, $(-2, 0)$ and $(-2, 2)$.

(a) Rotate shape *A* 180° about $(0, 2)$. Label the image *B*.

(b) Rotate shape *B* 90° clockwise about $(1, 0)$. Label the image *C*.

(c) Rotate shape *C* 90° anticlockwise about $(2, -2)$. Label the image *D*.

(d) Rotate shape *D* 90° anticlockwise about $(0, -3)$. Label the image *E*.

(e) Rotate shape *E* 90° anticlockwise about $(-5, 0)$. Label the image *F*.

138

Key Facts

An **enlargement** makes the shape larger (or smaller). The original and the enlargement must be exactly the same shape. All angles in both shapes stay the same.

A *mathematical enlargement* always has a centre of enlargement as well as a scale factor.

Drawing an enlargement
Draw an enlargement of triangle A with scale factor 3 about the centre of enlargement C.

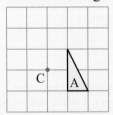

Join the centre *C* to one vertex (corner) with a dotted line

Multiply the length of the dotted line by the scale factor (do this by measuring or by counting squares) then draw the longer dotted line from C

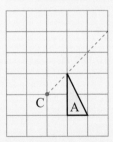

This shows where the top vertex will move to.

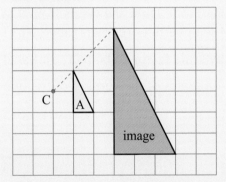

image

The rest of the enlarged shape can be drawn from this new vertex.

M4.17

For questions ① to ③, copy the diagram and then draw an enlargement using the scale factor and centre of enlargement (C) given. Leave room for the enlargement!

1

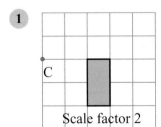

Scale factor 2

2

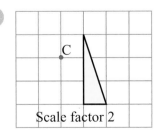

Scale factor 2

3

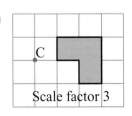

Scale factor 3

139

4 Look at your diagram for question **3**.

(a) Write down the area of the original shape.

(b) Write down the area of the enlarged shape.

(c) How many times bigger is the area of the enlarged shape? Compare this to the scale factor.

5

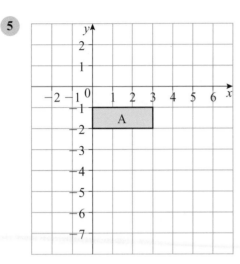

(a) Copy the grid and rectangle *A*. Enlarge rectangle *A* by scale factor 2 about (0, 0). Label the image *B*.

(b) Write down the area of *A*.

(c) Write down the area of *B*.

(d) How many times bigger is the area of *B*? Compare this to the scale factor.

6 (a) Draw the *x*-axis from 0 to 6. Draw the *y*-axis from 0 to 6. Draw the triangle *A* with vertices (corners) at (1, 3), (1, 4), (3, 4).

(b) Enlarge triangle *A* by scale factor 2 about (1, 5). Label the image *B*.

(c) Write down the co-ordinates of the vertices of triangle *B*.

USE YOUR MATHS! – Mobile phones

1 Do you have a mobile phone?

2 If yes, which one?

3 Why did you choose this phone?

4 When do you use your phone most often?

| Monday to Friday (during the day) | or | Monday to Friday (during the evening) | or | At the weekend |

5 How many minutes do you spend on the phone per day?

| 0 | or | 1–5 | or | 6–15 | or | 16–30 | or | 31–60 | or | more than 60 |

6   How many texts do you send per day?

| 0 | or | 1–5 | or | 6–10 | or | 11–15 | or | more than 15 |

7   What are the advantages and disadvantages of having a mobile phone?

8   Collect the above class data together with your teacher. Discuss the main findings.

Mobile phone bills

Contracts

You often pay a fixed monthly amount which allows you a certain number of minutes of phone calls and a certain number of text messages. You may have to pay extra if you exceed your limit.

Pay As You Go

You pay money in advance (sometimes by buying cards which allow you a certain amount of money on your phone). As soon as you have used up all your money, you have to buy more phone credit in advance.

Remember

Text messages are usually cheaper to send than making phone calls.

The best deal?

A tariff is a way of paying to use a mobile phone. The best tariff depends on how many minutes you use your phone for and what time of the day you use the phone.

Task

Compare these two tariffs.

TARIFF P	TARIFF Q
4p per minute	£9 per month
anytime	plus 1p per minute anytime

The best choice depends on how many minutes are used.

1   20 minutes on tariff P would cost 20 × 4p = 80p. Copy and complete this table for tariff P.

Minutes	0	20	40	100	200	300	400
Cost (£)	0	0·80	1·60				

141

2 (a) Copy the axes opposite onto squared paper.

(b) Plot points from the tariff P table and join them up to make a straight line.

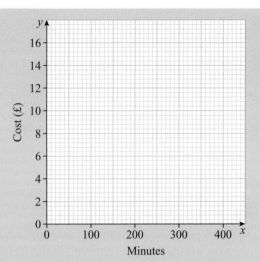

3 20 minutes on tariff Q would cost £9 then add on (20 × 1p) which is £0·20. 20 minutes cost £9·20.

Copy and complete this table for tariff Q.

Minutes	0	50	100	200	300	400
Cost (£)	9					

4 Plot points from the tariff Q table using the *same axes* as before. Join them up to make a straight line.

Your graph should look like this.

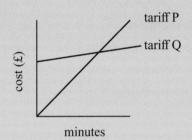

5 After how many minutes do the 2 lines cross?

6 What is the cost on both tariffs when the 2 lines cross?

7 If the number of minutes you use your mobile phone is less than your answer to question **5**, which tariff is cheaper for you?

8 If the number of minutes you use your mobile phone is more than your answer to question **5**, which tariff is cheaper for you?

9 Compare these two tariffs.

TARIFF Y £5 per month plus 2p per minute	TARIFF Z 4.5p per minute anytime

(a) Repeat questions **1** to **4** for these new tariffs.

(b) After how many minutes is the cost the same for both tariffs?

(c) Which tariff would you advise if you use your mobile phone for 150 minutes?

(d) Which tariff would you advise if you use your mobile phone for 320 minutes?

TEST YOURSELF ON UNIT 4

1. Identifying and labelling angles

    (a) Name the shaded angle below.   (b) Is AD̂B acute, obtuse or reflex?

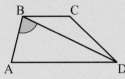 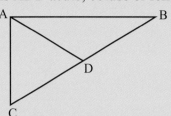

2. Finding angles

Find the angles marked with the letters. Give reasons for your answers.

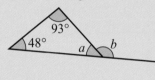 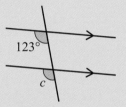 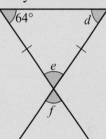

3. Using reflection symmetry and rotational symmetry

For each shape below, write down how many lines of symmetry it has and the order of rotational symmetry.

(a)   (b)   (c)

4. Recognising common quadrilaterals

Name the shapes below and for each shape, write down
 (i) how many lines of symmetry it has and
(ii) its order of rotational symmetry

(a)   (b)   (c)   (d)

5. Finding angles in quadrilaterals

Find the angles marked with letters.
Give reasons for your answers.

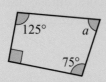

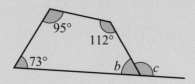

6. Finding angles in polygons

Find the angles marked with the letters.

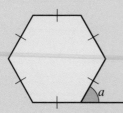 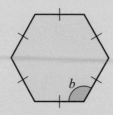 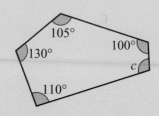

7. Recognising congruent shapes

Which shapes are congruent to shape A?

A   B   C   D   E

8. Using co-ordinates

Write down the co-ordinates of

(a) B   (b) E

(c) Write down the co-ordinates of any letter which forms an isosceles triangle with points F and R.

9. Translating shapes

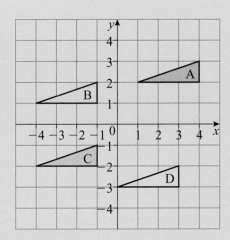

Use vectors to describe the
following translations.

(a) *A* to *C*

(b) *A* to *D*

(c) *D* to *B*

(d) *B* to *A*

10. Reflecting shapes in mirror lines

(a) Reflect the shape in the
broken mirror line.

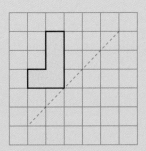

(b) Copy the shape below.
Draw a reflection of the shape.
Show your mirror line.

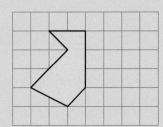

11. Rotating shapes

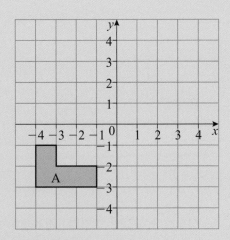

Copy the grid and shape *A*
opposite.

(a) Rotate shape *A* 90°
anticlockwise about (0, 0).
Label the image *B*.

(b) Rotate shape *A* 180° about
(−1, −2). Label the image *C*.

12. Enlarging shapes

Copy the diagrams below and then draw an enlargement using the scale factor and centre of enlargement (C) given:

(a)

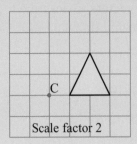

Scale factor 2

(b)

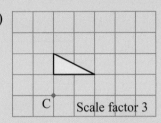

Scale factor 3

Mixed examination questions

1

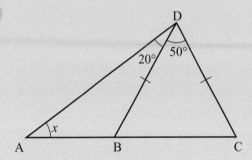

ABC is a straight line.
BD = *CD*.
Angle *BDC* = 50°.
Angle *ADB* = 20°.

Work out the size of the angle marked *x*.
Give reasons for your answer.   (EDEXCEL)

2 Here is a shape.

(a) Copy the shape above and draw on all the lines of symmetry.

Here is a regular hexagon.

(b) Write down the order of rotational symmetry of this regular hexagon.
                                                (EDEXCEL)

146

3 Copy the grid and triangle below.

Translate the shape by the vector $\begin{pmatrix} 2 \\ 3 \end{pmatrix}$

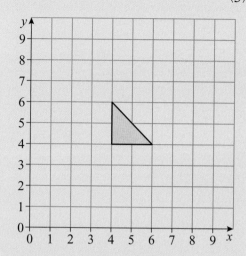

(AQA)

4

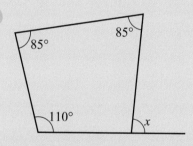

Calculate the size of angle x in the diagram opposite.

(CEA)

5 (a) Ravi has drawn these triangles on one centimetre square paper.

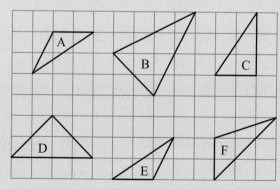

(i) Which two triangles contain a right angle?

(ii) Which two triangles are isosceles?

(iii) Which two triangles are congruent?

(OCR)

147

6 (a) In the diagram below, AB is parallel to CD.

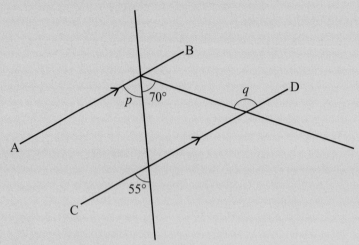

Work out angle *p* and angle *q*.

Give a reason for each answer.

(b) The exterior angle of a regular polygon is 40°.

How many sides does the polygon have? (OCR)

7 Copy the grid and shape below.

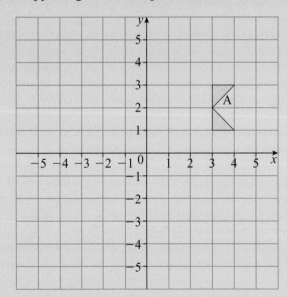

(a) Reflect the shape A in the diagram in the line *x* = 2
Label the new shape B.

(b) Rotate the shape A through 90° anticlockwise about the
point (0, −2)
Label the new shape C. (CEA)

8 This is a centimetre grid.

Draw a kite with an area of 12 cm².
One side has been drawn for you.

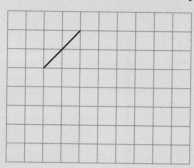

(AQA)

9 *ABC* is an equilateral triangle and *BCDE* is a square.

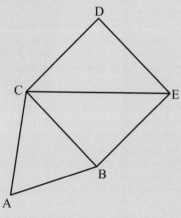

Diagram not drawn to scale.

Find the size of $A\widehat{C}E$.
You must explain each step of your calculation and show all
your working.

(WJEC)

10 Copy then enlarge this triangle with centre C and scale factor 3.

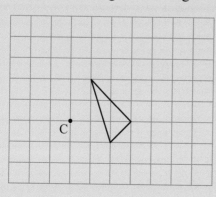

(OCR)

NUMBER 3

5

In this unit you will learn how to:

- add, subtract and multiply decimals
- divide decimals by whole numbers
- round off to decimal places
- estimate and use a calculator
- round off to significant figures
- check answers
- convert between fractions and percentages
- find percentage increases and decreases
- use reverse percentages
- convert between percentages and decimals
- use simple interest
- find ratios
- deal with direct proportion
- share in a given ratio
- ⟨ USE YOUR MATHS! ⟩ – money for your holiday

Adding and subtracting decimals

M5.1

1 Work out

(a)
$$18.6 + 13.4$$

(b)
$$30.75 + 7.8$$

(c)
$$13.0 + 0.39$$

(d)
$$17.5 - 6.2$$

(e)
$$8.36 - 2.8$$

(f)
$$14.0 - 2.6$$

2

0·71	0·54	0·96	0·37
0·22	0·8	0·63	0·41
0·46	0·29	0·04	0·61
0·39	0·2	0·78	0·59

This grid is full of pairs of numbers which add up to 1. Write down every pair (there are 8 pairs of numbers).

3 Work out the following (remember to line up the decimal point):

(a) $1·7 + 3·27$

(b) $5·16 + 4·99$

(c) $0·082 + 3·07$

(d) $6 + 0·31$

(e) $8·28 + 4·19$

(f) $38·64 + 13·8$

(g) $47·3 - 21·8$

(h) $63·7 - 28·8$

(i) $38·4 - 16$

(j) $7 - 4·4$

(k) $12 - 6·3$

(l) $7·7 - 5·39$

4 Carla buys some cups of coffee and some cakes.
One cake costs £2·60
One cup of coffee costs £1·90
Carla spends exactly £10·90
How many cups of coffee and cakes does Carla buy?

5 Geri has £40. She spends £13·87 on food and £15·50 on travel.
How much money does she have left?

6

TV	£487·50
computer	£874·99
DVD player	£88·45
printer	£124·75

Dan has £1600 to spend. Can he afford to buy all the items opposite? If so, how much money will he have left?

151

7

0·281	0·049	0·213	0·12
0·251	0·18	0·17	0·28
0·13	0·06	0·087	0·019
0·202	0·02	0·098	0·24

This grid is full of pairs of numbers which add up to 0·3. Write down every pair (there are 8 pairs of numbers).

8 Jack likes to go to the cinema and have a meal out on a Wednesday night. During March he goes to the cinema four times, has three pizzas and one curry. What is the total cost for all these during March?

cinema ticket	£11·70
pizza	£13·50
curry	£18·20

9 Which is larger?

A (sum of 7·22 and 8) or B (difference between 23 and 7·68)

10 Find the missing digits

(a)
$$
\begin{array}{r}
\square\cdot5\square \\
-\ 4\cdot\square3 \\
\hline
3\cdot7\ 3
\end{array}
$$

(b)
$$
\begin{array}{r}
4\cdot\square7 \\
+\ \square\cdot9\square \\
\hline
9\cdot0\ 3
\end{array}
$$

(c)
$$
\begin{array}{r}
3\cdot17\square \\
-\ \square\cdot4\square8 \\
\hline
0\cdot\square48
\end{array}
$$

Multiplying decimals

$$0\cdot\underline{3} \times 0\cdot\underline{05} = \frac{3}{10} \times \frac{5}{100} = \frac{15}{1000} = 0\cdot\underline{015}$$

When we multiply two decimal numbers together, the answer has the same number of figures after the decimal point as the total number of figures after the decimal point in the question.

1 Copy the questions below and put the decimal point in the correct place in each answer.

(a) $3·8 \times 0·7 = 266$

(b) $0·3 \times 0·78 = 234$

(c) $8·6 \times 6 = 516$

(d) $0·17 \times 0·29 = 493$

(e) $3·1 \times 0·94 = 2914$

(f) $3·28 \times 2·8 = 9184$

(g) $0·619 \times 3·6 = 22284$

(h) $27 \times 0·19 = 513$

(i) $0·05 \times 1·67 = 835$

(j) $8 \times 1·084 = 8672$

2 Work out

(a) $0·9 \times 0·4$

(b) $-0·2 \times 0·8$

(c) $0·03 \times 0·7$

(d) $-0·4 \times -0·04$

(e) $0·03 \times -0·6$

(f) $0·5 \times 0·007$

3 Find the total cost of 7 bottles of tomato ketchup at £1·63 for each bottle *and* 4 large packets of crisps at £1·28 for each packet.

4 If 1 kg of cheese costs £5·29, find the cost of 4 kg.

5 A new car tyre costs £41·49.
What is the total cost of 4 new tyres?

6 Find the total cost of 6 batteries at £1·47 each.

7 Wire costs £1·76 per metre. How much change from a £20 note will I get if I buy 7 metres of wire?

8 Copy below and fill in the empty boxes.

(a) $\boxed{} \times 0·6 = 0·18$

(b) $0·8 \times \boxed{} = -0·048$

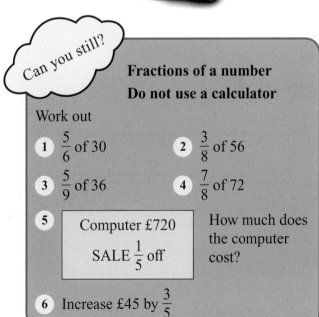

Can you still?

Fractions of a number

Do not use a calculator

Work out

1 $\dfrac{5}{6}$ of 30

2 $\dfrac{3}{8}$ of 56

3 $\dfrac{5}{9}$ of 36

4 $\dfrac{7}{8}$ of 72

5 Computer £720   SALE $\dfrac{1}{5}$ off   How much does the computer cost?

6 Increase £45 by $\dfrac{3}{5}$

9 A packet of 25 teeth flossers costs £2·16.

Mia uses one flosser each day.

What is the least amount of money Mia must spend so that she has enough flossers for October, November and December?

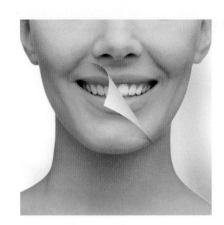

10 Here are 4 rules:

× 10		× 0·1		× 100		× 0·01

Copy each chain of numbers below and fill in the empty boxes with the correct rule (Remember: × 0·1 means ÷ 10 and × 0·01 means ÷ 100).

(a) 3·9 → ☐ → 39 → ☐ → 390 → ☐ → 3·9 → ☐ → 0·39

(b) 670 → ☐ → 67 → ☐ → 6·7 → ☐ → 670 → ☐ → 6·7

(c) 83·2 → ☐ → 8320 → ☐ → 832 → ☐ → 8·32 → ☐ → 0·832

(d) 0·24 → ☐ → 24 → ☐ → 2·4 → ☐ → 240 → ☐ → 0·24

Dividing decimals by whole numbers

(a) 11 ÷ 8

$$1 \cdot 3\ 7\ 5$$
$$8\overline{)11 \cdot {}^30\ {}^60\ {}^40}$$
↑ ↑ ↑
Note the extra zeros

(b) 7·3 ÷ 4

$$1 \cdot 8\ 2\ 5$$
$$4\overline{)7 \cdot {}^33\ {}^10\ {}^20}$$
↑ ↑
Note the extra zeros

M5.3

Work out

1 $3\overline{)18 \cdot 6}$

2 $4\overline{)36 \cdot 48}$

3 $6\overline{)20 \cdot 46}$

4 $6\overline{)15 \cdot 36}$

5 $7\overline{)34 \cdot 3}$

6 $9\overline{)39 \cdot 15}$

Work out

7 $18 \cdot 52 \div 4$ **8** $14 \cdot 82 \div 6$ **9** $205 \cdot 2 \div 6$ **10** $-18 \cdot 93 \div 6$

11 $1 \cdot 085 \div 5$ **12** $-26 \cdot 67 \div 7$ **13** $1 \cdot 96 \div 4$ **14** $70 \cdot 28 \div 7$

15 $-8 \cdot 7 \div 5$ **16** $-0 \cdot 58 \div 8$ **17** $0 \cdot 02352 \div 6$ **18** $0 \cdot 3724 \div 7$

19 Tom, Sally and Cherie club together to buy some flowers for their dear old Gran. The flowers cost £37·35. How much does each person pay?

20 Hannah and three of her friends go to the cinema.
The tickets cost £23.
What is the cost of 1 ticket?

21 Four identical boxes weigh 193 kg in total. How much does each box weigh?

22 A multipack containing 4 soap bars costs £2·52. Single soap bars can be bought for 67p each. How much do you save on each bar by buying the multi-pack?

23 A piece of wood is 4·23 m long. It is cut into 9 equal parts. How long is each part?

24 The Johnson family pay Andrew £186 for 20 hours cleaning each week. One Saturday the family have a party and ask Andrew to come in on Sunday and do 5 hours cleaning. They pay him 50% more for working on a Sunday. How much does Andrew earn for this Sunday work?

Decimal places

Rounding off to 1 decimal place

If the figure in the 2nd decimal place is 5 or more, round up. Otherwise do not.

3·8<u>7</u>2 = 3·9   14·4<u>5</u> = 14·5   2·4<u>3</u>7 = 2·4
   ↑   ↑   ↑

5 or more   5 or more   less than 5
round up   round up   round down

Rounding off to 2 decimal places

If the figure in the 3rd decimal place is 5 or more, round up. Otherwise do not.

3·87<u>2</u> = 3·87   15·52<u>5</u> = 15·53   2·43<u>7</u> = 2·44
  ↑   ↑   ↑

less than 5   5 or more   5 or more
round down   round up   round up

Note

5·96 rounded to the nearest whole number is 6

5·96 rounded to 1 decimal place is 6·0 (the zero is needed)

M5.4

1 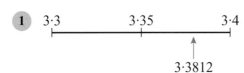 Round 3·3812 to 1 decimal place.

2 Round these numbers to 1 decimal place.

    (a) 6·31   (b) 5·83   (c) 8·37   (d) 6·75

    (e) 0·352   (f) 9·841   (g) 12·618   (h) 15·747

3 Which numbers below round to 7·3 (to 1 decimal place)?

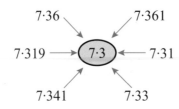

4 Round these numbers to 2 decimal places.

(a) 2·346   (b) 7·053   (c) 13·333   (d) 2·074

(e) 0·2365   (f) 23·676   (g) 0·9393   (h) 7·086

5 Which numbers below round to 8·16 (to 2 decimal places)?

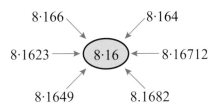

6 Round these numbers to 3 decimal places.

(a) 2·1683   (b) 5·6414   (c) 8·3257   (d) 4·2318

(e) 7·2515   (f) 13·7109   (g) 17·3298   (h) 41·61352

7 Work out these answers on a calculator and then round the answers correct to 2 decimal places.

(a) $9·76 \div 7$ (b) $0·38 \times 0·81$ (c) $2·57^2$ (d) $3186 \div 416$

(e) $0·89 \times 0·37$ (f) $19·32 \div 17$ (g) $3·9 \times 0·518$ (h) $0·87^2$

(i) $0·38 \div 51$ (j) $\sqrt{7·6}$ (k) $\sqrt{17}$ (l) $5·9 \div 37$

8 (a) Measure the sides of each triangle below. Write down each length, in cm, correct to 1 decimal place.

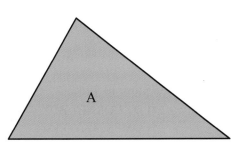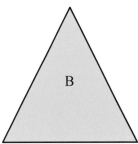

(b) For each triangle, add together the lengths of the 3 sides to find the perimeter.

9 Kavya rounds off 7·9994 to 2 decimal places and writes the answer 8·00. Noah says the answer is 7·99. Who is correct and explain why?

Key Facts

Jack worked out $7·02 \times 8·9$ equals $624·78$. He can check his answer by rounding off numbers in the question.

$7·02$ is roughly 7 $8·9$ is roughly 9

so $7·02 \times 8·9$ is roughly $7 \times 9 = 63$

Clearly Jack's answer is wrong. He put the decimal point in the wrong place. His answer should have been $62·478$.

M5.5

1. A quick way of adding lots of figures on a shopping bill is to round every number to the nearest pound (eg. £2·37 becomes £2, £0·94 becomes £1, £0·36 becomes £0 and so on).

   Use this method to estimate the total for each bill below:

   (a) | | |
   |---|---|
   | APPLE GRNNY SMTH | |
   | 0·540 kg @ £1·08/kg | £0·58 |
   | CLEMENTINES | £1·69 |
   | GRAPEFRUIT RED | £0·38 |
   | CONFERENCE PEARS | £1·49 |
   | CHICORY 160G | £1·08 |
   | ORGANIC CARROTS | £0·84 |
   | ORGNC/WATERCRESS | £1·39 |
   | BANANAS | |
   | 0·710 kg @ £0·74/kg | £0·53 |
   | MANGE TOUT 200G | £1·39 |
   | ORGNC/WATERCRESS | £1·39 |
   | CELERY | £0·53 |
   | ORGANIC CARROTS | £0·84 |
   | SALAD CRESS | £0·23 |
   | SALAD CRESS | £0·23 |
   | TTD CHC GNG BISC | £1·09 |
   | GRAPES RD SEEDLS | |
   | 0·425 kg @ £2·99/kg | £1·27 |

   (b) | | |
   |---|---|
   | RTB BAGUETTE | £0·95 |
   | RTB BAGUETTE | £0·95 |
   | APPLES COX | |
   | 1·495 kg @ £1·49/kg | £2·23 |
   | SATSUMAS | |
   | 0·985 kg @ £1·49/kg | £1·47 |
   | JS CEYLON TEA | £0·82 |
   | JS CEYLON TEA | £0·82 |
   | JS SLC HVST FHSE | £0·69 |
   | JS SLC HVST FHSE | £0·69 |
   | ONIONS LARGE | |
   | 0·225 kg @ £0·64/kg | £0·14 |
   | *240W BULBS | £0·45 |
   | *LDT CORNET BOX | £3·29 |
   | *COMP C/TKY/VEG | £1·46 |
   | JS U/S BRT BUTTR | £1·09 |
   | *2 100W BULBS | £0·49 |
   | GOUDA WHEEL | £3·66 |
   | JS CHICKEN BURGR | £1·09 |

   (c) Use a calculator to work out the exact total bill above.
   Was the estimate larger or smaller than the exact total bill?

2 Do not use a calculator.

Use sensible **rough** answers to match each question below to the correct answer:

A | 7.1×4.9 P | 101.7375

B | 41×4.95 Q | 34.79

C | $8139 \div 80$ R | 70.9

D | 0.99×61 S | 202.95

E | $29.6 + 41.3$ T | 60.39

3 Keira earns £97 each week. *Estimate* how much Keira earns in one year (52 weeks) by rounding off to sensible rough numbers.

4 Josh burns off 590 kcals each time he visits the Gym. *Estimate* how many kcals he burns off during 21 trips to the Gym?

5 Do *not* use a calculator.

From the table below, choose the most sensible **rough** answer from A, B or C.

	Calculation	A	B	C
(a)	7.78×8.95	32	72	720
(b)	3.1×97	300	90	30
(c)	4.16×6.99	28	15	280
(d)	$603 \div 4.93$	12	60	120
(e)	$88.7 \div 0.97$	90	300	900
(f)	604×10.46	4000	6000	600
(g)	$68.6 \times 39 + 271$	400	100	3000
(h)	2.12×70.4	700	140	7
(i)	7.13^2	14	50	200
(j)	$728 \div 9.88$	70	700	350
(k)	48% of £28 300	£28	£280	£14 000
(l)	9% of £394.60	£20	£40	£200

6 Madison travels 603 miles during one weekend.
Petrol costs £1.62 per litre and her car uses one litre of petrol for every 8 miles.
The total cost of the petrol is roughly £120.
Is this true or false? Explain your answer fully.

7

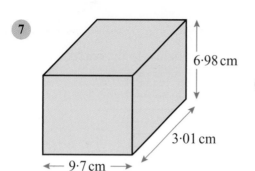

6·98 cm

3·01 cm

←— 9·7 cm —→

The volume of this box is
6·98 × 3·01 × 9·7
Estimate the volume of
this box.

8 36 × 563 = 20 268

Layla thinks that
3·6 × 5·63 = 202·68

Is this answer likely to
be correct?

Explain your answer
fully.

9 Ian thinks that
20·268 ÷ 3·6 = 5·63

True or false?

Explain your answer
fully.

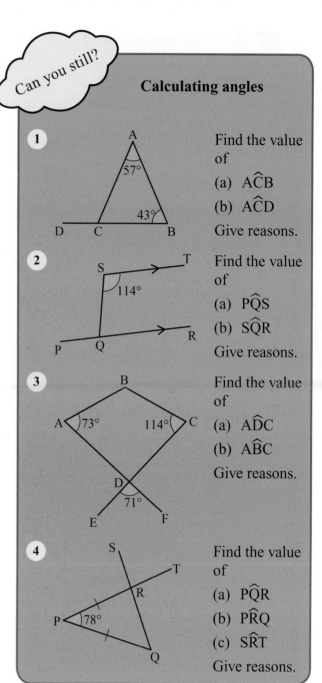

Can you still?

Calculating angles

1 Find the value
of

(a) AĈB

(b) AĈD

Give reasons.

2 Find the value
of

(a) PQ̂S

(b) SQ̂R

Give reasons.

3 Find the value
of

(a) AD̂C

(b) AB̂C

Give reasons.

4 Find the value
of

(a) PQ̂R

(b) PR̂Q

(c) SR̂T

Give reasons.

Using a calculator

Remember: in a money question, 2·8 on a calculator means £2·80

Use ▯ button for fractions

Use $x^{\blacksquare}$ button for powers

1 Work out the following. Give answers to the *nearest whole number*.

(a) $6 \cdot 1 + \dfrac{3 \cdot 8}{1 \cdot 65}$

(b) $9 \cdot 7 - \dfrac{6 \cdot 1}{4 \cdot 82}$

(c) $\dfrac{1 \cdot 8 + 4 \cdot 81}{3 \cdot 7}$

(d) $(8 \cdot 1 - 3 \cdot 06) \times (4 \cdot 7 + 2 \cdot 93)$

(e) $\dfrac{11 \cdot 3 - 6 \cdot 28}{4 \cdot 6}$

(f) $\dfrac{(8 \cdot 91 + 3 \cdot 6)}{0 \cdot 69}$

(g) $\dfrac{(5 \cdot 3 - 1 \cdot 21)}{0 \cdot 07}$

(h) $\dfrac{19 \cdot 2 + 13 \cdot 71}{1 \cdot 08}$

(i) $\dfrac{(28 \cdot 01 + 17 \cdot 6)}{(32 - 29 \cdot 7)}$

(j) $\dfrac{82 \cdot 1 - 13 \cdot 7}{31 + 1 \cdot 6}$

(k) $\dfrac{47 \cdot 28}{3 \cdot 8 - 0 \cdot 19}$

2

1		2		3		4
	5					
6				7	8	
		9				
			10			
11		12				

Copy the grid opposite.
Use a calculator to fill in
the grid using the clues
(*ignore any decimal points*).

Clues across

1. $3 \cdot 8 + 1 \cdot 7 + 1 \cdot 42$

3. $7 \times (3 \cdot 6 - 1 \cdot 9)$

5. $\dfrac{17 \cdot 6}{0 \cdot 4} - 3 \cdot 88$

7. $4 \cdot 9 \times 150$

9. $(0 \cdot 62 + 0 \cdot 08) \times 70$

10. $-24 \cdot 1 - 2 \cdot 3 + 61 \cdot 2$

11. $-900 \times (-0 \cdot 09)$

12. $4 \cdot 9 \times \left(\dfrac{40}{0 \cdot 8}\right)$

Clues down

1. $\dfrac{5 \cdot 1 - 1 \cdot 7}{0 \cdot 5}$

2. $3 \cdot 9 \times 4 \cdot 8 \times 13 \cdot 4$

3. $(3 \cdot 1 + 1 \cdot 8) \times (6 \cdot 1 - 3 \cdot 8)$

4. $121 - (31 \cdot 2 - 4 \cdot 85)$

6. $\dfrac{13 \cdot 8 + 9 \cdot 12}{0 \cdot 25}$

8. $(15 \cdot 1 - 7 \cdot 6) \times 3 \cdot 5 + 5 \cdot 2$

10. $\dfrac{18 \cdot 1 - 1 \cdot 1}{0 \cdot 38 + 0 \cdot 12}$

1 Use a calculator to match each question below to the correct answer:

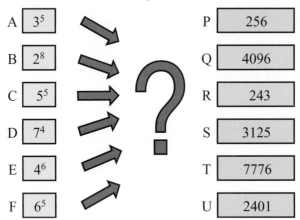

A	3^5		P	256
B	2^8		Q	4096
C	5^5		R	243
D	7^4		S	3125
E	4^6		T	7776
F	6^5		U	2401

2 Work out and give the answer correct to 2 decimal places.

(a) $3 \cdot 1^3 \times (5 \cdot 9 - 1 \cdot 312)$

(b) $\dfrac{\sqrt{5 \cdot 12}}{(7 \cdot 8 + 0 \cdot 314)}$

(c) $\sqrt{3 \cdot 8^2 - 2 \cdot 17}$

(d) $18 \cdot 8 \div (2 \cdot 8^2 - 2 \cdot 95)$

(e) $\dfrac{(17 \cdot 2 + 11 \cdot 25)}{(3 \cdot 89 + 1 \cdot 63)}$

(f) $\dfrac{17 \cdot 2 + 11 \cdot 25}{3 \cdot 89 + 1 \cdot 63}$

(g) $\sqrt{\dfrac{16 \cdot 18 - 3 \cdot 892}{12 \cdot 62 + 19 \cdot 31}}$

(h) $\dfrac{8 \cdot 312}{(5 \cdot 6^2 - 4 \cdot 218)}$

(i) $\dfrac{5 \cdot 1^2 + 6 \cdot 34}{17 \cdot 162 - 2 \cdot 8^2}$

(j) $\dfrac{3 \cdot 81^2 + 2 \cdot 6^3}{1 \cdot 41^2 - 1 \cdot 317}$

3 Copy and complete.

+	$\dfrac{3}{8}$		$2\dfrac{1}{2}$	$1\dfrac{2}{3}$
$\dfrac{1}{4}$				
$\dfrac{3}{5}$		$\dfrac{19}{20}$		
			$4\dfrac{5}{6}$	
		$2\dfrac{13}{20}$		

4 Copy this crossword puzzle and complete it using the clues below.
[The answers are calculator words]

1		2		3			4	
		5				6		
					7			
			8			9		10
		11						
						12		
13								
		14						

Across

2: $(3{\cdot}08 + 0{\cdot}701637) \times 10^6$ readable

5: $2 \times 71 \times 5$ greasy

6: $\sqrt{638401} + 3^2 + 1$ sticky

7: $555 - 44 + 3$ belongs to him

9: $0{\cdot}6 - 0{\cdot}22$ good when you're tired

11: $8 \times 4 \times (27 - 8)$ get out your wellies

13: $3^3 \div 30$ green light

14: $2000^2 - 68462$ surround

Down

1: 60 million $+ 436000 + 34$ hibernates in winter

3: $8 \times 9 \times 10 + 4^2 + 3$ for hair

4: $21 \times (40^2 + 67)$ not tight

6: $2^4 \times 5^3 \times 0{\cdot}41 - 1$ part of a boat

8   $33333 - 1325$ not a good idea

10: $24 \times 25 + (1 + 2 + 3 + 4)$ you might need a spade

12: $10^3 - 65{\cdot}5 \times 10$ female

For significant figures we approach from the left and start counting as soon as we come to the first figure which is not zero. Once we have started counting, we count any figure, zeros included.

(a) Round 8·0374 to 3 significant figures (3 s.f.)   8·<u>03</u>74

↑

(Count 3 figures. The 'next' figure is 7 which is more than 5 so round up.)

8·<u>03</u>74 = 8·04 (to 3 s.f.)

(b) 0·<u>065</u>4516 = 0·0655 (to 3 s.f.)

(c) <u>64</u>82·7 = 6400 (to 2 s.f.)

↑

Notice that we need the two noughts after the '4' as the original number 6382·7 is approximately 6400 not just 64.

M5.8

1 Which numbers below round to 3·96 (to 3 s.f.)?

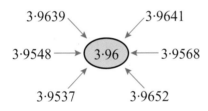

2 Write the following to the number of significant figures shown.

(a) 13·82 (2 s.f.)   (b) 7·891 (1 s.f.)

(c) 6·412 (2 s.f.)   (d) 0·83554 (3 s.f.)

(e) 1736·8 (3 s.f.)   (f) 51·382 (3 s.f.)

(g) 31777 (2 s.f.)   (h) 0·05483 (2 s.f.)

(i) 28639 (1 s.f.)   (j) 73·6294 (4 s.f.)

Mixed algebra

Simplify

1 $a^2 + a^2$

2 $a^2 \times a^2$

3 $7m + 1 + 2m$

4 $(m^4)^3$

Expand

5 $m(m + 4)$

6 $2a(4a - 3)$

Factorise

7 $8n - 6$

8 $m^2 + 5m$

9 $4ab + 10a$

10 $5n^2 - 20n$

3 Copy the grid below.

Use a calculator to fill in the grid using the clues (**ignore any decimal points**). You **must** round answers to the number of significant figures shown.

1		2			3	4
6	7					
			8			
9		10				
		11			12	
13				14		

Clues across	**Clues down**

Clues across

1. 1.9×9.46 (4 s.f.)

3. $3 \div 0.27$ (2 s.f.)

6. $2754.4 \div 0.3$ (2 s.f.)

8. 3.81^2 (4 s.f.)

9. $\dfrac{38 + 69.4}{0.48}$ (3 s.f.)

11. 2.2^3 (2 s.f.)

12. $(3.6 + 5.12) \times 1.01$ (2 s.f.)

13. $5.6^2 + 0.417$ (3 s.f.)

14. $\dfrac{3.1}{(2.83 - 1.9)}$ (2 s.f.)

Clues down

1. $18 \div 9.1$ (3 s.f.)

2. 30.8^2 (1 s.f.)

4. $1797.4853 \div 13$ (6 s.f.)

5. 0.24×0.17 (2 s.f.)

7. $0.36^2 + 1.7^2$ (3 s.f.)

9. $29 \div 13$ (3 s.f.)

10. $\dfrac{33}{0.12} \div 142.9$ (3 s.f.)

12. $99 - 16.182$ (2 s.f.)

Checking answers

- Here are five calculations followed by sensible checks. Some checks involve 'undoing' the calculation

  (a) $22 \cdot 2 \boxed{\div} 6 = 3 \cdot 7$ check $3 \cdot 7 \boxed{\times} 6 = 22 \cdot 2$

  (b) $31 \cdot 7 \boxed{-} 4 \cdot 83 = 26 \cdot 87$ check $26 \cdot 87 \boxed{+} 4 \cdot 83 = 31 \cdot 7$

  (c) $42 \cdot 8 \boxed{\times} 30 = 1284$ check $1284 \boxed{\div} 30 = 42 \cdot 8$

  (d) $\sqrt{17} = 4 \cdot 1231$ check $4 \cdot 1231^2$

  (e) $3 \cdot 7 + 17 \cdot 6 + 13 \cdot 9 + 6 \cdot 2$ check $6 \cdot 2 + 13 \cdot 9 + 17 \cdot 6 + 3 \cdot 7$
                                                         (add in reverse order)

- Calculations can also be checked by rounding numbers to a given number of significant figures. This gives an estimate which helps to check if the answer is correct.

  (f) $\dfrac{6 \cdot 1 \times 32 \cdot 6}{19 \cdot 3} = 10 \cdot 3$ (to 3 s.f.)

  Check this answer by rounding each number to 1 significant figure and estimating.

  $$\frac{6 \cdot 1 \times 32 \cdot 6}{19 \cdot 3} \approx \frac{6 \times 30}{20} \approx \frac{180}{20} \approx 9$$

  '$\approx$' means 'approximately equal to'.   This is close to $10 \cdot 3$ so the actual answer probably is $10 \cdot 3$

M5.9

1. Use a calculator to work out the following then check the answers as indicated.

   (a) $92 \cdot 5 \times 20 = \boxed{}$ check $\boxed{} \div 20 = \boxed{}$

   (b) $14 \times 328 = \boxed{}$ check $\boxed{} \div 328 = \boxed{}$

   (c) $63 - 12 \cdot 6 = \boxed{}$ check $\boxed{} + 12 \cdot 6 = \boxed{}$

   (d) $221 \cdot 2 \div 7 = \boxed{}$ check $\boxed{} \times 7 = \boxed{}$

   (e) $384 \cdot 93 \div 9 \cdot 1 = \boxed{}$ check $\boxed{} \times 9 \cdot 1 = \boxed{}$

   (f) $13 \cdot 71 \times 25 \cdot 8 = \boxed{}$ check $\boxed{} - 25 \cdot 8 = \boxed{}$

   (g) $95 \cdot 4 \div 4 \cdot 5 = \boxed{}$ check $\boxed{} \times 4 \cdot 5 = \boxed{}$

   (h) $8 \cdot 2 + 3 \cdot 1 + 19 \cdot 6 + 11 \cdot 5$ check $11 \cdot 5 + 19 \cdot 6 + 3 \cdot 1 + 8 \cdot 2$

   (i) $\sqrt{39} = \boxed{}$ check $\boxed{}^2$

   (j) $3 \cdot 17 + 2 \cdot 06 + 8 \cdot 4 + 16$ check $16 + 8 \cdot 4 + 2 \cdot 06 + 3 \cdot 17$

2 The numbers below are rounded to 1 significant figure to *estimate* the answer to each calculation. Match each question below to the correct answer.

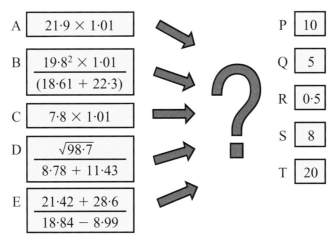

A $21 \cdot 9 \times 1 \cdot 01$

B $\dfrac{19 \cdot 8^2 \times 1 \cdot 01}{(18 \cdot 61 + 22 \cdot 3)}$

C $7 \cdot 8 \times 1 \cdot 01$

D $\dfrac{\sqrt{98 \cdot 7}}{8 \cdot 78 + 11 \cdot 43}$

E $\dfrac{21 \cdot 42 + 28 \cdot 6}{18 \cdot 84 - 8 \cdot 99}$

P   10

Q   5

R   0·5

S   8

T   20

3 Do *not* use a calculator.

$$281 \times 36 = 10\,116$$

Work out

(a) $10\,116 \div 36$ (b) $10\,116 \div 281$ (c) $28 \cdot 1 \times 3 \cdot 6$

4 Mavis is paid a salary of £49 620 per year. Work out a rough estimate for her weekly pay. (Give your answer correct to one significant figure.)

5 In 1996, the population of France was 61 278 514 and the population of Greece was 9 815 972. Roughly how many times bigger is the population of France compared to the population of Greece? (Hint: round the numbers to 1 significant figure).

6 *Estimate*, correct to 1 significant figure:

(a) $41 \cdot 56 \div 7 \cdot 88$ (b) $\dfrac{5 \cdot 13 \times 18 \cdot 777}{0 \cdot 952}$ (c) $\dfrac{1}{5}$ of £14 892

(d) $\dfrac{0 \cdot 0974 \times \sqrt{104}}{1 \cdot 03}$ (e)   52% of 0·394 kg   (f) $\dfrac{6 \cdot 84^2 + 0 \cdot 983}{5 \cdot 07^2}$

(g) $\dfrac{2848 \cdot 7 + 1024 \cdot 8}{51 \cdot 2 - 9 \cdot 98}$ (h) $\dfrac{2}{3}$ of £3124   (i) $18 \cdot 13 \times (3 \cdot 96^2 + 2 \cdot 07^2)$

Key Facts

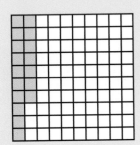

Per cent means 'out of 100'.

Fraction shaded $= \dfrac{17}{100}$

Percentage shaded $= 17\%$

Changing percentages into fractions

$41\% = \dfrac{41}{100}$

$18\% = \dfrac{18}{100} \overset{\div 2}{\underset{\div 2}{=}} \dfrac{9}{50}$

cancel when you can

$35\% = \dfrac{35}{100} \overset{\div 5}{\underset{\div 5}{=}} \dfrac{7}{20}$

cancel when you can

Changing fractions into percentages

(a)

$50\% = \dfrac{50}{100} \overset{\div 50}{\underset{\div 50}{=}} \dfrac{1}{2}$ so $\dfrac{1}{2}$ means 50%

To change a fraction into a percentage, multiply the fraction by 100

(b) Change $\dfrac{7}{24}$ into a percentage

$\dfrac{7}{24} \times 100$ Use calculator

$\dfrac{7}{24} \times 100 = 29 \cdot 16666\ldots$

$= 29\%$ (to the nearest whole number)

M5.10

1. 5 out of every 100 Britons donate blood at least once a year. Write down the percentage of Britons who donate blood at least once a year.

2. 70% of people in Great Britain drive to work. What percentage of people do *not* drive to work?

3. 12 out of every 100 British people are left-handed. Write down the percentage of British people who are left-handed.

4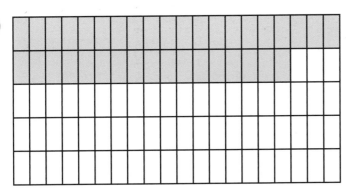

(a) What fraction of the large rectangle is pink?

(b) What percentage of the large rectangle is pink?

5 Change these percentages into fractions. Cancel the answers when possible.

(a) 10%   (b) 3%   (c) 11%   (d) 40%   (e) 75%   (f) 15%

(g) 80%   (h) 22%   (i) 32%   (j) 95%   (k) 48%   (l) 5%

6 Carl gave Michelle 30% of his DVD's. What *fraction* of his DVD's did Carl give to Michelle?

7 Nina used 55% of the petrol in her car when travelling from Manchester to Newcastle. She then used another 25% of the petrol travelling from Newcastle to Durham and back again. What fraction of her petrol did she use in total?

8 Approximately 67% of the earth's surface is covered with water. What percentage of the earth's surface is land?

9 Change these fractions into percentages.

(a) $\frac{1}{4}$ (b) $\frac{7}{20}$ (c) $\frac{3}{25}$ (d) $\frac{9}{25}$ (e) $\frac{7}{10}$ (f) $\frac{17}{20}$ (g) $\frac{21}{50}$

10 Silvio scored 13 out of 25 in a test. Caroline scored 16 out of 25 in the test. Write down how much more Caroline scored as a percentage.

11 Cleator Moor, near Whitehaven in Cumbria, has the highest percentage of Christians in the country (89%). What percentage of the people in Cleator Moor are *not* Christians?

12 Use a calculator to change these fractions into percentages (give your answers to the nearest whole number).

(a) $\dfrac{12}{17}$ (b) $\dfrac{8}{29}$ (c) $\dfrac{5}{16}$

13 In a cricket match, Joe Root scores $\dfrac{29}{49}$ of his team's runs. What percentage of his team's runs did he score? Give the answer to one decimal place.

14 Jane spends $\dfrac{11}{20}$ of her money on her rent. She spends 18% of her money on food. What percentage of her money does she have left over?

15 Write the numbers below in order of size, starting with the smallest.

$\dfrac{11}{25}$,   42%,   0·4, $\dfrac{9}{20}$

Polygons

1 Write down the order of rotational symmetry of a rhombus.

2 How many lines of symmetry does a rectangle have?

3 Calculate the size of an interior angle of a regular octagon.

4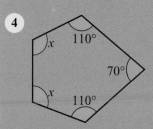
Calculate the value of angle x.

5 A regular polygon has an exterior angle equal to 20°. How many sides does the polygon have?

6 Draw a polygon with *only one* line of symmetry.

🔑 # Key Facts

Expressing one number as a percentage of another number

Write the two numbers as a fraction of each other then multiply by 100 to change into a percentage.

Suppose there are 25 cars in the staff car park. 9 of the cars were made in Japan. What percentage of the cars were made in Japan?

$$\dfrac{9}{25} \times 100 = \dfrac{9}{\underset{1}{25}} \times \dfrac{\overset{4}{100}}{1} = \dfrac{36}{1} = 36\%$$

1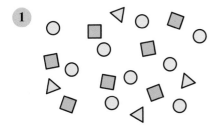

What percentage of these shapes are:

(a) squares

(b) circles

(c) triangles

2 Mehur scored 13 out of 20 in his maths exam and 18 out of 50 in his science exam.

(a) What percentage did Mehur score in his maths exam?

(b) What percentage did Mehur score in his science exam?

(c) Which exam did Mehur do better in?

3 In a college of 800 students, there are 472 females.
What percentage of the students are male?

4 In survey A, 150 people were asked about smoking. 45 people said they smoke. In survey B, 84 out of 240 people said they smoke. In which survey was there a greater percentage of smokers and by what percentage?

5 2 twins, Meg and Charlie, sat 5 exams. The results are opposite.

Find the percentage that Meg scored in *each* subject.

Write down who got the higher marks in most subjects.

Subject	Meg	Charlie
English	$\frac{17}{20}$	79%
Maths	$\frac{14}{25}$	50%
Science	$\frac{23}{50}$	52%
Art	$\frac{26}{40}$	62%
Geography	$\frac{42}{60}$	75%

For the remaining questions, use a calculator and give your answers to the nearest whole number.

6 A chocolate bar weighs 68 g. If 47 g of the bar is nougat, work out what percentage of the bar is nougat.

7
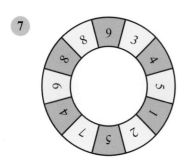
$1^2 = 1 \times 1 = 1$
$2^2 = 2 \times 2 = 4$
$3^2 = 3 \times 3 = 9$
$4^2 = 4 \times 4 = 16$
$\left. \right\}$ These are the first 4 square numbers.

Look at the picture opposite.
What percentage of the numbers are square numbers?

8

Germany	1,800,000
Russia	1,700,000
France	1,384,000
Austria–Hungary	1,290,000
Britain	743,000
Italy	615,000
Roumania	335,000
Turkey	325,000
Others	454,000
Total	8,646,000

In the 'horror' of the First World War, the numbers of people killed from the main countries are shown above.

Work out the percentage of people killed who came from
(a) Britain (b) France (c) Germany.
What a tragic waste of life!

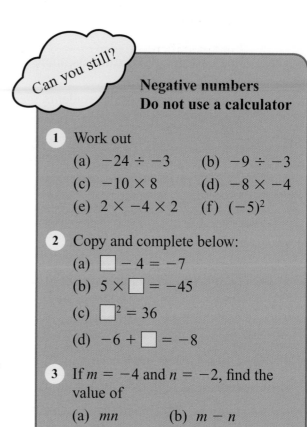

Can you still?

Negative numbers
Do not use a calculator

1 Work out
   (a) $-24 \div -3$ (b) $-9 \div -3$
   (c) -10×8 (d) -8×-4
   (e) $2 \times -4 \times 2$ (f) $(-5)^2$

2 Copy and complete below:
   (a) $\square - 4 = -7$
   (b) $5 \times \square = -45$
   (c) $\square^2 = 36$
   (d) $-6 + \square = -8$

3 If $m = -4$ and $n = -2$, find the value of
   (a) mn (b) $m - n$
   (c) m^2 (d) $n^2 - m$

9
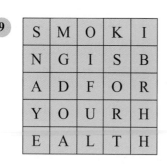

S	M	O	K	I
N	G	I	S	B
A	D	F	O	R
Y	O	U	R	H
E	A	L	T	H

What percentage of the letters in the square opposite are:

(a) the letter H

(b) vowels (A, E, I, O, U)

172

10

Drink	Number of people
juice	21
wine	18
cola	32
lemonade	21
beer	34
cider	12
total	138

Peter asks people what their favourite drink was. The results are shown in the table above.

Find the difference in the percentage of people who chose cola compared to cider.

Percentage increase and decrease

Find the given percentage then '*add on*' for '*increase*' or '*subtract*' for '*decrease*'.

(a) Increase £70 by 10%

10% of 70 = 70 ÷ 10 = 7

70 + 7 = £77
  ↑
increase

(b) Decrease £90 by 20%

$$\underset{}{20\% \text{ of } 90} = \overbrace{(90 \div 10)}^{10\%} \times 2 = 18$$

90 − 18 = £72
  ↑
decrease

M5.12

1. Find the odd one out

   (a) 50% of £30   (b) 20% of £80   (c) 25% of £60

2. Find the odd one out

   (a) 5% of £160   (b) 25% of £36   (c) 10% of £80

3 An egg is made up of 60% egg white, 30% yolk and the rest is shell.

    (a) What percentage of the egg is shell?

    (b) If the egg weighs 50 g, what is the weight of the yolk?

4 Find 15% of: (hint: work out 10% and 5% then add together)

    (a) 80   (b) 60   (c) 120   (d) 200   (e) 50   (f) 30

5 A music store is having a sale, with 25% *off* all prices. A guitar normally costs £360. What will it cost in the sale?

6 After one year, a car *loses* 20% of its value. If the car cost £7000 when it was bought, how much will it cost after one year?

7 A shop increases all its prices by 5%. If the price of a computer was £840, what is the new price?

8 A 750 g Cornflake packet has 10% extra free. How much does it weigh now?

In questions **9** to **17** below:

(a) How much is the price reduced by?   (b) What is the sale price?

9
Computer £600
SALE
20% off

10
Jacket £90
SALE
10% off

11
Bike £90
SALE
25% off

12
Dress £80
SALE
75% off

13
Watch £92
SALE
50% off

14
Table £420
SALE
30% off

15
Digital Radio £90
SALE
$33\frac{1}{3}$% off

16
Bed £350
SALE
40% off

17
Bracelet £64
SALE
75% off

18 Rosie earns £22 000 each year. She gets a pay rise of 4%. How much does she now earn each year?

Key Facts

Harder percentages

$1\% = \dfrac{1}{100}$ { To find 1% of a number, divide the number by 100 }

Find 23% of a number.
Divide the number by 100 to find 1% then multiply by 23 to find 23% of the number.

VAT is Value Added Tax. It is extra money that must be paid when buying many goods. The money is used by the Government to help run the country. It is usually 20%.

A printer costs £250 + VAT.   VAT = 20%

20% of 250 = (250 ÷ 100) × 20 = 50

add the tax

printer costs 250 + 50 = £300

M5.13

Use a calculator when needed.

1 48 000 people watch Liverpool play Everton. 62% of the people are Liverpool supporters. How many Liverpool supporters watch the match?

2 53% of the students in a school are girls. If there are 1300 students in the school, how many are girls?

3 Match each question to the correct answer below.

(The answers have been rounded off to the nearest penny.)

A 37% of £8·65      P £1·48

B 9% of £16·40   Q £1·87

C 12% of £15·62   R £3·20

4 Work out, correct to the nearest penny:

(a) 12% of £17·60   (b) 26% of £91   (c) 214% of £8·50

(d) 129% of £6·87   (e) 267% of £11·27   (f) 18% of £28·53

(g) 6·5% of £174   (h) 9·2% of £9·25   (i) 12·5% of £38·17

5 Sean has £850. He uses 37·2% of his money to buy a new music centre.
He also spends 6·4% of his money on a meal out.
How much money does Sean now have?

Give answers to the nearest penny
below when needed.

6 (a) Decrease a price of £75
by 7%

(b) Decrease a price of £320
by 8·5%

(c) Increase a price of £7·40
by 11%

(d) Decrease a price of £21
by 6·3%

(e) Increase a price of £48
by 26%

(f) Reduce a price of £9
by 83%

(g) Reduce a price of £463
by 62%

(h) Decrease a price of £9·85
by 3·2%

7 A computer costs £1099. Tom gets
a 14% discount. How much will
Tom pay for the computer?

8 A railcard gives a 20% discount.
How much would a £9·65 train
journey cost if the railcard was
used?

9 The population of Hatton is 11 500.
If the population decreases by 2%,
what is the new population?

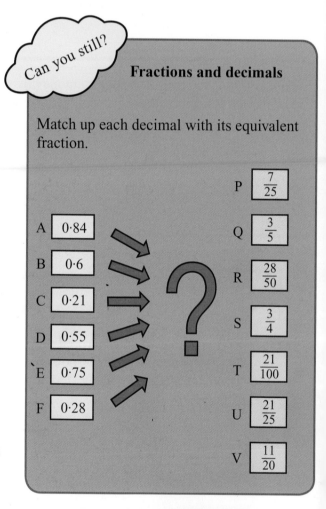

Can you still?

Fractions and decimals

Match up each decimal with its equivalent fraction.

A 0·84   P $\frac{7}{25}$

B 0·6   Q $\frac{3}{5}$

C 0·21   R $\frac{28}{50}$

D 0·55   S $\frac{3}{4}$

E 0·75   T $\frac{21}{100}$

F 0·28   U $\frac{21}{25}$

V $\frac{11}{20}$

10 Three friends plan to go on a holiday to Greece. The total price is £1560. The price of the holiday is reduced by 35%. How much do each of the friends pay for the holiday?

11 A bike costs £412 + VAT. If VAT is 20%, work out how much the bike costs altogether.

12 A new watch costs £275 + VAT (20%)

(a) What is the total price of the new watch?

After a year-and-a-half the shop puts the watch in a sale when the price is reduced by 15%.

(b) How much does the watch cost in the sale?

13 80 examiners are chosen to mark 480 exam papers each.
25% of the examiners decide not to do any marking. All the exam papers are marked by the remaining examiners.
How many exam papers must each examiner now mark?

14 A new car costs £2320 + VAT (20%)

(a) What is the total price of the new car?

Its value decreases by 27% after one year.

(b) How much does the car cost after 1 year?

15

fridge	£265
TV	£480
kettle	£36

The price of the fridge is reduced by 12%, the TV by 22% and the kettle by 15%.

What is the total cost of the 3 items including VAT at 20%?

Key Facts

Multiplier for percentage changes

Increase £60 by 10%

We need the original £60 (this is 100%) plus the extra 10%.

This is 110% of £60

Answer with $\dfrac{110}{100} \times 60$ or $1 \cdot 1 \times 60$

The answer is £66

Note $\dfrac{110}{100}$ or $1 \cdot 1$ is called the **multiplier**

E5.1

1. Increase £70 by 20%. Which calculation below will give the answer?

   | A 20×70 | B $1 \cdot 2 \times 70$ | C $0 \cdot 8 \times 70$ | D $1 \cdot 02 \times 70$ |

2. Decrease £90 by 30%. Which calculation below will give the answer?

   | P $\dfrac{130}{100} \times 90$ | Q $\dfrac{30}{100} \times 90$ | R $\dfrac{70}{100} \times 90$ | S $1 \cdot 3 \times 90$ |

3. Use a multiplier to do the following:

   (a) Reduce £60 by 40%   (b) Increase £80 by 20%

   (c) Increase £120 by 25%   (d) Decrease £130 by 10%

4. Max has had 40 days off work following an accident The doctor says Max must have 40% more time off work. Use a multiplier to work out how many days he has off work in total.

5. A teapot costs £30 plus VAT at 20%. How much does the teapot cost?

6. Alyssa earns £32 000 each year and gets a 5% pay rise. Gabriel earns £35 000 but has to take a 5% pay cut. Who now earns more and by how much?

Reverse percentages

A balloon ride costs £100.
Its price is increased by 10%
so the balloon ride now costs
£110.
Question ?
If a balloon ride costs £110
after a 10% increase, what
was the price before the
increase?

Oliver says '10% of 110 = 11
so original price = 110 − 11 = £99'

It should be £100 so Oliver is wrong.

 Key Facts

In the question above, a 10% increase means the multiplier is 110% or 1·1

To find the original price, reverse the percentage so divide by 110% or 1·1

original price = £110 ÷ 1·1 = £100

The price of a radio is decreased by 50% and now costs £30.
What was the original price?

Decrease = 50% so multiplier = 100% − 50% = 50% or 0·5

Reverse the percentage so original price = £30 ÷ 0·5 = £60

E5.2

1 The price of a jacket is reduced by 25% and now costs £60. Find

(a) the multiplier   (b) the original price

2 The cost of a holiday increases by 50% and now costs £900. Find

(a) the multiplier   (b) the original cost

3 Copy and complete the table below:

	Old price	% change	New price
(a)		50% increase	£120
(b)		20% decrease	£160
(c)		10% decrease	£81
(d)		20% increase	£480

4 The Harris family reduce their weekly food bill by 30%. It is now £98. How much did they spend on food each week before this reduction?

5 A magnifying glass increases the lengths by 150%. A rectangle appears to be 50 mm by 35 mm. What are the real measurements of the rectangle?

6 VAT is 20%. A TV costs £660 after VAT is added on. How much does the TV cost without VAT?

7 VAT is 20%. Each item below includes VAT in the cost. Find the cost of each without VAT.

computer	£960
cooker	£900
bike	£360

8 The population of rabbits in a park increases by 25%. The population of squirrels decreases by 10%. There are now 1000 rabbits and 360 squirrels. How many more rabbits were there than squirrels before the percentage changes?

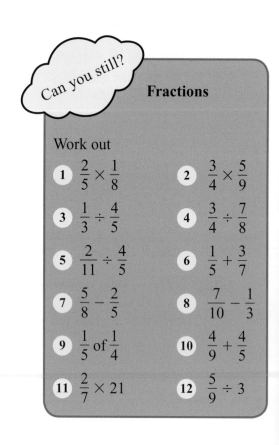

Can you still!?

Fractions

Work out

1 $\dfrac{2}{5} \times \dfrac{1}{8}$ **2** $\dfrac{3}{4} \times \dfrac{5}{9}$

3 $\dfrac{1}{3} \div \dfrac{4}{5}$ **4** $\dfrac{3}{4} \div \dfrac{7}{8}$

5 $\dfrac{2}{11} \div \dfrac{4}{5}$ **6** $\dfrac{1}{5} + \dfrac{3}{7}$

7 $\dfrac{5}{8} - \dfrac{2}{5}$ **8** $\dfrac{7}{10} - \dfrac{1}{3}$

9 $\dfrac{1}{5}$ of $\dfrac{1}{4}$ **10** $\dfrac{4}{9} + \dfrac{4}{5}$

11 $\dfrac{2}{7} \times 21$ **12** $\dfrac{5}{9} \div 3$

Percentages and decimals

Note

$$80\% = \frac{80}{100} = 0\cdot80 = 0\cdot8 \qquad \text{but} \qquad 8\% = \frac{8}{100} = 0\cdot08$$

To change decimals into percentages, the first two numbers after the point give the percent:

$$0\cdot07 = \frac{7}{100} = 7\% \qquad \text{but} \qquad 0\cdot7 = 0\cdot70 = \frac{70}{100} = 70\%$$

M5.14

1 Which of the following are true?

(a) 3% = 0·03   (b) 3% = 0·3   (c) 70% = 0·07   (d) 70% = 0·7

(e) 2% = 0·2   (f) 2% = 0·02   (g) 4% = 0·4   (h) 40% = 0·4

2 Change these decimals into percentages:

(a) 0·84   (b) 0·67   (c) 0·02   (d) 0·8   (e) 0·2   (f) 0·08

3 Match up each percentage with its equivalent decimal (warning: one of the decimals is not needed).

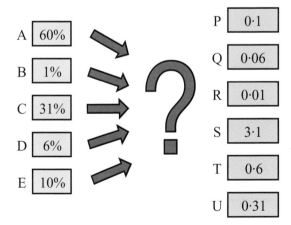

A 60%   B 1%   C 31%   D 6%   E 10%

P 0·1   Q 0·06   R 0·01   S 3·1   T 0·6   U 0·31

4 Change these percentages into decimals:

(a) 3·5%   (b) 6·7%   (c) 100%   (d) 120%   (e) 248%   (f) 192%

5 Copy and complete:

Percentage	Decimal	Fraction
21%		
	0·07	
		$\dfrac{19}{100}$
25%		
	0·3	
		$\dfrac{7}{10}$

6 Toni says that 0·3 is greater than 28%.
Patrick does not agree. Explain fully who is correct.

7 Copy and complete:

Decimal	Percentage	Fraction
0·32		
	43%	
0·06		
		$\dfrac{7}{50}$
	80%	
		$\dfrac{3}{20}$

Simple interest

Interest is the extra amount earned on money
which is invested or the extra amount charged
when money is borrowed.
Simple interest is calculated using the sum
of money first borrowed or invested.
The simple interest is usually a percentage
per annum (year).

Find the simple interest on £440 invested at 6% per annum for 5 years.

Interest for 1 year = 6% of 440

So total simple interest for 5 years = $\dfrac{6}{100} \times 440 \times 5 = £132$

1. Find the simple interest on £680 at 5% per annum for 3 years.

2. Find the simple interest on £1900 at 3% per annum for 4 years.

3. Mr Thomas borrows £400 to buy a pool table for his children. He is charged 9% per annum simple interest. He pays back all the money in 3 years. How much does he pay back in total?

4. Skye invests £6500. She receives 4% per annum simple interest. How much simple interest does she receive over 7 years?

5. Jason borrows £350 to buy a surfboard. He repays all the money over 4 years with a simple interest rate of 5% per annum. He pays back an equal amount each month. How much will each monthly payment be?

Simple interest $= \dfrac{PRT}{100}$ where P = money invested or money borrowed (the principal)

R = rate of interest per year

T = number of years

Find the simple interest on £3000 for 5 years at 8% per annum.

Simple interest $= \dfrac{3000 \times 8 \times 5}{100} = £1200$

6. Megan borrows £1500. She is charged 4% per annum simple interest. She pays back all the money in 3 years. How much does she pay back in total?

7 The table opposite shows
the money invested in a
bank account, the simple
interest rate and how long
the money is left in the
bank. Find out the total
amount of money in each
bank account after the time period shown.

	Money	Interest rate per annum	Time
(a)	£2600	3%	6 years
(b)	£7000	6%	6 months
(c)	£850	9%	10 years
(d)	£9500	2%	3 years 6 months

8 Faith borrows £4000 for a car. She is charged 6·29% per annum simple
interest. She must pay back all the money in 5 years. How much money must
she pay back in total?

Can you still?

Transformations

(You may use tracing paper)

1

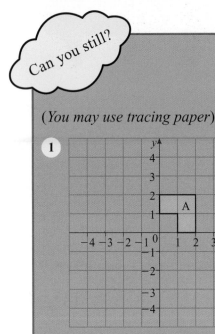

(a) Copy the grid. Copy shape A.

(b) Rotate shape A 180° clockwise
about (0, 0). Label the image (new
shape) B.

(c) Enlarge shape B by scale factor 2
about (0, 0). Label the image C.

2

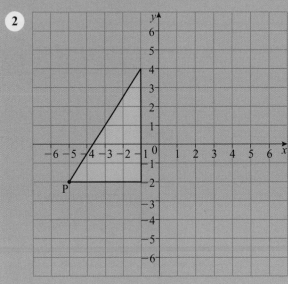

(a) Copy the grid. Copy shape A.

(b) Translate shape A with $\begin{pmatrix} 5 \\ -4 \end{pmatrix}$
and label the image B.

(c) Reflect shape B in the x-axis
and label the image C.

(d) Write down the final co-
ordinates of vertex P
after the translation and
reflection.

Key Facts

We use ratio to compare parts of a whole.

   In this diagram, there are 6 black squares and 2 white squares.

We say the *ratio* of black squares to white squares is 6 to 2.

This is written as 6 : 2

Both numbers in the ratio 6 : 2 can be divided by 2 so we can reduce the ratio 6 : 2 to its simplest form of 3 : 1

(a) In a class of 24 children, 14 are girls. Find the ratio of boys to girls. Give the answer in its simplest form.

There are 10 boys
Ratio of boys to girls = 10 : 14
(10 and 14 can both be divided by 2)
Ratio of boys to girls = 5 : 7

(b) Are the ratios 15 : 25 : 30 the same as 3 : 5 : 6?
15, 25 and 30 can all be divided by 5

$15 \div 5 = 3$
$25 \div 5 = 5$
$30 \div 5 = 6$

so 15 : 25 : 30 = 3 : 5 : 6

M5.16

Copy and fill in the boxes below:

1   The ratio of black to white is ☐ : ☐

2  The ratio of black to white is ☐ : ☐

3 ● ○ ● ● ○ ●   The ratio of black to white is ☐ : ☐

4 ○ ○ ○ ○ ○

(a) Copy and colour in the circles to show the ratio of black to white is 3 : 2.

(b) Leah says that the ratio 3 : 2 is the same as the ratio 2 : 3. Explain fully whether Leah is correct or not.

185

5 Copy and colour in the circles to show the ratio of white to black is 1 : 2

6 On a bus, there are 35 people. 25 of the people are female. Find the ratio of males to females. Give the ratio in its simplest form.

7 For the human body, write down the following ratios. Write the answers in their simplest form (example: thumbs to fingers is 2 : 8 = 1 : 4)

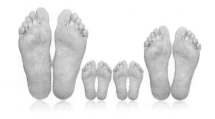

(a) feet to toes   (b) ears to nose

(c) eyes to fingers

8 For each diagram below, write down the ratio of red to yellow in its simplest form.

(a)    (b)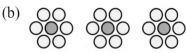

(c) 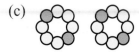   (d)

9 Maaike makes some models using cubes of different colours.

(a) Model 1 must have red to blue in the ratio 1 : 2. She uses 4 red cubes. How many blue does she use?

(b) Model 2 must have yellow to green in the ratio 2 : 3. She uses 6 yellow cubes. How many green does she use?

(c) Model 3 must have green to blue in the ratio 3 : 5. She uses 10 blue cubes. How many green does she use?

(d) Model 4 must have white to yellow in the ratio 3 : 2. She uses 8 yellow cubes. How many white does she use?

(e) Model 5 must have white to black to red in the ratio 2 : 1 : 3. She uses 3 black cubes. How many white does she use? How many red does she use?

10

Some sports students choose an activity for the morning as shown opposite.

(a) Write down the ratio of students choosing football compared to dance.

(b) Alan says that half as many more students choose football compared to hockey. Explain whether he is correct or not.

1 Change the following ratios to their simplest form.

(a) 15 : 10   (b) 8 : 12   (c) 9 : 15   (d) 10 : 22

(e) 30 : 20   (f) 42 : 49   (g) 12 : 16   (h) 35 : 20

(i) 18 : 24   (j) 18 : 30   (k) 40 : 25   (l) 24 : 60

(m) 8 : 4 : 2   (n) 6 : 9 : 12   (o) 40 : 15 : 25   (p) 8 : 18 : 14

2 One evening, a vet sees 16 dogs and 10 cats.
Find the ratio of dogs to cats.
Give the ratio in its simplest form.

3 Is the ratio 9 : 15 : 24 equivalent to 6 : 10 : 16?
Explain your answer fully.

4 Frank spends £3 on Monday and 50p on Tuesday. Find the ratio of the
money spent on Monday to the money spent on Tuesday (remember to
change all the money to pence then give the answer in its simplest form).

5 Tanya is 1·6 m tall and Sid is 2 m tall.
Find the ratio of Tanya's height to Sid's
height (remember: 1 m = 100 cm so
2 m = 200 cm and 1·6 m = 160 cm).
Give the answer in its simplest form.

6 Write the ratios below in their simplest form. Remember to get the units the
same first.

(a) 50 cm : 1 m   (b) 1 m : 20 cm   (c) 2 m : 20 cm   (d) 3 m : 50 cm

(e) 25 cm : 2 m   (f) 75 cm : 3 m   (g) 5 m : 40 cm   (h) 5 cm : 2 m

(i) 50p : £2   (j) 50p : £5   (k) 5p : £2   (l) 80p : £8

7

> 2·5 : 6 = 25 : 60 = 5 : 12 (whole number ratio)
>
> multiply both numbers by 10

Write each ratio below in their simplest whole number form.

(a) 1·5 : 2·7   (b) 2·3 : 5·2   (c) 1·25 : 0·5   (d) 4·4 : 9·25

8 Which ratio below is the odd one out?
Explain your answer fully.

A $9 : 1.5 : 7.8$ B $1.2 : 0.2 : 1$ C $6 : 1 : 5$

9 Mr and Mrs Cowan want a swimming pool with the ratio of the length to the width equal to $3 : 2$. Which swimming pool below should they choose?

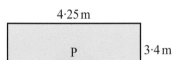

4·25 m
P
3·4 m

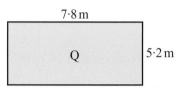

7·8 m
Q
5·2 m

6·2 m
R
4·6 m

Direct proportion

5 doughnuts cost 80p.

How much will 12 doughnuts cost?

Find the cost of 1 doughnut and then find the cost of 12.
5 doughnuts cost 80p
1 doughnut costs $80 \div 5 = 16$p
12 doughnuts cost $16\text{p} \times 12 = 192\text{p} = £1.92$

M5.18

Do not use a calculator.

1 Magazines cost £21 for 7. Find the cost of 3 magazines.

2 9 pizzas cost £45. How much will 7 pizzas cost?

3 8 rubbers cost 88p. How much will 5 rubbers cost?

4 7 shirts cost £84. Find the cost of 4 shirts.

5 4 cups of tea cost £3·60. How much will 5 cups of tea cost?

For the rest of the exercise you may use a calculator if needed.

6 Toni used 450 g of mince to make chilli con carne for 4 people. How much mince would have to be used to make chilli con carne for 10 people?

In questions **7** and **8**, copy and complete the tables.

7

Pounds	Dollars
42	79·80
1	
8	
32·50	
75	

8

Pounds	Euros
9·20	15·18
1	
5	
15	
125	
63·40	

9 17 adults can go the cinema for £116·45. Three of the adults drop out. How much does the cinema cost for the remaining adults?

10 250 g of butter costs £3.
400 g of butter costs £4·60.
Which weight of butter is the better buy?
Explain your answer fully.

11 300 g of dog food costs £3·60.
500 g of dog food costs £6·20.
Which is the better value?
Explain your answer fully.

12 500 g of cereal costs £1·98.
750 g of cereal costs £2·95.
Which is the better value?
Explain your answer fully.

Can you still?

Standard form

1 Write in standard form
(a) 0·078   (b) 0·00119
(c) 1690   (d) 186·7

2 Which is larger:
$7·4 \times 10^{-6}$ or $7·4 \times 10^{-7}$?

3 Use a calculator to work out
(a) $(4·6 \times 10^9) \times (3·7 \times 10^8)$
(b) $(5·9 \times 10^{-8})^2 \times (1·8 \times 10^7)$
(c) $\dfrac{(4 \times 10^{11})^2}{8 \times 10^9}$

189

13 This recipe for macaroni cheese serves 6 people.

150 g	cheese
300 g	plain flour
250 g	margarine
1	onion
3	eggs
30 g	butter
3	tablespoons of cold water

How much of each ingredient is needed to serve 18 people?

14 This recipe for chocolate sponge serves 8 people.

220 g	butter
220 g	sugar
2	tablespoons of boiling water
4	eggs
220 g	self-raising flour
2	tablespoons of cocoa

How much of each ingredient is needed for 12 people?

15 This recipe for pancakes serves 4 people.

120 g	plain flour
280 ml	milk
2	eggs

How much of each ingredient is needed for 6 people?

16 This recipe for pizza serves 5 people.

250 g	cheese
180 g	dough
150 ml	tomato sauce
25 g	pepperoni

How much of each ingredient is needed for 9 people?

17 Amelia receives €83·30 for £70 when in Paris. How many euros would she receive for £90?

Sharing in a given ratio

Share 40 oranges between Al and Jordan in the ratio 5 : 3.

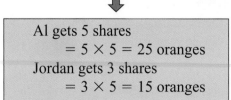

Al : Jordan
= 5 : 3
Total of 8 shares

→

40 oranges
so each share = 40 ÷ 8
= 5 oranges

⬇

Al gets 5 shares
= 5 × 5 = 25 oranges
Jordan gets 3 shares
= 3 × 5 = 15 oranges

1 (a) Divide 300 g in the ratio 3 : 7   (b) Divide 450 g in the ratio 7 : 2

(c) Divide 60 minutes in the ratio 3 : 1   (d) Divide £800 in the ratio 5 : 1 : 2

(e) Divide £360 in the ratio 2 : 3 : 4   (f) Divide 5000 g in the ratio 8 : 5 : 7

2 Colin and Lily share a bag of 35 sweets in the ratio 2 : 3. How many sweets does each person get?

3 A metal bar is 27 cm long. If it is cut into 2 parts in the ratio 2 : 7, how long is each part?

4 The ratio of men to women to children visiting the Eiffel Tower one day was 4 : 5 : 6. If 975 people visited the Eiffel Tower, find out how many were:

(a) men   (b) women   (c) children

5 £320 is shared between Omar, Molly and Sachin in the ratio 3 : 1 : 4. How much will each person get?

6 Mr Hope has a BMW and a Mini. He puts 75 litres of petrol into the 2 cars so that the ratio of the petrol in the BMW to the Mini is 16 : 9. How much petrol is put into each car?

7 Ribena is diluted with water in the ratio 1 : 6.

(a) If 9 ml of ribena is used, how much water should be added?

(b) If 60 ml of water is used, how much ribena should be added?

8 Some money is shared between Hamish and Rory in the ratio 11 : 4. If Rory gets £60, how much will Hamish get?

9 Gravel and cement are mixed in the ratio 5 : 3 to make mortar.

(a) If 30 shovels of gravel are used, how many shovels of cement are needed?

(b) If 12 shovels of cement are used, how many shovels of gravel are needed?

10 For a school trip there needs to be a ratio of adults to young people of 2 : 17. How many adults are needed for a trip with 85 young people?

11 An orange paint is made by mixing red and yellow in the ratio $2:3$.

   (a) How much yellow must be used if 16 litres of red are used?

   (b) How much red must be used if 36 litres of yellow are used?

   (c) How much red and how much yellow must be used to make 80 litres of orange?

12 A father and son's ages are in the ratio $15:2$. If the father is 30 years old, how old is the son?

13 Bread is made from flour and yeast in the ratio $30:1$

   (a) How much yeast is mixed with 870 g of flour?

   (b) How much flour is needed to mix with 350 g of yeast?

14 A recipe is made from flour, butter and sugar in the ratio $6:3:2$. How much flour and sugar is needed if 270 g of butter is used?

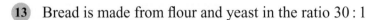

E5.3

1

The angles x, y and z in a triangle are in the ratio $5:1:3$.

Find the sizes of angles x, y and z.

2 Some money was shared between Lizzie, Nikhil and Isaac in the ratio $4:3:7$. Nikhil got £80 less than Isaac. How much money did Nikhil get?

3 If $\dfrac{5}{9}$ of the animals in a Rescue Centre are dogs, what is the ratio of dogs to the other animals?

4 Tom and his sister share a £20 000 lottery win, in the ratio $13:7$. Tom then shares his winnings between himself, his daughter and his son in the ratio $4:3:3$. How much money does Tom keep?

5 A school trip needs 1 teacher for every 15 students.

   (a) 5 teachers are available. What is the maximum number of students that can go on the trip?

   (b) Only 53 students wish to go on the trip. How many teachers are needed?

6 Purple paint is made from red and blue paint in the ratio $2:5$. If 35 litres of blue are used, how much purple paint would be mixed *in total*?

7 Three retired soldiers have a number of medals in the ratio $4:1:3$. The first soldier has 6 more medals than the second soldier. How many medals does the third soldier have?

8 The angles p, q, r and s in a quadrilateral are in the ratio $3:1:2:4$

   Find the sizes of angles p, q, r and s.

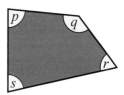

9 Henry's parents loan him £60 000 to buy a flat for £200 000. When Henry sells the flat for £240 000, his parents want the same percentage of the value of the flat back as they invested. How much money do his parents get back?

USE YOUR MATHS! – Money for your holiday

Exchange rate

This is the amount of foreign money you will get in exchange for £1.

At the time of writing:

£1 = 1·45 euros (Europe)	£1 = 51·18 rubles (Russia)
£1 = 1·82 dollars (USA)	£1 = 19·84 pesos (Mexico)
£1 = 196 yen (Japan)	£1 = 6·84 riyals (Saudi Arabia)
£1 = 11·98 rand (South Africa)	£1 = 2·39 dollars (Australia)

Converting pounds into foreign money

| Multiply the number of pounds by the chosen exchange rate |

Examples

£1 = 1·82 dollars (USA)

so £10 = 10 × 1·82 = 18·2 dollars

£1 = 51·18 rubles (Russia)

so £300 = 300 × 51·18 = 15 354 rubles.

Converting foreign money into pounds

| Divide the foreign money by the chosen exchange rate |

Examples

£1 = 196 yen (Japan)

4508 yen = 4508 ÷ 196 = £23

£1 = 1·45 euros

150 euros = 150 ÷ 1·45 = £103·448276

= £103·45 (to the nearest penny)

| Beware! |

When converting your money, the bank (or whatever organization you use) will charge you a fee. This is called the 'commission'.

Different organizations charge different amounts of commission. Always look around for the best deal.

Task

Using the exchange rate at the start of this section, convert the following amount of money.

1 £200 into euros

2 £350 into pesos

3 £150 into Australian dollars

4 £900 into rand

5 300·3 American dollars into pounds

6 11 904 pesos into pounds

7 13 328 yen into pounds

8 £454 into riyals

9 1015 euros into pounds

10 17 970 rand into pounds

11 A digital radio costs £164 in the UK. Sarah sees a similar digital radio for 31 360 yen in Japan. In which country is the digital radio cheaper?

12 Jonathan was lucky enough to have two holidays last year, one in France and one in Australia. A can of cola was 1·16 euros in France and 1·68 dollars in Australia. In which country was the can of cola cheaper?

13 Candice comes back from holiday in Mexico with 992 pesos. Shabina returns from holiday in the USA with 98·28 dollars. Who has more money left?

14 Stephen takes 547·2 riyals to a Bureau de Change to convert them into pounds. The Bureau de Change charges 4% commission. How much money does Stephen get back?

15 Maggie takes 2047·2 rubles to a bank to change them into pounds. The bank charges 3% commission. How much money does Maggie get back?

TEST YOURSELF ON UNIT 5

1. Add, subtract and multiply decimals

Work out

(a) $0·6 \times 0·03$ (b) $0·08 \times 6$ (c) $0·7^2$ (d) $21·2 \times 0·3$

(e) The cost of a taxi is £4 plus £1·35 per mile.
Three friends need to travel 5 miles.
It would cost each person £3·45 to use a bus.
Which is cheaper and by how much – using a taxi or a bus?

2. Dividing decimals by whole numbers

Work out

(a) $8\overline{)18·00}$ (b) $0·768 \div 6$ (c) $3·6 \div 5$

(e) 4 friends split the cost of a meal equally. If the meal costs £63, how much does each friend have to pay?

3. Rounding off to decimal places

(a) Round these numbers to 1 decimal place.

(i) 8·23   (ii) 6·35   (iii) 4·16   (iv) 14·34   (v) 8·162

(b) Round these numbers to 2 decimal places.

(i) 3·387   (ii) 2·186   (iii) 15·384   (iv) 0·895   (v) 28·183

4. Estimating and using a calculator

Without using a calculator, choose the most sensible *rough* answer from A, B or C.

	Calculation	A	B	C
(a)	$41·2 \div 8·14$	320	50	5
(b)	$68·6 - 19·14$	50	30	90
(c)	$789 \times 10·33$	800	8000	80
(d)	$8·95^2$	80	150	20

(e) Estimate the value of $\dfrac{3·98^2 + 4·1}{1·97 + 3·02}$

Use a calculator to work out

(f) $\dfrac{6·8^2}{15·8 - 15·79}$ (g) $2\dfrac{1}{5} + 3\dfrac{5}{7}$ (h) $\dfrac{\sqrt{28 - 12}}{0·5^2}$

5. Rounding off to significant figures

Write the following to the number of significant figures (s.f.) shown.

(a) 17·81 (3 s.f.)   (b) 23·69 (2 s.f.)   (c) 31·685 (3 s.f.)

(d) 213182 (3 s.f.)   (e) 384·67 (2 s.f.)   (f) 0·61087 (3 s.f.)

6. Checking answers

Do not use a calculator.

(a) If $310 \times 23 = 7130$, does $7130 \div 310 = 23$?

(b) If $2646 \div 42 = 63$, does $2646 \div 63 = 42$?

(c) If $2646 \div 42 = 63$, does $63 \times 42 = 2646$?

(d) If $386 \times 17 = 6562$, work out $65·62 \div 17$

7. Converting between fractions and percentages

Change these fractions into percentages.

(a) $\dfrac{51}{100}$ (b) $\dfrac{3}{10}$ (c) $\dfrac{7}{25}$ (d) $\dfrac{11}{20}$

(e) What percentage of these shapes are stars?

(f) Ned scored 9 out of 25 in his English test. Faye scored 8 out of 29 in her English test. Who got the higher percentage and by how much was it higher? (*You may use a calculator*)

(g) Mr Seymour wants to buy a car for £12 000. He pays a deposit of £1000. What is the deposit as a percentage of the total cost of the car? (*You may use a calculator*. Give your answer to the nearest whole number.)

8. Finding percentage increases and decreases

(a)

     What is the sale price of this TV?

(b) A music system costs £628 + VAT. If VAT = 20%, work out how much the music system costs in total?

(c) Increase £610 by 4%

(d) Decrease £385 by 12%

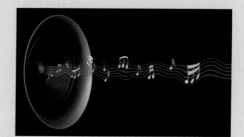

9. Using reverse percentages

(a) The price of a phone is reduced by 10%.
The phone now costs £72.
What was the price of the phone before the reduction?

(b) VAT is 20%.
A computer costs £600 after VAT is added on.
How much does the computer cost without VAT?

10. Converting between percentages and decimals

(a) Pair off each percentage below with its equivalent decimal.

| 75% | 1·4 | 34% | 70% | 0·07 |
| 0·7 | 0·34 | 140% | 0·75 | 7% |

(b) How much greater is 0·6 than 58%?
Give your answer as a decimal.

11. Using simple interest

(a) Find the simple interest on £1700 at 4% per annum for 6 years.

(b) Sue borrows £800 to buy a TV. She repays all the money over
3 years with a simple interest rate of 6% per annum. How much
does Sue pay back in total?

12. Finding ratios

(a) $\frac{4}{9}$ of the children in a class are boys.

Write down the ratio of boys to girls.

(b) Write down the ratio of blue
to pink in its simplest form.

Change the following ratios to their simplest form:

(c) 9 : 24   (c) 60 : 15   (c) 50 cm : 2 m   (d) 25p : £3

(g) Write the ratio 1·2 : 3 in its simplest whole number form.

13. Dealing with direct proportion

(a) 4 apples cost £1·68.
How much do 7 apples cost?

(b) 250 g is needed to make 10 cakes.
How many cakes can be made from 400 g?

(c) 200 g of chocolates cost £1·96 and 350 g of chocolate cost £3·50.
Which weight is the better value?

(a) £3000 is shared between Ally, Jane and Rob in the ratio $11:4:5$.
How much money does each person get?

(b) Lemon squash is diluted using squash and water in the ratio $1:8$.
If 72 ml of water is used, how much squash must be added?

(c) Green paint is made from blue and yellow paint in the ratio $3:7$.
If 42 litres of yellow are used, how much blue paint must be used?

(d) Some sweets are shared between Riley and Sanjay in the ratio $5:9$.
Sanjay gets 28 more sweets than Riley. How many sweets does Riley get?

Mixed examination questions

1 Daniel buys

      one loaf of bread costing £1·18
      one tub of spread costing 94p
      two jars of strawberry jam.

Daniel pays with a £5 note.
He gets 39p change.

Work out the cost of **one** jar of strawberry jam.   (EDEXCEL)

2 Copy and complete this bill.

Dwayne's Plumbing
3 Pipe Way, Looe

Mrs Leak
Flood Lane
Looe

Date 1st November 2013

Bath	£1295.00
Sink	£475.00
Labour	£350.00

Total before Value added Tax (VAT)   ....

VAT at 20%   ....

Total to pay   ....

(AQA)

3 Amir is mixing antifreeze and water.
He has 6 litres of a mixture of antifreeze and water in the ratio 1 : 3.

How much antifreeze must he add to make the ratio 1 : 1?   (OCR)

4 Work out the difference in value between $\frac{1}{4}$ and 30%.   (EDEXCEL)

5 Boxes of Tasty Tea come in three sizes

    size A   60 bags for £1·80
    size B   80 bags for £2·24
    size C   150 bags for £4·80

Find out which size is the best bargain.

Show clearly your method and all your working.   (CEA)

6 Amira and Sian travelled by ship to Ireland for a five-day holiday.

(a) Amira exchanged £750 into euros before departing.
The exchange rate was £1 = 1·20 euros.
How many euros did Amira receive?

(b) On the first night, they stayed at a hotel in Dublin.
Amira had booked online before departing and had paid £85.
Sian paid 96 euros at the hotel.
Using the same exchange rate, calculate the difference **in pounds**
between the amounts they each paid.   (WJEC)

7 Talil is going to make some concrete mix.
He needs to mix cement, sand and gravel in the ratio 1 : 3 : 5 by weight.

Talil wants to make 180 kg of concrete mix.

Talil has

    15 kg of cement
    85 kg of sand
  100 kg of gravel

Does Talil have enough cement, sand and gravel to make the
concrete mix?   (EDEXCEL)

8 (a) Use your calculator to work out $\dfrac{\sqrt{2\cdot5^2 + 3\cdot75}}{3\cdot9 - 1\cdot7}$

Write down all the figures on your calculator display.
You must give your answer as a decimal.

(b) Write your answer to part (a) correct to 2 decimal places.   (EDEXCEL)

9 A school only has pupils in Year 7, Year 8 and Year 9.

The table shows information about pupil absence on one day.

	Year 7	Year 8	Year 9
Number of pupils in year group	380	400	420
Number of pupils absent	28	32	36

The target for daily attendance is 93% or more for the whole school.

Did the school meet the target that day? (AQA)

10 Hugh is a travelling salesman. He claims 24·6p for each km he travels and £27·60 for meals on each day he is travelling.

If he travels more than 700 km in any week he adds 12·5% to his total claim.

Last week Hugh travelled 915 km in 5 days.

How much did Hugh claim for last week? (CEA)

11 Pat and Julie share some money in the ratio 2 : 5
Julie gets £45 more than Pat.

How much money did Pat get? (EDEXCEL)

12 Jay sells Christmas trees. This year he sells 75 trees which is 25% more than he sold last year. How many trees did he sell last year?

13 (a) Estimate $108 \times 7·8$

(b) Estimate how many books costing £7·95 each can be bought with £48

(c) Estimate $\sqrt{75}$ (CEA)

14 Minnie invested £250 for 3 years at 4% simple interest.

Work out the total interest Minnie gets (EDEXCEL)

15 Potatoes cost £9 for a 12·5 kg bag at a farm shop.
The same type of potatoes cost £1·83 for a 2·5 kg bag at a supermarket.

Where are the potatoes the better value, at the farm shop or at the supermarket?
You must show your working. (EDEXCEL)

WATCH YOUR MONEY

In this unit we will explore bank accounts and buying on credit.

WATCH YOUR MONEY! – Bank accounts 1

Most people have an account with a bank or a building society. Money is kept safely in the bank. Bills can be paid directly from the bank or with a debit card. Cash can be withdrawn or cheques can be used.

Writing a cheque

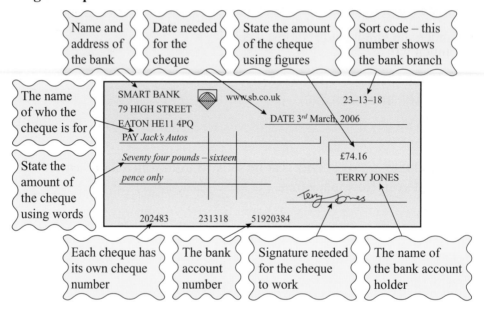

- Name and address of the bank
- Date needed for the cheque
- State the amount of the cheque using figures
- Sort code – this number shows the bank branch
- The name of who the cheque is for
- State the amount of the cheque using words
- Each cheque has its own cheque number
- The bank account number
- Signature needed for the cheque to work
- The name of the bank account holder

Note

- The amount in words must match the amount in figures.
- The cheque must be used within six months of the date.
- If you make a mistake when filling out a cheque, you may correct it so long as you write your signature by the mistake.
- The bank will not pay the money for your cheque if you do not have enough money in your bank account.

Cheque guarantee card

Once you are over 18, your bank may allow you a cheque guarantee card. If the cheque guarantee card number is written on the back of the cheque, the bank will definitely pay the money (the maximum amount is usually £100).

Being overdrawn

If you spend more money than is in your bank account without arranging with the bank beforehand, you will go overdrawn. The bank will charge you extra money and you will *owe* them *even more money*. You will then have to sort it out quickly or could run into even greater difficulties.

Opening a bank account

You can open a bank account now if you have not already done so. Visit any bank and they will help you to open an account but *shop around*. Some banks will *pay you extra money* if you have some money in your bank account. This is called '*interest on your bank account*'. Also find out how '*kind*' the bank is if you go '*slightly*' overdrawn. Will the bank charge you lots of money?

WYM 6.1

1 Pat has £56 in her account. Her bank will charge her £30 if she goes overdrawn. She pays out two cheques, one for £39.19 and another for £27. How much will she now owe the bank?

2 Zak's bank has agreed that he may go up to £50 overdrawn without paying a penalty. If he breaks the agreement, he will have to pay a £35 charge. Zak has £32 in his account. He makes 3 payments of £28, £16·29 and £34·96. How much will Zak now owe the bank?

3 Chloe has the same agreement with her bank as Zak in Question **2**.

Chloe has £93 in her account. She makes 3 payments of £61·14, £73·06 and £25·32. How much will Chloe now owe the bank?

4 Colin sends the following cheque to his phone company.

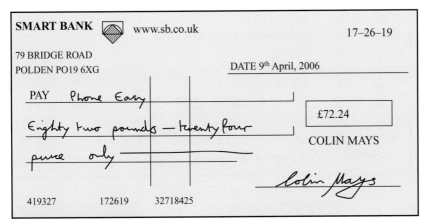

By looking at the cheque earlier in this section, write down:

(a) the sort code   (b) the bank account number

(c) the website address for the bank   (d) the cheque number.

(e) The bank will *not* cash this cheque. Explain why.

5 Lara has £128.16 in her bank account. She makes payments of £17·11, £32·68 and £41·23. What is the biggest cheque she could now pay out *without* going overdrawn?

6 Investigate different banks. Find out if they pay interest on bank accounts. How much can you go overdrawn before you are charged? How much would the bank charge you if you went too much overdrawn? Discuss as a class.

WATCH YOUR MONEY – Bank accounts 2

To keep track of your money, the bank or building society will send you a regular '**statement**'.

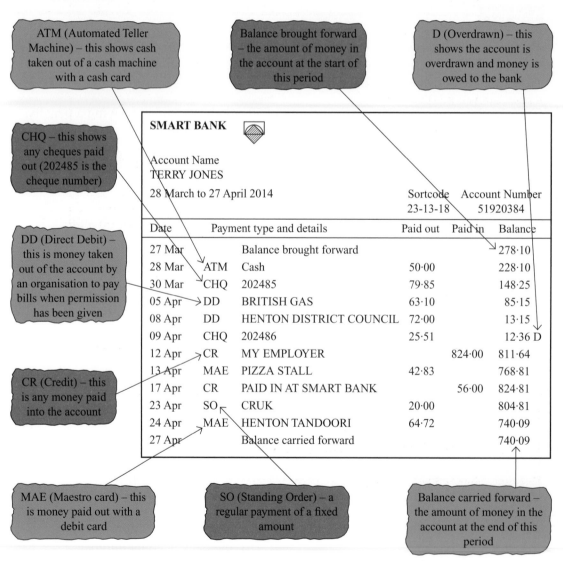

ATM (Automated Teller Machine) – this shows cash taken out of a cash machine with a cash card

Balance brought forward – the amount of money in the account at the start of this period

D (Overdrawn) – this shows the account is overdrawn and money is owed to the bank

CHQ – this shows any cheques paid out (202485 is the cheque number)

DD (Direct Debit) – this is money taken out of the account by an organisation to pay bills when permission has been given

CR (Credit) – this is any money paid into the account

MAE (Maestro card) – this is money paid out with a debit card

SO (Standing Order) – a regular payment of a fixed amount

Balance carried forward – the amount of money in the account at the end of this period

SMART BANK

Account Name
TERRY JONES

28 March to 27 April 2014

Sortcode 23-13-18 Account Number 51920384

Date	Payment type and details		Paid out	Paid in	Balance
27 Mar		Balance brought forward			278·10
28 Mar	ATM	Cash	50·00		228·10
30 Mar	CHQ	202485	79·85		148·25
05 Apr	DD	BRITISH GAS	63·10		85·15
08 Apr	DD	HENTON DISTRICT COUNCIL	72·00		13·15
09 Apr	CHQ	202486	25·51		12·36 D
12 Apr	CR	MY EMPLOYER		824·00	811·64
13 Apr	MAE	PIZZA STALL	42·83		768·81
17 Apr	CR	PAID IN AT SMART BANK		56·00	824·81
23 Apr	SO	CRUK	20·00		804·81
24 Apr	MAE	HENTON TANDOORI	64·72		740·09
27 Apr		Balance carried forward			740·09

SMART BANK

Account Name

COLIN MAYS

3 April to 2 May 2014

Sortcode
17-26-19

Account Number
32718425

Date	Payment type and details	Paid out	Paid in	Balance
2 Apr	Balance brought forward			416·25
3 Apr	CHQ 419330	63·10		1
5 Apr	DD POLDEN WATER	58·17		294·98
9 Apr	CR MY EMPLOYER		750·00	2
14 Apr	MAE PETROLGO	28·64		3
16 Apr	DD MID ELECTRICITY	67·00		949·34
18 Apr	CHQ 419331	4		823·74
19 Apr	SO MR. S. JONES	38·45		5
22 Apr	CR PAID IN AT SMART BANK		6	850·29
23 Apr	MAE HORTON STORE	43·26		7
28 Apr	MAE AQUAPLAY	21·95		8
2 May	Balance carried forward			9

For questions **1** to **9**, write down the correct amount of money for each box above.

10 Explain what 'DD' shows on a bank statement.

11 Explain what 'ATM' shows on a bank statement.

12 Explain what 'D' shows on a bank statement.

If you do not have enough money to buy an item, you might buy *on credit*. There are different ways of doing this such as hire purchase, credit cards, store cards, bank overdrafts and personal loans.

Make sure you know the true cost of buying on credit.

This section deals with hire purchase.

> Hire purchase allows you to buy items straight away but you pay for them in instalments (usually monthly).
>
> You probably will not own the items until all the instalments have been paid. If you stop paying the instalments, the items could be taken back.

> Computer £650
> (or a 20% deposit plus 24 monthly payments of £27·50 each month.)

If you buy the computer on credit:

deposit = 20% of £650 = £130

24 monthly payments = 24 × £27·50 = £660

total credit price = £130 + £660 = £790

How much extra does the hire purchase cost you?

extra cost = £790 − £650 = £140

       ↑   ↑

     Credit Cash

      price   price

You would have to decide if you do not mind paying this *extra money* to be able to get this computer.

GET WISE

If shops and other places offer interest-free periods, find out exactly what you have to pay in the end. It may *cost* you a lot of *extra money*.

1　A washing machine costs £420. You can buy it for a 10% deposit plus 36 equal monthly payments of £14.

(a)　How much is the deposit?

(b)　How much are the 36 monthly payments?

(c)　What is the total credit price?

(d)　How much extra does the hire purchase cost?

2　A TV costs £560. You can buy it for a 15% deposit plus 36 equal monthly payments of £15·50.

(a)　How much is the deposit?

(b)　How much are the 36 monthly payments?

(c)　What is the total credit price?

(d)　How much extra does the hire purchase cost?

3　Copy and complete the table below:

	Item	Cash price (£)	Deposit (£)	Number of monthly instalments	Each monthly (£) instalment	Total credit price (£)	Extra cost of hire (£) purchase
(a)	Cooker	735	100	24	30		
(b)	Bike	390	80	24	15		
(c)	Car	12 400	3000	48	224		
(d)	Phone	230	40	12	17·50		
(e)	Dishwasher	465	55	36	14·99		

4

New windows £3250	Pay a 20% deposit then *nothing for 2 years*. Followed by 12 equal monthly payments of £299.

How much extra does the hire purchase cost?

5

Boiler　　　　　　　　£4100

Pay a £1000 deposit then *nothing for 1 year*.
Finally 48 equal monthly payments of £85.

How much is saved by paying the cash price?

Make sure you know the true cost of buying on credit.

This section deals with credit cards and store cards.

Credit cards

- A credit card can be used to buy items now and pay for them at a later date. They can be used to get cash but this can be expensive to do.

- Credit cards are good if the person pays off the bill within a certain number of days. If the bill is not paid off, interest is charged which means the person will *owe even more money*.

- People usually have to be 18 or over to get a credit card (not everyone is able to get a credit card).

- Each person has a credit limit. If the person tries to spend more than this, the card will not work or the person will get a penalty charge.

Monthly payment

If a person cannot pay off the bill in full, at least £5 or 5% of the total bill (whichever is the greater) has to be paid. The percentage may be different for some credit cards. If the person does not pay this, there will be a penalty charge and the person will *owe even more money*.

APR (annual percentage rate)

Look at the APR to compare the cost of borrowing for different credit cards. The APR is given as a yearly percentage. It takes into account all the costs involved and the method of repayment.

In general, the *lower the APR*, the *better the deal*.

Store Cards

Credit cards can be an expensive way to borrow money over a long period of time. A store card often has a higher APR than a standard credit card so is even more expensive. The advantage of a store card is that you can spread out the cost of buying items and many stores give special offers with their cards at times.

Richard's tale

Richard has a credit card with a credit limit of £3000.
Each month the interest rate is 1·32%.

During the first year of his credit card he spends up to
his limit and at the end of January he owes £2998.

1 The credit card company want a payment of 5% of
£2998. How much is this?

2 Richard cannot afford this payment so ignores it.
The monthly interest of 1·32% of £2998 is added
onto his debt. How much does he now owe? (Give
your answer to the nearest penny.)

3 Richard did not make his monthly payment so has
a penalty charge of £20. How much does he now
owe?

4 The credit card company notice that Richard has
gone over his credit limit and decide to increase his
limit to £5000. How much money is Richard now
allowed to spend before reaching this limit?

5 Over the next 4 months Richard spends happily and
his credit card debt increases by another £1879.
How much does he now owe?

6 The monthly payment is due. This is 5% of what
Richard now owes. How much is the monthly
payment? (Give your answer to the nearest penny)

7 Richard can afford no more than £200.
How much more would he need to make the
monthly payment?

8 He fails to make this monthly payment.
The monthly interest of 1·32% of his debt is added
onto his debt. How much does he now owe? (Give
your answer to the nearest penny)

9 Richard gets a penalty charge of £20 for not making
his monthly payment. How much does he now owe?

10 Richard is now over his £5000 credit limit.
He is getting more and more into debt. Maybe
the credit card company will raise his credit limit
again? What would be your advice to Richard?
Discuss with your teacher the advantages and
disadvantages of credit cards.

ALGEBRA 2

In this unit you will learn how to:

- find numbers in sequences
- find rules for arithmetic sequences
- change the subject of a formula
- draw straight line graphs
- find gradients of lines and use $y = mx + c$
- draw curves from equations
- read graphs
- use travel graphs
- ⟨ USE YOUR MATHS! ⟩ – hidden car costs

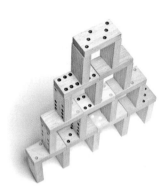

Sequences

- A number sequence is a list of numbers in special order.

- Each number in a sequence is called a *term*.

- The terms are connected by a rule.

  For example: 3, 8, 13, 18, 23… the rule is $+5$ each time.

  Note – if the rule is adding or subtracting the same number each time, the sequence is an *arithmetic* sequence.

- To find the rule that links the numbers, study the gaps.

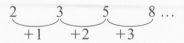

  2 3 5 8 …   You can now see the pattern so the next
    $+1$ $+2$ $+3$ number will be $8 + 4 = 12$

1 The numbers in boxes make a sequence. Find the next term.

(a) 2   5   8   11   ☐

(b) 15   13   11   9   ☐

(c) 3   4   6   9   ☐

In each of questions **2** to **15**, (a) copy the sequence and write the *next 2 numbers*, (b) what is the rule for the sequence?   (c) is this an arithmetic sequence?

2   2, 6, 10, 14, …   **3**   7, 9, 11, 13, …   **4**   7, 15, 23, 31, …

5   16, 13, 10, 7, …   **6**   23, 19, 15, 11, …   **7**   5, 14, 23, 32, …

8   4, 10, 16, 22, …   **9**   10, 19, 28, 37, …   **10**   5, 7, 10, 14, …

11   1, 2, 4, 7, …   **12**   18, 17, 15, 12, …   **13**   80, 75, 65, 50, …

14   5, 3, 1, −1, …   **15**   2, 0, −2, −4, …

In questions **16** to **25** write down the missing numbers.

16   7, 11, ☐, 19, ☐   **17**   8, 11, ☐, 17, ☐

18   21, 16, ☐, 6, ☐   **19**   32, 26, 20, ☐, ☐

20   5, 12, ☐, 26, ☐   **21**   −10, −8, ☐, −4, ☐

22   3, 0, ☐, −6, ☐   **23**   61, 57, 53, ☐, ☐

24   ☐, 2, 0, −2, ☐   **25**   4, 5, 7, 10, ☐, ☐

26 Do you remember the triangular numbers below?

1   3   6   10

Write down the next 3 triangular numbers?

27 Shape 1   Shape 2   Shape 3   How many lines are needed for

☐   ☐   ☐

(a) shape 4,

(b) shape 5?

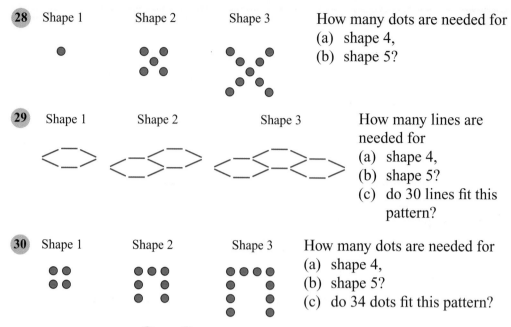

28 Shape 1   Shape 2   Shape 3   How many dots are needed for
(a) shape 4,
(b) shape 5?

29 Shape 1   Shape 2   Shape 3   How many lines are needed for
(a) shape 4,
(b) shape 5?
(c) do 30 lines fit this pattern?

30 Shape 1   Shape 2   Shape 3   How many dots are needed for
(a) shape 4,
(b) shape 5?
(c) do 34 dots fit this pattern?

In each of questions **31** to **45**, (a) copy the sequence and write the *next 2 numbers*,

(b) what is the rule for the sequence?   (c) is this an arithmetic sequence?

31 1, 2, 4, 8, …   **32** 1, 3, 9, 27, …   **33** 1, 4, 9, 16, …

34 800, 400, 200, 100, …   **35** 2, 5, 10, 17, …   **36** $\frac{1}{2}$, 1, $1\frac{1}{2}$, 2, …

37 1, 3, 6, 10, …   **38** 2, 6, 18, 54, …   **39** 243, 81, 27, 9, …

40 2, 20, 200, 2000, …   **41** 1, 8, 27, 64, …   **42** 1·3, 1·7, 2·1, 2·5, …

43 2, 16, 54, 128, …   **44** 21, 28, 36, 45, …   **45** 300, 30, 3, 0·3, …

Finding rules for arithmetic sequences

 # Key Facts

A sequence is *arithmetic* if the difference between successive terms is always the same number.

This number is called the *common difference d*.

eg. 7, 11, 15, 19, … has common difference $d = 4$
    22, 17, 12, 7, … has common difference $d = -5$

$$\text{nth term} = a + (n - 1)d$$

for all arithmetic sequences
where a is the first term in the sequence.

$$5, 8, 11, 14, \ldots \qquad a = 5 \qquad d = 3$$
$$n\text{th term} = a + (n - 1)d = 5 + (n - 1) \times 3$$
$$= 5 + 3n - 3$$
$$n\text{th term} = 3n + 2$$

M7.2

1. Here is a sequence: 3, 8, 13, 18, …

   The first term is 3 and the common difference is 5.

   $n\text{th term} = a + (n - 1)d = 3 + (n - 1) \times 5$

   Multiply out the bracket and write the nth term in its simplest form.

2. Here is a sequence: 8, 10, 12, 14, …

   Write down (a) the first term

              (b) the common difference

              (c) the nth term in its simplest form.

3. For each sequence below, write down the first term and common difference then use them to find the nth term.

   (a) 3, 9, 15, 21, …

   (b) 4, 11, 18, 25, …

   (c) 13, 23, 33, 43, …

   (d) 12, 10, 8, 6, …

   (e) 1, 9, 17, 25, …

   (f) 17, 13, 9, 5, …

   (g) 40, 31, 22, 13, …

   (h) 2·5, 3, 3·5, 4, …

   Can you still?

   Mixed algebra

   Find the value of each expression if $m = 5$ and $n = -4$.

   1. $3mn$ | 2. m^2 | 3. $m^2 + n$

   4. $5n$ | 5. n^2 | 6. $2n + m$

   7. $\dfrac{8m}{n}$ | 8. $\dfrac{4m}{m + n}$ | 9. $n(2m - n)$

   Solve these equations:

   10. $4n - 3 = 13$

   11. $\dfrac{n}{5} = 7$ | 12. $-8n = 40$

   13. $55 = 9n + 1$

   14. $7n + 3 = 6$

4 The rule for the number sequences below is 'multiply by 3 then add 1'

Find the missing numbers.

(a) $3 \rightarrow 10 \rightarrow 31 \rightarrow 94 \rightarrow$ ☐

(b) ☐ $\rightarrow 7 \rightarrow 22 \rightarrow 67 \rightarrow 202$

5 The rule for the number sequences below is 'multiply by 2 and take away 1'

Find the missing numbers.

(a) $2 \rightarrow 3 \rightarrow 5 \rightarrow 9 \rightarrow$ ☐

(b) ☐ $\rightarrow 7 \rightarrow 13 \rightarrow 25 \rightarrow 49$

6 Write down the term-to-term rule for each sequence below:

(a) 70, 64, 58, 52, …   (b) 144, 72, 36, 18, …

(c) 3·5, 5, 6·5, 8, …   (d) 2, 6, 18, 54, …

Here is a sequence of shapes made from sticks.

Let n = shape number and s = number of sticks

  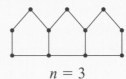

$n = 1$ $\qquad$ $n = 2$ $\qquad$ $n = 3$
$s = 5$ $\qquad$ $s = 9$ $\qquad$ $s = 13$

The next shape in the sequence is

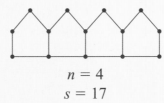

$n = 4$
$s = 17$

Make a table of values.

n	1	2	3	4
s	5	9	13	17

first term = 5

common difference = 4

nth term = $a + (n - 1)d = 5 + (n - 1) \times 4 = 5 + 4n - 4 = 4n + 1$

This means $s = 4n + 1$

For shape number 50, $s = 4n + 1 = 4 \times 50 + 1 = 201$ sticks

(much quicker than drawing pictures!)

1 Here is a sequence of shapes made from squares. Let n = shape number and w = number of white squares.

 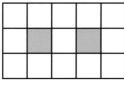 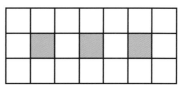

$n = 1$ $n = 2$ $n = 3$
$w = 8$ $w = 13$ $w = 18$

(a) Draw the next shape in the sequence.

(b) How many white squares are in shape number 4?

(c) Complete the table of values.
The first term is 8 and the
common difference is 5.

n	1	2	3	4
w	8	13	18	

Use these to find a formula for the number of white squares (w) for the shape number n.
Use values of n to check if your formula is correct.

(d) Use your formula to find out how many white squares are in shape number 20.

For each of the sequences in questions **2** to **6**,

(a) Draw the next shape in the sequence.

(b) Let n = shape number and s = number of sticks.
Complete a table of values for n and s.

(c) Use the first term and the common difference to find a formula for the number of sticks (s) for the shape number n.

(d) Use the formula to find out how many sticks are in shape number 50.

2

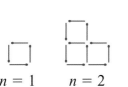

$n = 1$ $n = 2$ $n = 3$
$s = 4$ $s = 10$ $s =$

3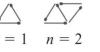

$n = 1$ $n = 2$ $n = 3$

4

 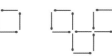 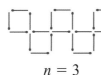

$n = 1$ $n = 2$ $n = 3$

215

5

$n = 1$ $n = 2$ $n = 3$

6

$n = 1$ 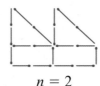 $n = 2$ 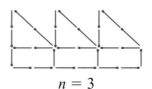 $n = 3$

7 This table can seat 5 people.

The diagrams below show how many people can be seated when tables are joined together.

   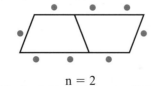 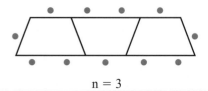

n = 1   n = 2   n = 3

(a) Draw the diagram for 4 tables.

(b) Let p = number of people and n = number of tables. Make a table of values and use it to find a formula for the number of people according to how many tables.

(c) How many people could be seated with 20 tables?

8 Ponds are surrounded by paving slabs as shown below:

    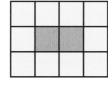   

$n = 1$ $n = 2$ $n = 3$

(a) Draw the next shape in the sequence.

(b) How many yellow paving slabs surround each pond?

(c) Find a formula for the number of yellow slabs (y) surrounding each pond n (use a table of values to help you).

(d) How many yellow slabs surround pond number 50?

(e) Would 24 yellow slabs fit this design? Explain your answer fully.

Changing the subject of a formula

(a) $a = 3b$

Make b the subject of the formula.

$a = 3 \times b$

$\dfrac{a}{3} = \dfrac{\cancel{3} \times b}{\cancel{3}}$

$\dfrac{a}{3} = b$ we say that $b = \dfrac{a}{3}$

(b) $p = 5q + 8$

Make q the subject of the formula.

$\boxed{p} = \boxed{5q}\,\boxed{+8}$

$\boxed{p} - 8 = \boxed{5q}\,\boxed{+8} - 8$

$p - 8 = 5q$

$\dfrac{p - 8}{5} = \dfrac{\cancel{5}q}{\cancel{5}}$

$\dfrac{p - 8}{5} = q$ we say that $q = \dfrac{p - 8}{5}$

E7.1

Copy and complete each statement below:

1   If $x = y + 5$ then $x \,\square\, 5 = y$

2   If $x = y + 8$ then $x \,\square\, 8 = y$

3   If $a = b - 3$ then $a \,\square\, 3 = b$

4   If $a = b + 9$ then $a \,\square\, 9 = b$

5   If $a = 6b$ then $\dfrac{a}{\square} = b$

6   If $x = y - 2$ then $x \,\square\, 2 = y$

7   Make x the subject of each formula given below:

(a) $y = x - 9$ (b) $y = \dfrac{x}{12}$ (c) $y = x + 6$ (d) $y = x + 20$

(e) $y = 8x$ (f) $y = 10x$ (g) $y = x - 4$ (h) $y = x - 25$

(i) $y = \dfrac{x}{3}$ (j) $y = \dfrac{x}{15}$ (k) $y = x + 100$ (l) $y = 18x$

8   Match up pairs of formulas which are the same. There will be one odd formula left over.

A $a = b + 5$

B $a = 5b$

C $a = b - 5$

P $b = \dfrac{a}{5}$

Q $b = a - 5$

R $b = 5a$

S $b = a + 5$

9 $p = 3q$ Make q the subject of the formula.

10 $a = 7b$ Make b the subject of the formula.

11 $x = \dfrac{y}{9}$ Make y the subject of the formula.

12 Copy and fill each box below:

(a) $x = 3y + 2$
$x - \square = 3y + 2 - \square$
$x - \square = 3y$
$\dfrac{x - \square}{\square} = y$

(b) $x = 4y - 9$
$x + \square = 4y - 9 + \square$
$x + \square = 4y$
$\dfrac{x + \square}{\square} = y$

13 $a = 2b - 5$ Make b the subject of the formula.

14 $p = 9q + 7$ Make q the subject of the formula.

15 $a = 7b + 1$ Make b the subject of the formula.

16 $x = 3y - 10$ Make y the subject of the formula.

17 Make x the subject of each formula given below:

(a) $y = 2x + 8$ (b) $y = 6x - 5$ (c) $y = 8x - 10$

(d) $y = \dfrac{x}{3} + 2$ (e) $y = \dfrac{x}{5} - 6$ (f) $y = \dfrac{x}{2} - 4$

Drawing straight line graphs

M7.4

1 Write down the equations of the lines marked A, B and C.

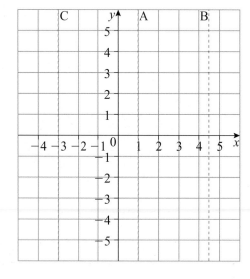

2 Write down the equations of the lines marked P, Q, R and S.

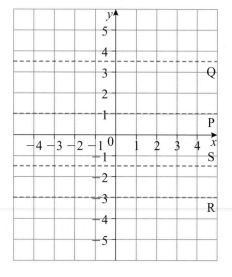

3 (a) Draw axes like those in question **2**.

(b) Plot the points A(4, 3), B(−3, −2), C(4, −1), D(−3, 3).

(c) Write down the equation of the line passing through

    (i) A and C   (ii) B and D   (iii) A and D

4

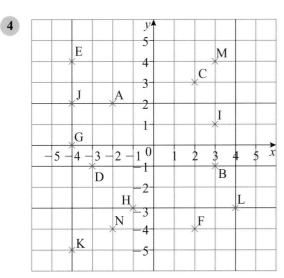

(a) J lies on the line $y = 2$. Which other letter lies on $y = 2$?

(b) Which letter lies on $x = 4$?

(c) Which letters lie on $y = -1$?

(d) Which letters lie on $x = -4$?

(e) How many letters lie on $y = -3$?

(f) Which letter lies on $y = 2$ *and* $x = -4$?

(g) Which letter lies on $x = 4$ *and* $y = -3$?

5 The outside edge of Frank's face below is made by straight lines.

Write down the equation of each line (2 of the lines will have the same equation).

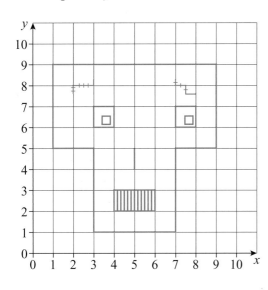

Can you still?

Mixed algebra

Simplify

1 $3a \times 4b$ **2** $5a \times 7a$

3 $a^2 + a^2$ **4** $a^2 \times a^2$

5 $(m^3)^2$ **6** $4n^2 + 3n - n^2$

Expand

7 $4(a - c)$ **8** $m(m + 3n)$

9 $2a(a - 4b)$ **10** $5n(3n - 2p)$

Factorise

11 $6m + 9n$ **12** $ab - bc$

13 $a^2 - 7a$ **14** $15n^2 + 10mn$

219

Sloping lines

Draw the straight line $y = x + 3$.

When $x = 1$, $y = x + 3 = 1 + 3 = 4 \rightarrow (1, 4)$

When $x = 2$, $y = x + 3 = 2 + 3 = 5 \rightarrow (2, 5)$

When $x = 3$, $y = x + 3 = 3 + 3 = 6 \rightarrow (3, 6)$

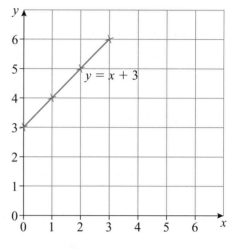

Note

When working out the y-values, we usually write them in a table.

x	0	1	2	3
y	3	4	5	6

M7.5

(Check all your graphs with a computer or graphical calculator if your teacher wants you to!)

For questions **1** to **3**, you will need to draw axes like those below:

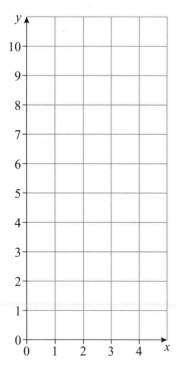

1 Complete the table below then draw the straight line $y = x + 4$

x	0	1	2	3
y				

2 Complete the table below then draw $y = 2x$

x	0	1	2	3
y				

3 Complete the table below then draw $y = 3x + 1$

x	0	1	2	3
y				

220

4 Using *x*-values from 0 to 5, complete a table then draw the straight line
$y = 6 - x$.

5 (a) Using *x*-values from 0 to 3, draw $y = x$ and $y = 6 - 2x$ on the *same graph*.

(b) Write down the co-ordinates where the two lines meet.

6 Find the value of these when $x = -2$:

(a) $x + 3$ (b) $3x$ (c) $x - 2$ (d) $2x$ (e) $2x + 3$

7 Find the value of *y* when $x = -3$:

(a) $y = x + 1$ (b) $y = 2x$ (c) $y = x - 3$ (d) $y = 3x$ (e) $y = 3x - 2$

In questions **8** and **9**, you will need to draw axes like these:

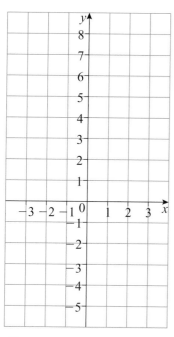

8 Complete the table below then draw the straight line $y = x - 2$

x	-2	-1	0	1	2
y					

9 Complete the table below then draw the straight line $y = 2x + 4$

x	-2	-1	0	1	2
y					

10 (a) Using *x*-values from -2 to 2, complete a table then draw the straight line $y = 3x - 2$ (make sure you draw the axes big enough).

(b) Use your graph to find the value of *x* when $y = -6$.

11 (a) Draw $y = 3 - 2x$ using *x*-values from -3 to 3.

(b) Use your graph to find the value of *x* when $y = 4$.

12 Draw an *x*-axis from -3 to 3 and a *y*-axis from -10 to 8. Using the *same* set of axes, draw

$$y = 4x \qquad\qquad y = 2x - 3$$
$$y = 1 - 2x \qquad\qquad y = 3x - 4$$

Label each line clearly.

Have you ever seen signs like this?

This is the gradient – how steep the hill is.

The '**1 in 10**' means that the hill goes up 1 m for every 10 m across.

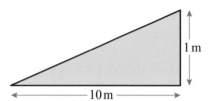

Gradient = 1 in 10 = $\dfrac{1}{10}$

The steeper the hill, the bigger the gradient.

Gradient = $\dfrac{\text{vertical distance}}{\text{horizontal distance}}$

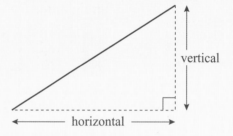

(a) Find the gradient of this line

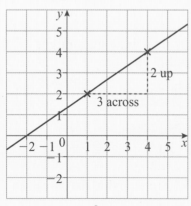

Gradient = $\dfrac{2 \text{ up}}{3 \text{ across}} = \dfrac{2}{3}$

(b)

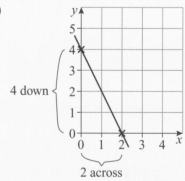

Gradient = $\dfrac{4 \text{ down}}{2 \text{ across}} = \dfrac{-4}{2} = -2$

If a line slopes downwards to the right, it has a *negative gradient*.

Find the gradient of each line.

1

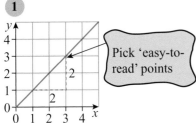

Pick 'easy-to-read' points

2

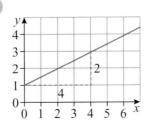

3

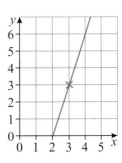

4

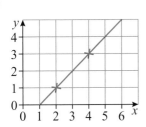

5

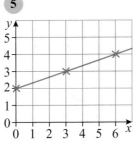

6

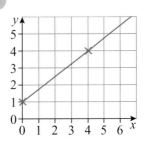

7 Find the gradient of each line below:

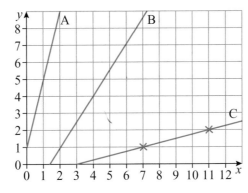

8 Find the gradient of the line joining:

(a) A and B

(b) A and D

(c) C and D

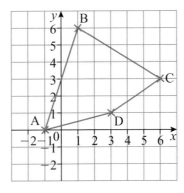

223

Find the gradient of each line.

9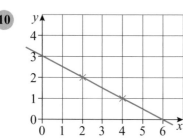

10

11

Can you still?

Angles

Find the angles marked with the letters.

1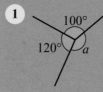

2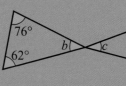

3

4

5

6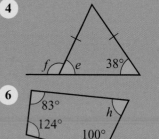

7 Work out the size of an interior angle of a regular decagon (10 sides).

12 Find the gradient of each line below:

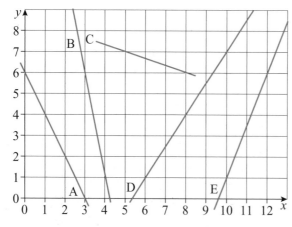

13 Draw axes on squared paper. Draw a line with gradient -4. Ask a friend to check the gradient.

14 Draw axes on squared paper. Draw a line with gradient $\frac{2}{5}$. Ask a friend to check the gradient.

M7.7

Use a graphical calculator or computer if possible.

1 You will need to draw axes like these:

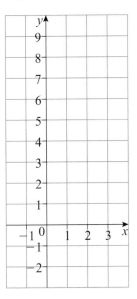

(a) Complete the table below then draw the straight line $y = 2x + 3$.

x	1	2	3
y			

(b) Use another table to draw $y = 2x$ on the same grid.

(c) Draw $y = 2x + 1$ on the same grid.

(d) Draw $y = 2x - 1$ on the same grid.

(e) Find the gradient of each line.

(f) What do you notice about the gradient of each line and its equation? *Discuss* with your teacher.

(g) Look at where each line cuts the y-axis. For each line what do you notice about this value and its equation? Discuss with your teacher.

2 Draw the following lines and repeat parts (e), (f) and (g) from question **1**.

$y = -3x + 1$

$y = -3x + 4$

$y = -3x$

$y = -3x - 2$

$y = -3x - 5$

3 Write down the co-ordinates of the point where the line $y = 4x - 5$ cuts the y-axis.

Decimals

Do not use a calculator.

Work out

1 0.3×0.08 **2** $6.2 \div 5$

3 $15 - 0.16$ **4** 1.3×0.9

5 What change from £30 do I get if I buy 7 magazines at £3.85 each?

6 Write the decimals below in order of size, starting with the smallest.

0.8   0.79   0.084   0.82   0.09

Key Facts

The equation of a straight line may be written in the form

$$y = mx + c$$

m is the gradient of the line

c is the point y-value at the point where the line cuts the y-axis – this is known as the *'y-intercept'*

M7.8

1 Which lines below have the same gradient?

$y = 3x + 1$ $y = 3x - 2$ $y = 2x + 3$ $y = 3 + 4x$ $y = 7 + 3x$

2 Write down the gradient and y-intercept of each of the following lines:

(a) $y = 3x + 4$ (b) $y = 2x - 5$ (c) $y = 8x - 1$ (d) $y = x + 6$

(e) $y = -4x - 2$ (f) $y = -4x + 3$ (g) $y = -x - 2$ (h) $y = -5x + 2$

(i) $y = 3 - x$ (j) $y = 4 - 2x$ (k) $y = \frac{1}{3}x - 7$ (l) $y = \frac{1}{2} - 4x$

3 Write down the equation of each of the 3 lines below:

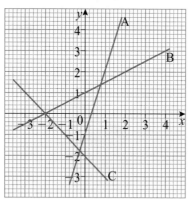

4 Which lines below are parallel?

$y = x + 2$ $y = 3 + 4x$ $y = 5 - x$ $y = 4x - 2$ $y = 2x + 4$

Drawing curves from equations

Draw $y = x^2 + 3$, using x-values from -3 to 3.

Substitute each x-value into the equation to find the y-value.

For example, when $x = 2$, $y = 2^2 + 3 = 4 + 3 = 7$

when $x = -3$, $y = (-3)^2 + 3 = 9 + 3 = 12$

$-3 \times -3 = 9$

draw a table

x	-3	-2	-1	0	1	2	3
y	12	7	4	3	4	7	12

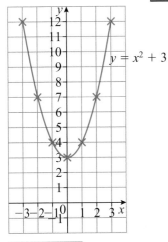

$y = x^2 + 3$

- draw axes so that *all* the points can be plotted

- plot each point

- join up all the points with a smooth curve

- label the curve with its equation

M7.9

For questions **1** to **3**, you will need to draw axes like these:

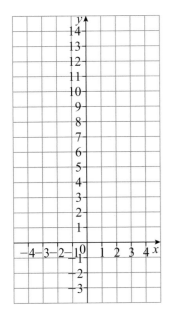

1 Complete the table below then draw the curve $y = x^2$

x	-3	-2	-1	0	1	2	3
y							

2 Complete the table below then draw the curve $y = x^2 + 1$

x	-3	-2	-1	0	1	2	3
y							

3 Complete the table then draw $y = x^2 - 3$

x	-3	-2	-1	0	1	2	3
y							

4 (a) Complete the table below for $y = 2x^2$ ($2x^2$ means 'x^2 then multiply by 2').

x	-3	-2	-1	0	1	2	3
y	18				2		

$$x = 1 \text{ so } y = 2x^2 = x^2 \times 2 = (1)^2 \times 2 = 1 \times 2 = 2$$

(b) Draw an x-axis from -3 to 3 (use 2 cm for 1 unit) and a y-axis from 0 to 18 (use 1 cm for 2 units).

Plot the points from the table and draw the curve $y = 2x^2$.

5 (a) Complete the table below for $y = 3x^2$ ($3x^2$ means 'x^2 then multiply by 3').

x	-3	-2	-1	0	1	2	3
y		12					

(b) Draw an x-axis from -3 to 3 (use 2 cm for 1 unit) and a y-axis from 0 to 28 (use 1 cm for 2 units). Draw the curve $y = 3x^2$.

6 Using x-values from -3 to 3, complete a table then draw $y = 2x^2 + 1$ (make sure you draw the axes big enough).

7 Using x-values from -3 to 3, complete a table then draw $y = 3x^2 - 2$ (make sure you draw the axes big enough).

Curves with several terms

Using x-values from -3 to 3 draw $y = x^2 + 4x - 1$.

Do each part separately in the table then add together at the end to find y.

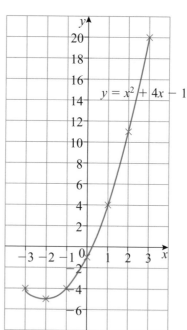

$y = x^2 + 4x - 1$

x	-3	-2	-1	0	1	2	3
x^2	9	4	1	0	1	4	9
$+4x$	-12	-8	-4	0	4	8	12
-1	-1	-1	-1	-1	-1	-1	-1
y	-4	-5	-4	-1	4	11	20

Note
A curve is called a 'quadratic' graph if the highest power of x is x^2.

228

1 (a) Complete the table for $y = x^2 + x + 2$.

x	-4	-3	-2	-1	0	1	2
x^2		9					
$+x$		-3					
$+2$	2	2	2	2	2	2	2
y		8					

(b) Draw an x-axis from -4 to 2 and a y-axis from 0 to 14. Draw the curve $y = x^2 + x + 2$ (the bottom of the curve should be curved $\smile$ *not* flat $\smile$).

In questions **2** and **3**, you will need to draw axes like these:

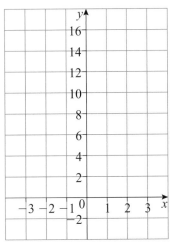

2 Complete the table below then draw the curve $y = x^2 + 2x$.

x	-3	-2	-1	0	1	2	3
x^2		4			1		
$+2x$		-4			2		
y		0			3		

3 (a) Complete the table then draw the curve $y = x^2 - x + 2$.

x	-3	-2	-1	0	1	2	3
x^2	9						
$-x$	3						
$+2$	2						
y	14						

(b) Read off the value of y from your graph when $x = 0.5$.

Reading graphs

1 The graph below shows how many cars pass through a car wash during one day.

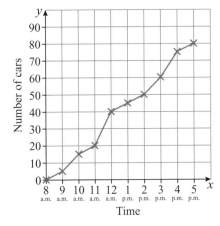

How many cars had passed through the car wash by the following times?

(a) 12 am   (b) 11:30 am

(c) 9:30 am   (d) 2:30 pm

(e) During which one hour period did *most* cars pass through the car wash. How many cars was this?

2 The graph below shows how to convert pounds into euros.

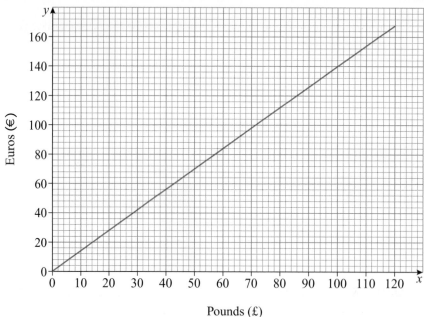

Use the graph to find how many euros are the same as:

(a) £20   (b) £80   (c) £50   (d) £240

Use the graph to find how many pounds are the same as:

(e) €56   (f) €84   (g) €140   (h) €560

(i) Tim spends €154 on clothes in Paris. How many pounds has he spent?

3 The number of people sitting down in a cinema was recorded every quarter of an hour. The results are shown below.

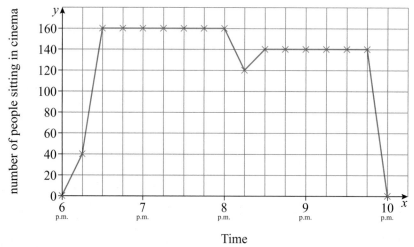

(a) How many people were sitting down at 7 pm?

(b) How many people were sitting down at 8:15 pm?

(c) When do you think the first film started?

(d) When do you think the second film started?

(e) How long did the first film last for?

(f) Which film was more popular?

1 Colin and Kris run a 400-metre race. The graph below shows how far they had run at different times.

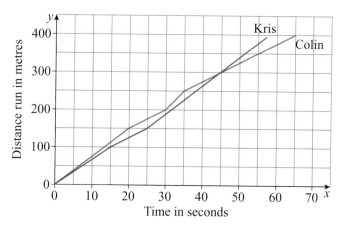

How far has Kris run after: (a) 15 seconds? (b) 25 seconds? (c) 60 seconds?

(d) How long does it take Colin to run the first 150 metres?

(e) How long does it take Colin to run the first 250 metres?

(f) After how many seconds have Colin and Kris run the *same* distance?

(g) Who won the race?

2 For each graph below find the speed of the journey from A to B (give the answer in km/h).

(a)
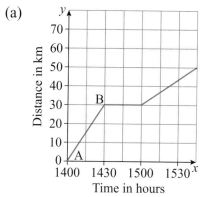

(b)
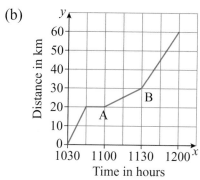

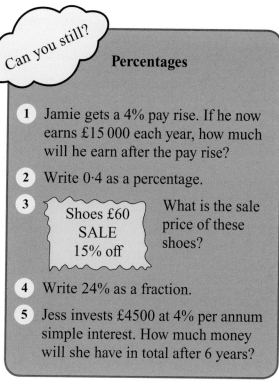

Can you still?

Percentages

1 Jamie gets a 4% pay rise. If he now earns £15 000 each year, how much will he earn after the pay rise?

2 Write 0·4 as a percentage.

3 Shoes £60 SALE 15% off — What is the sale price of these shoes?

4 Write 24% as a fraction.

5 Jess invests £4500 at 4% per annum simple interest. How much money will she have in total after 6 years?

231

3

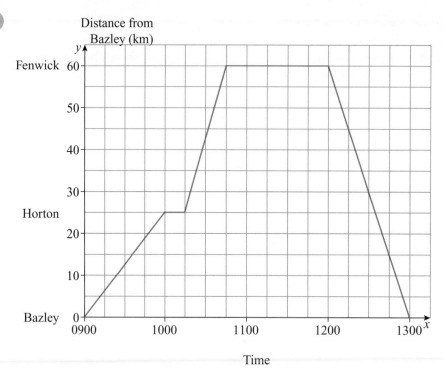

The graph above shows a car journey from Bazley.

(a) When did the car arrive back in Bazley?

(b) How long did the car stop in Horton?

(c) When did the car leave Horton after stopping?

(d) How long did the car stop in Fenwick?

(e) Find the speed (in km/h) of the car between Bazley and Horton.

(f) Find the speed (in km/h) of the car between Horton and Fenwick.

(g) Find the speed (in km/h) of the car from Fenwick back to Bazley.

4

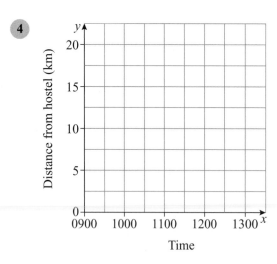

Copy the axes opposite then draw a travel graph to show the journey below.

'Some friends go for a long walk. They leave their hostel at 0900 and walk 4 km in $\frac{1}{2}$ hour at a steady speed. They walk 7 km during the next hour. They then rest for $\frac{1}{2}$ hour. They walk another 4 km in the next $\frac{1}{2}$ hour then return to the hostel in $1\frac{1}{2}$ hours at a steady speed.'

5 Water is poured at a constant rate into each of the containers A, B and C. Which of the graphs below fits each container?

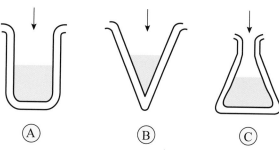

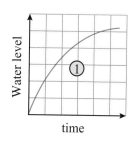

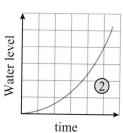

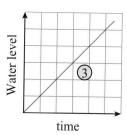

6 Which of the graphs below best fits each of the following statements:

(A) After a poor start, car sales have increased massively this year.

(B) The price of milk has remained the same over the past year.

(C) The world's population continues to rise rapidly.

(D) The price of computers has fallen steadily over the last year.

(E) The number of visitors to a seaside resort rose in the Summer then dropped off towards Winter.

(F) The number of people going to the cinema in the UK has increased steadily this year.

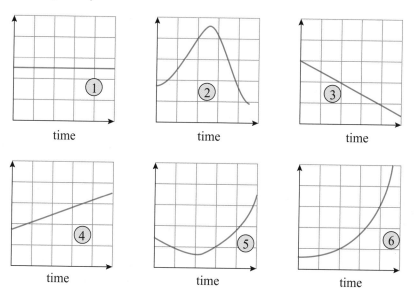

USE YOUR MATHS! – Hidden car costs

Most people want to learn to drive as soon as possible. How much it costs will depend on how many driving lessons are taken or how much driving practice is done with family members or friends.

> You cannot drive on a road without a provisional driving licence. This costs £50 (at the time of writing).

You must pass a theory test and a practical test.

> Theory test £31

> Practical test £62

If you drive with a family member or friend, you must be insured for driving the car. The cost of this will depend on the car and other factors.

A one hour driving lesson will often cost between £20 and £25.

Task A

Brooks Driving School
One hour lesson £23
10 one hour lessons £220

Car insurance for one month
Andrew for Uncle's car £68
Sneha for Mother's car £57

1. Andrew passes his test after 20 Brooks lessons plus two months of extra practice in his uncle's car. What is the total cost? (Remember to include the cost of the tests and provisional licence.)

2. Sneha passes her test after 34 Brooks lessons plus one month of extra practice in her mother's car. What is the total cost?

3. Andrew practises for 4 months using his uncle's car. He passes his theory test but fails his practical test. He now takes 14 Brooks lessons then does the practical test again. This time he passes. What is the total cost?

4. Sneha passes her theory test and passes her practical test at the third attempt. In total she has 36 Brooks lessons and five months of extra practice in her mother's car. What is the total cost?

You may want to buy and run a car after passing your driving test. There are many extra costs apart from the price of the car.

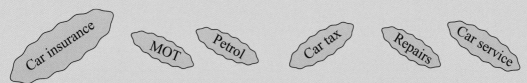

An MOT test each year checks the safety level of your car and costs £54·85 (at the time of writing). The car's carbon dioxide (CO_2) emissions are checked. You must pay car tax each year. Your car is put in a band depending on its CO_2 emissions. You pay a different car tax for each band as shown below.

Band	CO_2 emission (g/km)	12 months rate	6 months rate
A	Up to £100	£0·00	
B	101–110	£20·00	
C	111–120	£30·00	
D	121–130	£110·00	£60·50
E	131–140	£130·00	£71·50
F	141–150	£145·00	£79·75
G	151–165	£180·00	£99·00
H	166–175	£205·00	£112·75
I	176–185	£225·00	£123·75
J	186–200	£265·00	£145·75
K	201–225	£285·00	£156·75
L	226–255	£485·00	£266·75
M	Over 255	£500·00	£275·00

Task B

1   Andrew buys a band J car for £2000. His car insurance is £138 each month. He taxes the car at the 12 months rate, has an MOT plus a car service costing £112·50. In the first year, repairs and petrol amount to £1315.

   (a) How much does Andrew spend in total for this first year?

   (b) Ignoring the cost of the car, how much does Andrew spend on average each week during this first year? (Assume 1 year = 52 weeks.)

2   Sneha buys a band F car for £2500. During the first year she taxes the car every six months. Her weekly car insurance is £23·17. She has an MOT which then leads to £196 of repairs. Her car service costs £98·99 and she buys two new tyres for £86·50 in total. Ignoring the cost of the car and petrol, how much does she spend on driving each month during this first year?

1. Finding numbers in sequences

(a) Which sequence below is *arithmetic*?

| P | 3, 6, 12, 24, … | | Q | 1, 3, 6, 10, … | | R | 5, 9, 13, 17, … |

(b) Lucy says the next number in the sequence 1, 2, 4, … is 8. Aaron says the next number is 7. Who is correct? Justify your answer.

(c) Write down the next *2 numbers* on each sequence below:
   (i) 160, 80, 40, 20, …
   (ii) 25, 22, 19, 16, …
   (iii) 3, 6, 11, 18, …

2. Finding rules for arithmetic sequences

Find the *n*th term for each sequence below:

(a) 4, 7, 10, 13, …

(b) 3, 8, 13, 18, …

(c) Here is a sequence of shapes made from hexagons.

     $n = 1$ $n = 2$ $n = 3$

Let n = shape number and w = number of white hexagons.

Find a formula for the number of white hexagons (w) for the shape number n.

(d) Use the formula to find out how many white hexagons are in shape number 20.

3. Changing the subject of a formula

Make x the subject of each formula given below:

(a) $y = x + 3$ (b) $y = 4x$ (c) $y = x - 9$ (d) $y = 2x + 1$

(e) $y = 5x - 2$ (b) $y = \dfrac{x}{5}$ (g) $\dfrac{x}{7} = y$ (h) $y = \dfrac{x}{3} + 4$

4. Drawing straight line graphs

(a)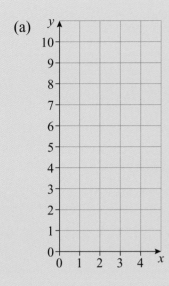

Draw these axes.

Complete the table below then draw $y = 4x + 1$

x	0	1	2
y			

(b) Draw the graph of $y = 7 - x$

(c) Draw the line $x = 2$ on the same graph as the one used in part (b). Write down the co-ordinates of the point where the line $y = 7 - x$ meets the line $x = 2$

5. Finding gradients of lines and using $y = mx + c$

Find the gradient of each line below:

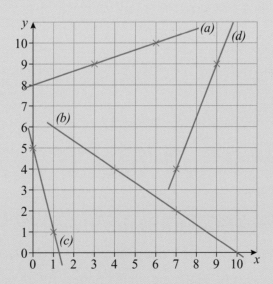

(e) Which line below cuts the y-axis at $(0, 3)$?

$y = 3x + 1$ $y = 2 + 3x$ $y = 2x + 3$ $y = 4 - 3x$

(f) Which lines below have a gradient equal to 5?

$y = 3x + 5$ $y = 5x - 4$ $y = 1 + 5x$ $y = 2 - 5x$

(g) Write down the gradient of the line $y = -x + 4$

6. Drawing curves from equations

(a) Complete the table below then draw the curve $y = x^2 + 2$.

x	-3	-2	-1	0	1	2	3
y							

(b) Complete the table below then draw the curve $y = 2x^2 + 3$.

x	-3	-2	-1	0	1	2	3
y							

7. Using graphs

The graph below shows the weights of Ed and Serena during one year.

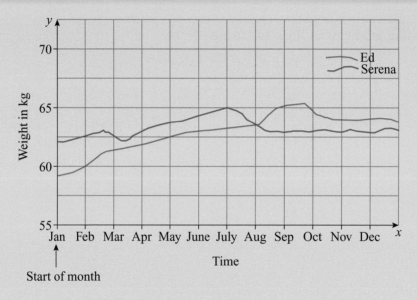

How much did Ed weigh at the start of:

(a) March? (b) September? (c) December?

(d) At the start of which month did Serena weigh 65 kg.

(e) How much did Serena weigh at the start of January?

(f) When did Ed and Serena weigh the same amount? How much did they weigh then?

(g) How much *more* did Serena weigh than Ed at the start of February?

(h) How much *more* did Ed weigh than Serena at the start of November?

Mixed examination questions

1 Here are the first seven terms in a number sequence.

  3   6   5   8   7   10   9

(a) Write down the next **two** terms in this number sequence.

Here are the first five terms in a different number sequence.

  5   9   13   17   21

(b) Find the 10th term in this number sequence.

(c) Write an expression, in terms of n, for the nth term of this number sequence.   (EDEXCEL)

2 Draw the graph of $y = 3x - 2$ for values of x from -1 to 3.   (EDEXCEL)

3 Katie went on a cycling trip from her home.
The diagram below shows the distance/time graph for her complete journey.

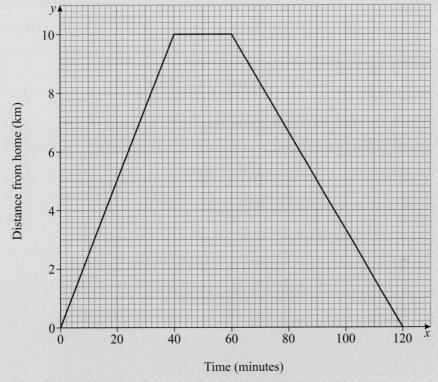

Time (minutes)

(a) What is the meaning of the horizontal line on the graph?

(b) How far did she travel in the first 30 minutes?

(c) How long did it take her to travel the first 4 kilometres?

(d) Where was Katie after 120 minutes?

(e) What was the average speed for the first 30 minutes?

(f) At what stage of the trip was she travelling at the fastest average speed?

(g) After how many minutes has she travelled a distance of 14 kilometres?

                                                                    (CEA)

4 Rearrange $v = u + 5t$ to make t the subject. (OCR)

5 (a) Here are the first five terms in two sequences.

What is the next term in each of these sequences?

(i) 4   7   10   13   16

(ii) 3   4   6   9   13

(b) Harry uses this set of rules to find the next term in a sequence.
 - If the number is even, divide by 2.
 - If the number is odd, multiply by 3 and add 1.

(i) Harry starts one sequence with 12.
These are the first four terms.

12   6   3   10

What are the next 3 terms in Harry's sequence?

(ii) A different sequence follows Harry's rules.
The second term in the sequence is 22.

What numbers could the first term have been? (OCR)

6 (a) Complete the table for $y = x^2 - 2$.

x	-3	-2	-1	0	1	2	3
y	7			-2			7

(b) Draw the graph of $y = x^2 - 2$. (OCR)

7 Work out the equation of the line shown.

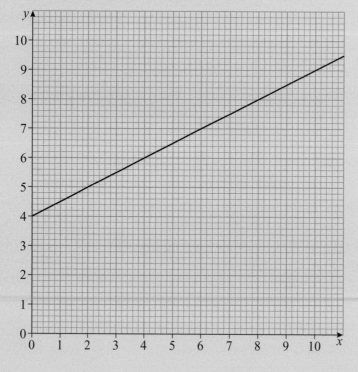

(AQA)

240

In this unit you will learn how to:

– use the probability scale

– use relative frequency

– find probabilities

– list possible outcomes

– use frequency trees

– deal with mutually exclusive events

– use Venn diagrams and set notation

– (USE YOUR MATHS!) – trim it

The probability scale

The probability of something happening is the likelihood or chance that it might happen.

If the probability of something happening is 'impossible', we say the probability is 0 (0% or 'no chance').

If the probability of something happening is 'dead certain', we say the probability is 1 (100% certain).

All the probabilities lie between 0 and 1.

0   1

impossible   unlikely   even chance   likely   certain

This is the 'probability scale'.

Think about the probability of these events. Place them on a probability scale.

A You will eat during the next week.   **B** You will get 'heads' if you toss a coin

C It will rain on the 10th February.   **D** You could swim to Australia without stopping.

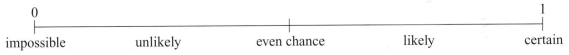

For each of these statements write one of these probabilities:

impossible   unlikely   even chance   likely   certain

1. It will rain on the 4th July.

2. Your teacher was born on a Monday.

3. You roll a dice and get a 3.

4. You will brush your teeth sometime tomorrow.

5. You will drive a bus home tomorrow evening.

6. You will have a birthday in the next year.

7. A baby will be born somewhere in the UK in the next hour.

8. You will choose a king if you pick one card from a pack of playing cards (there are 4 kings in a pack of 52 playing cards).

9. You will fly to the moon during the next year.

10. You will do *all* your maths homework for the rest of the year.

11. Think about the probability of the events below. Place them on a probability scale.

    (a) Someone in you family will win the National Lottery Jackpot next week.

    (b) You will wash your hair during the next week.

    (c) There will be a school holiday during the next year.

    (d) You will get 'tails' if you toss a coin.

    (e) All pupils in your class will wear correct school uniform every day next term.

12 Think about the probability of the events below. Place them on a probability scale.

(a) It will snow on Christmas Day.

(b) The first person to walk into your next maths lesson will be a girl.

(c) You will go to the toilet during the next 24 hours.

(d) You roll a dice and get an 'odd' number.

(e) You will get married one day.

Rearranging formulas

Make x the subject of each formula given below:

1 $y = x + 6$ **2** $y = 12x$

3 $y = \dfrac{x}{5}$ **4** $m = x - 7$

5 $m = 2x - 9$ **6** $a = 5x + 1$

7 $m = \dfrac{x}{4} + 6$ **8** $y + 4 = \dfrac{x}{3}$

Relative frequency

Sometimes it is useful to *estimate* the probability of something happening.

We collect data (maybe by doing an experiment). Each time the experiment is done is called a 'trial' (e.g. throwing a dice). We use these results to estimate the chance of something happening. This estimate is called the *relative frequency*.

$$\text{Relative frequency of 'X' happening} = \frac{\text{number of times 'X' happens}}{\text{total number of trials}}$$

Maggie thinks her dice is biased (not fair). She throws the dice 600 times. The table below shows her results.

Score	1	2	3	4	5	6
Frequency	96	84	186	72	78	84

(a) How many times should each number come up if the dice is fair?

(b) From Maggie's results, estimate the probability of getting a '3' (this is called the relative frequency).

(c) Do you think the dice is fair?

Answers

(a) 6 numbers, so each number should come up 100 times.

(b) Relative frequency of getting a '3' $= \dfrac{186}{600} = 0{\cdot}31$ (using a calculator)

(c) The dice is not fair (it landed on '3' nearly twice as often as it should).

1. Joe spins a coin 100 times. The coin lands on 'heads' 71 times and 'tails' 29 times.

   (a) How many times should 'heads' come up if the coin is fair?

   (b) From Joe's results, find the 'relative frequency' of getting 'heads'.

   (c) Do you think the coin is fair? Explain the answer you give.

2. Will thinks his dice is biased (not fair). He throws the dice 300 times. The table below shows his results.

Score	1	2	3	4	5	6
Frequency	51	46	47	54	53	49

   (a) How many times should each number come up if the dice is fair?

   (b) From Will's results, use a calculator to estimate the 'probability' of getting a '4'.

   (c) Janice throws the dice 500 times and estimates the 'probability' of getting a '4' to be 0·17. Should the results from Will or from Janice give the best estimate for the 'probability' of getting a '4'? Justify your answer.

   (d) Do you think the dice is fair? Discuss your answer with your teacher.

3. Mary throws a drawing pin 200 times. It lands 'point down' 78 times.

   (a) Use a calculator to find the relative frequency that the drawing pin will land 'point down'.

   (b) How many times does the drawing pin land 'point up'?

   (c) Find the relative frequency that the drawing pin will land 'point up'.

4. Gavin has to feed 900 people. He asks 60 people to choose their favourite meal from a menu of 3 dishes. The results are shown opposite.

Cottage pie	18
Chicken kurma	12
Spaghetti bolognese	30

   (a) Estimate the probability that the first person to arrive for a meal would choose chicken kurma.

   (b) Based on Gavin's survey, how many servings of *each* meal should he prepare to feed all 900 people?

5 Lola is throwing a 10-sided dice. She throws the dice 500 times. The table below shows her results.

Score	1	2	3	4	5	6	7	8	9	10
Frequency	44	48	51	50	47	52	40	82	45	41

(a) How many times should each number come up if the dice is fair?

(b) From Lola's results, use a calculator to estimate the probability of getting each score (1 up to 10).

(c) Do you think the dice is fair? Explain the answer you give.

(d) What should Lola do if she wants to be even more certain about her answer to part (c)?

Can you still?

Transformations

1

Copy this grid. Copy shape A.

(a) Reflect shape A in the *x*-axis. Label the image (new shape) B.

(b) Translate shape B through $\begin{pmatrix} -3 \\ -1 \end{pmatrix}$. Label the new shape C.

(c) Describe *fully* the translation which moves shape C onto shape A.

(d) Which shapes are *congruent* to shape A?

2

Copy this grid. Copy shape A.

(a) Reflect shape A in the broken mirror line. Label the image (new shape) B.

(b) Translate shape B through $\begin{pmatrix} -4 \\ 1 \end{pmatrix}$. Label the new shape C.

$$\text{Probability} = \frac{\text{the number of ways the event can happen}}{\text{the total number of possible outcomes}}$$

A bag contains 5 black beads and 4 red beads.
I take out one bead.

(a) The probability of taking out a black bead is $\frac{5}{9}$

　　　We may write p (black) $= \frac{5}{9}$

(b) The probability of taking out a red bead $= \frac{4}{9}$

(c) The probability of taking out a red or black bead $= \frac{9}{9} = 1$　(This is 'dead certain')

(d) The probability of taking out a yellow bead $= 0$　(This is impossible)

M8.3

1　Mo has a bag of sweets.
She has 3 chews and 2 mints left.
She picks out a sweet.
What is the probability that she picks a mint?

2　Tina rolls a dice.

What is the probability that she rolls a:

(a) 1?　　　　　(b) 3?　　　　　(c) 4?　　　　　(d) 3 or 4?

3　Billy has 9 cards as shown below:

Billy picks a card at random.

What is the probability that he picks the letter:

(a) C?　　　　　(b) F?　　　　　(c) a vowel?

4 Rowan has a box of chocolates.

There are 5 truffles, 4 toffees and 2 nuts.

Rowan picks a chocolate.

Find the probability that he chooses a:

(a) toffee   (b) truffle   (c) toffee or nut

5 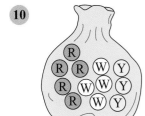 Thelma spins this spinner.

Find the probability that she gets

(a) a 5   (b) an even number   (c) an odd number

6 Ten discs numbered 1, 2, 2, 2, 3, 6, 8, 9, 9, 9, are placed in a bag. One disc is selected at random.

Find the probability that it is:

(a) an even number   (b) 2   (c) less than 6

7 Phil has 15 pencils in his pencil case. 7 pencils are red, 5 are blue and the rest are green.

Phil takes out a pencil at random.

What is the probability that he takes out:

(a) blue?   (b) green?   (c) red or green?   (d) yellow?

8 Sarah is taking part in a TV Quiz show. She must choose one box from a choice of 10 to win a prize. 4 boxes are empty, 5 boxes contain prizes for the home and 1 box has the 'star' prize.

What is the probability that Sarah will win:

(a) the 'star' prize?   (b) nothing?   (c) a prize for the home?

9 One card is picked at random from a pack of 52.

Find the probability that it is:

(a) the Queen of clubs   (b) a red card   (c) a spade

10 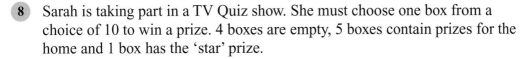 A bag contains 12 balls. There are 5 red, 4 white and 3 yellow.

(a) Find the probability of selecting a red ball.

(b) The 4 white balls are replaced by 4 yellow balls. Find the probability of selecting a yellow ball.

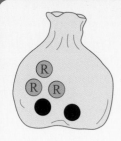

There are 3 red beads and 2 black beads in a bag. A bead is picked from this bag 75 times and replaced each time. How many red beads would you expect to get?

Probability of picking 'red' = $\frac{3}{5}$

Expect to get $\frac{3}{5}$ of 75

$$= (75 \div 5) \times 3$$
$$= 15 \times 3$$
$$= 45 \text{ reds.}$$

E8.1

1 A bag contains one green bead and 3 yellow beads. A bead is picked from this bag 80 times and replaced each time.

How many yellow beads would you expect to get?

2 A dice is thrown 180 times.

How many times would you expect to get

(a) a 4   (b) a 3   (c) an even number?

3 A coin is spun 60 times. How many tails would you expect to get?

4 A box has 30 pencils in it. The probability of picking a red pencil is $\frac{1}{6}$. How many red pencils are in the box?

5 A bag has 25 beads in it. The probability of picking a white bead is $\frac{3}{5}$. How many white beads are in the bag?

6 In a game this spinner is spun 60 times. How many wins would you expect?

7 The chance of Jim playing football in a games lesson is $\frac{1}{4}$. There are 16 lessons in a term. How many times will Jim expect to play football?

8 A bag contains 7 red discs, 8 black discs and 5 white discs. Sandra pulls out one at random and then puts it back. If she does this 80 times, how many times would she pick:

(a) a red disc?   (b) a white disc?   (c) a black disc?

9 The probability that a train will arrive *on time* the next day at Swindon is 0·8. If 60 trains arrive at Swindon the next day, how many will be *on time*?

10 The probability of getting a grade 4 or better in an English GCSE is 0.6.
If 300 young people take their English GCSE, how many would you expect
to get a grade 4 or better?

11 Ann keeps trying her luck in the National Lottery. The probability that the
first ball chosen will be hers is $\frac{6}{49}$. During one year, she plays 98 times.

How many times would she expect the first ball chosen to be hers?

12 There are 15 balls in a bag. Sandeep takes a ball from
the bag, notes its colour and then returns the ball to
the bag. Sandeep does this 20 times.

red	6
yellow	1
black	11
green	2

Here are the results.

(a) What is the smallest number of green balls there
could be in the bag?

(b) Sandeep says 'There cannot be any white balls in the bag because there
are no whites in my table'.

Explain why Sandeep is wrong.

(c) Sandeep takes one more ball from the bag. What is the most likely
colour of the ball?

13 The probability of it raining in November in
Aberdeen is $\frac{5}{6}$. How many days would you
expect it to rain in November?

14 A bag has only blue and white balls in it.
The probability of picking blue is $\frac{3}{4}$.

(a) What is the probability of picking a white ball?

(b) Ken picks a ball at random. He picks a white ball. What is the smallest
number of white balls there could be in the bag?

(c) Ken then picks out another white ball. What is the smallest number of
blue balls there could be in the bag?

15 I have two bags of beads.

12 red beads
16 blue beads

11 red beads
14 blue beads

Which bag has the greater probability of getting a red bead?
(You may *use a calculator* to help explain your answer.)

16 Each number below on the spinner is a square number less than 10.

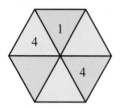

The probability of the spinner landing on an odd number is greater than the probability of it landing on an even number.

The probability of the spinner landing on a '4' is greater than the probability of it landing on a '1'.

What other numbers belong on the spinner?

17 A bag contains red and yellow beads only. The ratio of red to yellow is 3 : 7. There are 12 red beads.

(a) How many beads are in the bag in total?

(b) One bead is randomly removed. What is the probability that this is a yellow bead?

Ratio and percentages

1 Divide 540 g in the ratio 7 : 13.

2 Write 3·2 : 5·25 in its simplest whole number form.

3 Tony borrows £5000 and is charged 7·95% per annum simple interest. He pays back the money over 6 years. How much money does he pay back in total?

4 Zoe earns £350 each week. She is given a 4% pay rise. She multiplies £350 by 1·04 to find her new weekly pay. Will this give the correct amount? Justify your answer.

5 330 ml of lemonade costs 60p. 500 ml of lemonade costs 90p. Which size is the better value? Explain your answer fully.

6 Write 5 cm : 3 m in its simplest form.

Listing possible outcomes

When more than one event occurs, it is usually helpful to make a list of all the possible outcomes. Use a system when making the list.

If you throw 2 coins, they could land as:

1st coin	2nd coin
head	head
head	tail
tail	head
tail	tail

there are 4 possible outcomes

1   For breakfast, Ellie eats cereal or toast. She drinks juice or tea.
    Copy and complete the table below to show all the different breakfasts she
    might have.

food	drink
cereal	juice
	tea
toast	

2   Ivy throws a coin and a dice. She could get a 'head' and a '5' (H 5).
    She could get a 'tail' and a '5'. List the 12 possible outcomes.

3   Here are 2 spinners. If I spin both spinners,
    I could get a 3 and a 9 (3, 9).

    (a) List *all* the possible outcomes.

    (b) How many possible outcomes are there?

4   Alfonso sells ice-cream in tubs which contain 2 scoops. He has chocolate
    chip, vanilla and raspberry ripple. A tub could have one scoop of vanilla and
    one scoop of raspberry ripple or it could have 2 scoops of raspberry ripple.
    List all the different kinds of tubs which can be made.

5   At a restaurant, each person has a starter,
    main course and dessert.

    One evening the menu is:

        starter: melon or soup

        main course: lamb, turkey or pork

        dessert: apple pie, creme brulé or
        rhubarb crumble

    List all the different meals that could be ordered.

6   Four people, Tom, Sasha, Becky and Ronnie, work at a garage. Two people
    work at any one time. List all the possible pairs of people that could be
    working together at any one time.

7   Three coins are thrown together. List all the possible outcomes for the three
    coins. What is the probability of getting 3 heads?

8 You can choose from 4 possible drinks in a drinks machine.

| coke | fanta | sprite | diet coke |

Zak buys one drink for himself and one for his friend. Write down all the possible pairs of drink Zak and his friend could have.

9 Three dolls' houses A, B and C are displayed on a shelf in a shop window.

   (a) How many different arrangements are there?

   (b) What is the probability that A and B will *not* be next to each other?

10 Jack has 2 spinners. He spins both spinners and adds up the numbers to get a total. For example a '4' and a '3' give a total of 7.

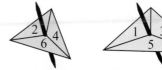

   (a) Copy and complete this grid to show all the possible outcomes and totals.

   (b) Find the probability of getting a total of 7.

   (c) Jack says there is a greater probability of getting a total of 9 than getting a total of 5. Is he correct? Justify your answer.

+	1	3	5
2	3		
4		7	
6			

11

+	1	2	3	4	5	6
1						
2						
3		5				
4						
5		7				
6						

2 dice are thrown. The numbers are then added together to get a total.

   (a) Copy and complete this grid to show all the possible outcomes and totals.

   (b) Find the probability of getting a total of 6.

   (c) Find the probability of getting a total which is an even number.

   (d) Find the probability of getting a score which is *more* than 9.

80 people take their driving test.
60 of these people paid to have driving lessons, the others were taught by family members. Of these 60 people, 47 passed their test. 59 people passed their test in total.

The different outcomes in a situation can be shown on a frequency tree.

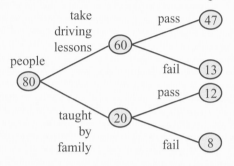

(a) If one person is chosen at random then the probability of having failed is
$\dfrac{21}{80} = 0.26$

(b) If one person is chosen at random from the people who took driving lessons then the probability of having failed is $\dfrac{13}{60} = 0.22$

There appears to be less chance of failing after taking driving lessons.

M8.5

1. In January snow is forecast for 17 days.
It actually snows on 11 of the days when it is forecast.
In January it actually snows on 14 days. Copy and complete the frequency tree.

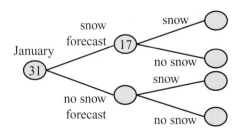

2 53 out of 150 people get enough daily
vitamins. In March, 16 of these people
get ill and 64 out of the 150 people get
ill in total.

(a) Copy and complete the frequency tree
below.

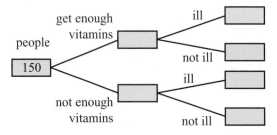

(b) If a person is chosen at random from those who do not get enough
vitamins, what is the probability that this person became ill?

3 Out of every 1000 people screened for a disease, 980 are given the 'all clear'
and invited back in 5 years time for their next routine test.
The remaining people are given more tests straight away. Of these there is
no disease evident in 16 of them. The other people have the disease and are
treated accordingly.
Draw a frequency tree to show the above information.

4

60% of 200 people visit the dentist
at least once each year. Of the people
who do not visit the dentist, 15% of them get toothache some time during
the year. In total 9% of the 200 people get toothache.

(a) Copy and complete the frequency tree.

(b) If one person is chosen at random from the people who visit the dentist,
what is the probability that this person did not get toothache?

Key Facts

Events are mutually exclusive if they cannot occur at the same time.

For example:
- selecting a queen
  selecting a '3' } from the same pack of cards

- tossing a 'head'
  tossing a 'tail'

The sum of the probabilities of mutually exclusive events is 1.

A bag contains balls which are either red, blue or yellow.

The probability of selecting a red is 0·3.

The probability of selecting a blue is 0·4.

What is the probability of selecting a yellow?

The probability of selecting a red *or* blue = 0·3 + 0·4 = 0·7 ('or' often suggests you *add* the probabilities).

Sum of probabilities = 1

Probability of selecting a yellow = 1 − p (red or blue)

$$= 1 - 0·7$$

$$= 0·3$$

M8.6

1. Which of the following pairs of events are mutually exclusive?

   (a) choose a club or an ace from a pack of cards.

   (b) win or lose a football match.

   (c) get a red light or green light on traffic lights.

   (d) the sun shines or it rains.

   (e) wear a blue tie or brown shoes.

   (f) get a '3' or a '4' on a dice.

2 Kerry has a drawer full of blue, black or red socks. The probability of choosing blue socks is 0·5. The probability of choosing black socks is 0·3.

(a) What is the probability of selecting blue *or* black socks?

(b) What is the probability of selecting red socks?

3 In a Games lesson, students play football, basketball or hockey.

The probability of playing football is 0·4.

The probability of playing basketball is 0·5.

(a) What is the probability of playing football or basketball?

(b) What is the probability of playing hockey?

4 Emma has one drink for her breakfast. The table shows the probability of her choosing each drink.

tea	coffee	orange juice	grapefruit juice
0·4	x	0·3	0·1

(a) What is the probability of Emma choosing orange juice or grapefruit juice?

(b) What is the probability of Emma choosing coffee?

(c) During the month of April, how many days would you expect Emma to choose tea?

5 Terry has a selection of shirts. The table shows the probability of Terry choosing a particular shirt colour.

blue	white	yellow	red	green
0·3	0·3	0·15	x	0·05

(a) What is the probability of Terry choosing a yellow or green shirt?

(b) What is the probability of Terry choosing a red shirt?

(c) For every 50 times that Terry chooses a shirt, how many times would you expect him to choose a white shirt?

6 The probability of pulling out a Queen from a pack of cards is $\frac{1}{13}$.
What is the probability of *not* pulling out a Queen?

7 Each time Cassie visits her grandfather he gives her some money.
The table shows the probability of her getting a particular amount of money.

£2	£5	£10	£20
x	$\frac{1}{4}$	$\frac{1}{8}$	$\frac{1}{16}$

(a) Find the probability of getting £5 or £10.

(b) Find the probability of not getting £20.

(c) Find the probability of getting £2.

(d) For every 16 visits to her grandfather, how many times would Cassie expect to get £10?

8 In a football match the probability of Everton winning is 0·5.
The probability of losing is 0·3.
What is the probability of Everton drawing?

9 A bag contains balls which are either yellow, blue or green.

The probability of selecting a yellow ball is 0·15.

The probability of selecting a blue ball is 0·55.

(a) Find the probability of selecting a green ball.

(b) Find the probability of selecting a ball which is *not* yellow.

10 4 people play a game of poker. The probability of each person winning the game is shown below in the table.

Darryl	Simon	Dan	Mark
0·35	0·25	0·25	x

(a) What is the probability of Darryl or Simon winning?

(b) What is the probability of Mark winning?

(c) If they play 60 times, how many times would you expect Dan to win?

11 The probability of getting a square number when you throw a dice is $\frac{1}{3}$. What is the probability of *not* getting a square number?

12 Every Friday night Jodie goes to a cinema, pub or restaurant. The probability of going to the cinema is $\frac{1}{2}$. The probability of going to the pub is $\frac{1}{4}$. What is the probability that Jodie goes to a restaurant?

Can you still?

Using co-ordinates

Draw x and y axes with values from -5 to 5. Plot the points below and join them up in order.

(a) $(-2, -3)$ $(-1, -3)$ $(0, -2)$ $(-2, 0)$ $(-2, 1)$ $(-3, 2)$
    $(-4, 1)$ $(-4, 3)$ $(-3, 4)$ $(-2, 4)$ $(0, 2)$ $(-1, 1)$
    $(-1, 0)$ $(1, -1)$ $(3, -1)$ $(3, 0)$ $(1, 2)$ $(0, 2)$

On the same grid, plot the points below and join them up in order.

(b) $(2, -1)$ $(4, -3)$ $(3, -4)$ $(2, -2)$ $(0, -2)$

On the same grid, plot the points below and join them up in order.

(c) $(-4, 1)$ $(-3, 3)$ $(-3, 4)$ $(-3, 2)$

(d) Draw a dot at $(-2, 3)$.

(e) Describe the picture.

Key Facts

A set is a collection of items, often written inside curly brackets, eg. A = {2, 4, 6, 8}.

Each member of a set is called an element.

The set of all items in a situation is called the Universal set $\mathscr{E}$.

$\mathscr{E}$ = {students in Year 10 in Henton High School}
H = {students who study History}
G = {students who study Geography}

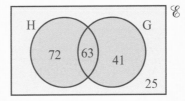

(a) 72 + 63 = 135 students study History.

(b) 63 students study History and Geography.

(c) 25 students do not study History or Geography.

(d) Number of students in Year 10 = 72 + 63 + 41 + 25 = 201

M8.7

1 The Venn diagram shows people in a band ($\mathscr{E}$).

G = {people who play the guitar}
S = {people who sing}

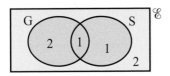

(a) How many people sing?

(b) How many people are in the band?

(c) How many people do not sing or play the guitar?

259

2 $\mathscr{E}$ = {houses in a street}

  G = {houses with a garage}

  R = {houses with a red door}

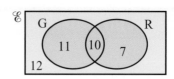

How many houses have

(a) a red door   (b) no garage or red door?

(c) a red door but no garage?   (d) a garage?

3 $\mathscr{E}$ = {athletes in a competition}

  P = {athletes who pole vault}

  L = {athletes who long jump}

The Venn diagram shows numbers
of athletes for the above.

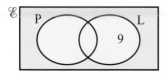

There are 101 athletes in the competition.

12 athletes do the long jump

10 athletes do the pole vault

Copy and complete the Venn diagram.

4   100 people are asked if they
drink tea or coffee each day.
The information is shown
in a Venn diagram.

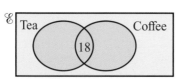

48 people drink tea each day.
41 people never drink tea or
coffee.

Copy and complete the
Venn diagram.

Can you still?

Fractions

1 $\frac{3}{5}$ of 30 children play football.

  Two thirds of the footballers wear a
blue shirt. How many children wear
a blue shirt?

2   Work out $\frac{3}{7} + \frac{2}{9}$

3   Work out $\left(\frac{1}{2} \times \frac{1}{2}\right) - \left(\frac{1}{6} \times \frac{1}{6}\right)$

4   How many $\frac{1}{6}$ m lengths of ribbon
can be cut from a $2\frac{2}{3}$ m length of
ribbon?

The Venn diagram shows some people who who exercise regularly.

G = {people who use the Gym}

J = {people who jog}

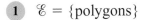

There are 48 + 23 + 16 + 13 = 100 people in total.
If one person is chosen at random then

(a) the probability of the person using the Gym = $\dfrac{71}{100}$

we say p(using Gym) $= \dfrac{71}{100}$

(b) p(not jogging) $= \dfrac{61}{100}$

M8.8

1 $\mathscr{E}$ = {polygons}

Q = {quadrilaterals}

R = {polygons which contain a right angle}

If one shape is chosen at random then find

(a) p(quadrilateral)

(b) p(polygon with no right angle)

(c) p(quadrilateral which contains a right angle)

2 $\mathscr{E}$ = {team of decorators}

P = {painters}

C = {carpet fitters}

The Venn diagram below shows how many people are in each of the sets above.

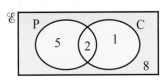

If a person is chosen at random then find

(a) p(being a painter)

(b) p(not a painter or carpet fitter)

(c) p(not being a painter)

261

3 The Venn diagram below shows a group of 200 people during the Winter season.

I = {people who ice skate}

S = {people who sledge}

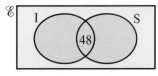

71 people ice skate.
54 people do not ice skate or sledge.

If a person is chosen at random then find

(a) p(person sledges)

(b) p(does not ice skate)

(c) p(ice skates but does not sledge)

4 $\mathscr{E}$ = {students in Year 10}

W = {students who wear a watch}

G = {students who wear glasses}

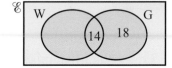

43 students wear a watch but do not wear glasses.
There are 150 students in Year 10.
If a student is chosen at random then find

(a) p(student wears a watch)

(b) p(does not wear glasses)

(c) p(does not wear a watch or glasses)

5 $\mathscr{E}$ = {120 people who play sport}

C = {people who play cricket}

T = {people who play tennis}

The Venn diagram shows how many people play each sport.

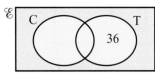

60 people play tennis and 35 people do not play cricket or tennis.

If a person is chosen at random then find

(a) p(plays cricket)

(b) p(does not play tennis)

(c) p(plays cricket and tennis)

Body mass index (BMI) is used to consider what a healthy weight is for a given height.

$$\text{BMI} = \frac{\text{Weight (in kg)}}{(\text{Height in m})^2}$$

Example: if a person's weight is 74 kg and height is 1·73 m, the person's

$$\text{BMI} = \frac{74}{1·73^2} = 24·7$$

This body mass index graph is used to examine whether a person has a healthy weight.

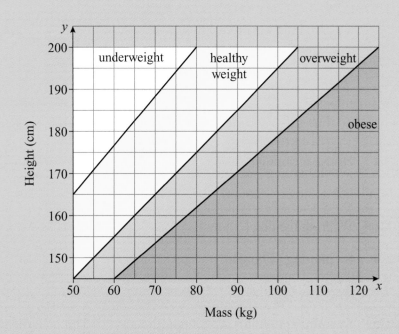

Task A

Jasmine is 1·64 m tall and weighs 71 kg
Rory is 1·82 m tall and weighs 62 kg
Mark is 1·75 m tall and weighs 100 kg

1   Work out the BMI for each person.

2   Use the chart above to decide if each person is underweight, healthy weight, overweight or obese.

A person will lose 400 g of fat from exercise if the person burns 3000 extra calories.

Jasmine would burn the number of calories shown below for each hour of the activity

Swimming	446
Mowing lawn	419
Aerobics	532
Cycling	630
House cleaning	274
Walking the dog	386
Badminton	608
Yoga	196
Rowing machine	827
Gardening	248

Mark would burn the number of calories shown below for each hour of the activity

Football	724
Circuit training	735
Aerobics	592
Rowing machine	836
Gardening	272
Golf	397
Cycling	680
House cleaning	314
Swimming	462
Fishing	273

Jasmine does the following extra activities each week

Sat	House cleaning (2 hours)
Sun	Gardening ($1\frac{1}{2}$ hours), Yoga ($\frac{1}{2}$ hour)
Mon	Walking the dog ($\frac{1}{2}$ hour)
Tue	Swimming (1 hour)
Wed	Aerobics ($\frac{1}{2}$ hour)
Thu	Swimming ($\frac{1}{2}$ hour), Cycling ($\frac{1}{2}$ hour)
Fri	Badminton (1 hour)

Mark does the following extra activities each week

Sat	Football (1 hour), Cycling ($\frac{1}{2}$ hour)
Sun	Golf (3 hours), Gardening (1 hour)
Mon	Swimming ($\frac{1}{2}$ hour)
Tue	House cleaning (1 hour)
Wed	Swimming ($\frac{3}{4}$ hour)
Thu	Gardening ($\frac{1}{2}$ hour)
Fri	Fishing ($3\frac{1}{2}$ hours)

Task B

1 Who will burn off more extra calories during one week? Show all your working out.

2 How much fat will Mark lose in one week?

3 Jasmine will be a healthy weight if she loses 1·2 kg. How many weeks will it take her to lose this amount?

TEST YOURSELF ON UNIT 8

1. Using the probability scale

Think about the probability of the events below. Place them on a probability scale.

0 ├──────┬──────┬──────┬──────┬──────┤ 1

(a) You will have a drink in the next 24 hours.

(b) You will get a '2' when you throw a dice.

(c) A car will drive on a motorway today in the UK.

(d) If I put a stone in one of my hands, you will guess correctly which hand has the stone.

(e) Your school will be 'transported' to the planet Mars today.

2. Using relative frequency

Sabrina throws a shoe into the air. The shoe lands on its left side, right side or on its bottom.

She does this 50 times. The table below shows her results.

left side	right side	bottom
16	21	13

Use a calculator to find the relative frequency that the shoe lands on its:

(a) left side

(b) right side

(c) bottom

(d) If Sabrina threw the shoe 200 times, how many times would she expect it to land on its right side?

3. Finding probabilities

(a) Fiona has 8 cards as shown below?

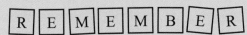

Fiona picks a card at random.

What is the probability that she picks the letter:

(i) B?   (ii) E?   (iii) R?   (iv) a vowel?

265

(b) 12 discs numbered 1, 2, 3, 3, 5, 6, 6, 8, 9, 9, 10, 15 are placed in a bag.
One disc is selected at random. Find the probability that it is:

    (i) a prime number   (ii) a 6   (iii) a multiple of 3

(c) This pointer is spun 60 times.
How many times would you
expect it to point to:

    (i) 2?

    (ii) an even number?

    (iii) a square number?

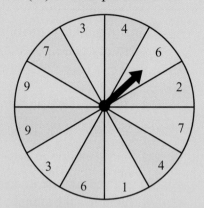

4. Listing possible outcomes

(a) Kyron throws a dice and spins the
spinner shown opposite.

He could get a '4' and a '3' (4, 3).
List *all* the possible outcomes.
How many possible outcomes are there?

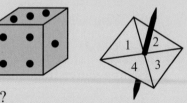

(b) Cath has to choose some of her school subjects from the option
blocks below:

A	B	C
french	history	art
german	geography	dt
spanish		

She must choose one subject from column A, one from column B and one
from column C. List *all* the different groups of choices she could make
(combinations).

(c) How many combinations are there?

5. Using frequency trees

Sally plays badminton against
Mark or Rohan. During the
year they play 50 games.
Sally plays 30% of her games
against Mark and loses 60%
of these games.
She wins 68% of all the games
she plays.
Copy and complete the frequency tree opposite.

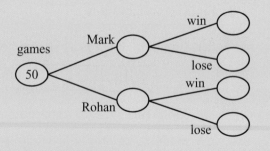

6. Dealing with mutually exclusive events

(a) The probability that Ivan is late in the morning is 0·01. What is the probability that Ivan is *not* late in the morning?

(b) A bag contains balls which are either white, green or blue.
The probability of selecting a white ball is 1/3.
The probability of selecting a green ball is 1/2.

   (i) What is the probability of selecting a white *or* green ball?

   (ii) What is the probability of selecting a blue ball?

(c) Gwen likes a wide range of music. The table below shows the probability of Gwen listening to a particular type of music.

rock	opera	jazz	classical
0·5	0·15	x	0·05

   (i) What is the probability of Gwen listening to opera or classical music?

   (ii) What is the probability of Gwen listening to jazz?

   (iii) For the next 50 times that Gwen listens to music, how many times would you expect her to listen to rock music?

7. Using Venn diagrams and set notation

$\mathscr{E}$ = {1000 pupils in a school}

Y = {pupils in Year 10}

L = {pupils who eat school lunches}

The Venn diagram shows numbers for the above.

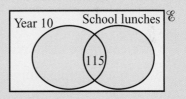

There are 190 pupils in Year 10.
280 pupils, not in Year 10, do not have school lunches.

If one person is chosen at random then find

(a) the probability that the pupil is in Year 10 but does not eat school lunches.

(b) the probability that the pupil eats school lunches.

Mixed examination questions

1 Each letter of the alphabet is written on a tile. The 26 tiles are placed in a bag.
One tile is chosen at random from the bag.
Write down the probability that the letter on the tile is

(a) Q,

(b) a letter from the word MATHEMATICS. (CEA)

2 A factory production line packs buttons into bags.
There are exactly 80 buttons packed into each bag.
There is a mixture of different coloured buttons in each bag.
A total of 600 bags of buttons were packed in a day.

The first 100 bags were checked and it was found that a total of 1200 red buttons had been used.
In the 600 bags of buttons it was found that the relative frequency of red buttons packed was 40%.

Calculate the relative frequency of red buttons packed in the final 500 bags. (WJEC)

3 The diagram shows a door lock.

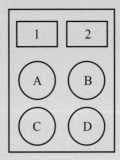

The code is a number followed by a letter.
Steve enters a code at random.

Work out the probability that he has entered the correct code. (AQA)

4 50 people are asked if they have a main computer and if they have an iPad.
The information is placed in a Venn diagram.

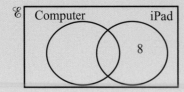

35 people have a main computer.
22 people have an iPad.

If one person is chosen at random then find the probability that the person does *not* have a main computer.

5 Riki has a packet of flower seeds.

The table shows each of the probabilities that a seed taken at random will grow into a flower that is pink or red or blue or yellow.

Colour	pink	red	blue	yellow	white
Probability	0·15	0·25	0·20	0·16	

(a) Work out the probability that a seed taken at random will grow into a white flower.

There are 300 seeds in the packet.

All of the seeds grow into flowers.

(b) Work out an estimate for the number of red flowers.   (EDEXCEL)

6 In their last 60 games, the England Cricket team have won the toss 40 times. Out of these 40 games they have lost $\frac{1}{5}$ of them, won 16 of them and drawn the rest.
In the games when they did not win the toss, they lost half of them, won 3 and drew the rest.

(a) Copy and complete the frequency tree below.

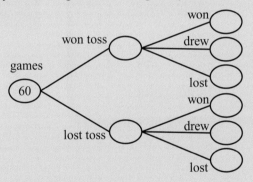

(b) Based on these results, what is the probability that England will not lose their next game?

7 John discovered that the probability that a girl has blue eyes is 0·6.

(a) What is the probability that a girl does **not** have blue eyes?

John asks 20 girls their eye colour. He writes some probabilities in the following table.

Colour of eyes	brown	green	blue	other
Probability	0·35	0·05		0·05

(b) Copy and complete John's table.

(c) Why do you think that John's calculated probability for blue eyes is not 0·6?   (CEA)

GEOMETRY 2

In this unit you will learn how to:

– read scales

– use and convert metric units

– deal with 'time' problems

– use speed, distance and time

– find perimeters of shapes

– find areas of triangles and rectangles

– find areas of trapeziums and parallelograms

– find circumferences of circles

– find areas of circles

– find surface areas and volumes of cuboids

– find surface areas and volumes of prisms

– find volumes of cylinders

– identify similar shapes

– ⟨ USE YOUR MATHS! ⟩ – better value

Reading scales

M9.1

For each of the scales work out:

    (a) the measurement indicated by each of the arrows.

    (b) the difference between the two arrows.

1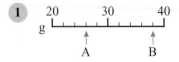

2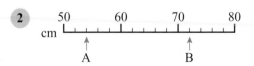

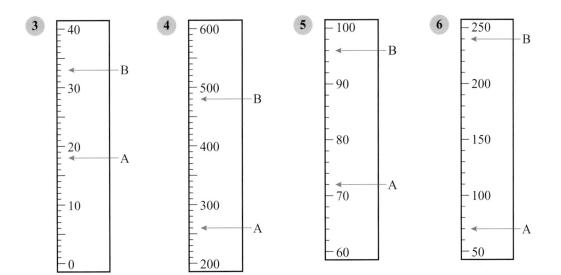

Write down the measurement shown by the arrow on each dial below.

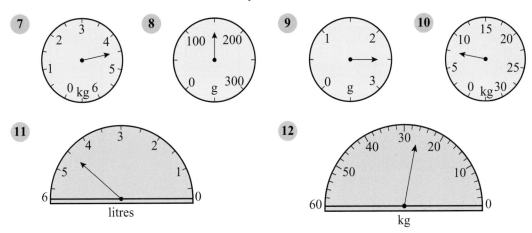

Write down the time shown by each clock below:

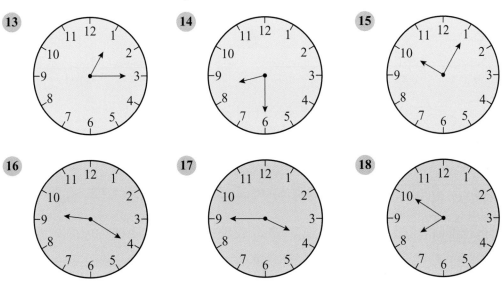

For each of the scales work out:

(a) the measurement indicated by each of the arrows.

(b) the difference between the two arrows.

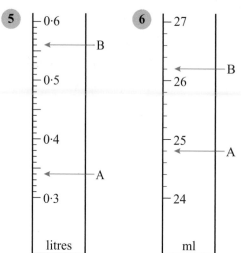

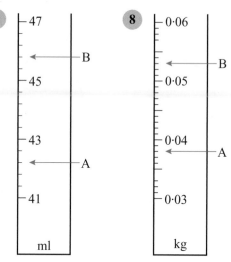

This is a fuel gauge on a car.
It is full with 50 litres of petrol.
How much petrol is there in the car now?

14 Here is another fuel gauge.
This is full with 60 litres of petrol.
How much petrol is there in the car now?

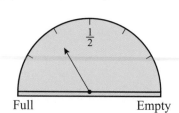

Write down the measurement shown by the arrow on each dial below.

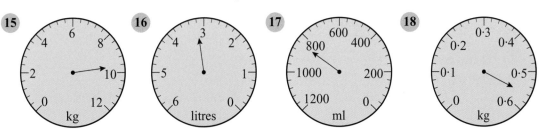

15 kg   **16** litres   **17** ml   **18** kg

Metric units

🔑 Key Facts

length	**mass**	**volume**
10 mm = 1 cm	1000 g = 1 kg	1000 ml = 1 litre or 1 l
100 cm = 1 m	1000 kg = 1 tonne	1 ml = 1 cm^3
1000 m = 1 km	1000 mg = 1 gram	100 cl = 1 litre

Examples

Convert the following metric units.

(a) 7000 g into kg ➡ ÷ 1000 ➡ 7 kg

(b) 2·5 m into cm ➡ × 100 ➡ 250 cm

(c) 4·32 tonnes into kg ➡ × 1000 ➡ 4320 kg

(d) 400 ml into litres ➡ ÷ 1000 ➡ 0·4 l

M9.3

Write down which metric unit you would use to measure the following.

1 The mass of a dog (kg or tonnes?)

2 The length of a garden (cm or m?)

3 The contents of a full wine glass (litres or ml?)

4 The length of a submarine.

5 The mass of a tank.

6 The mass of a nose stud.

7 Write each length in cm.

(a) 7 m   (b) 4·5 m   (c) 1·62 m   (d) 50 mm   (e) 0·3 m

8 Write each mass in g.

(a) 5 kg   (b) 3·6 kg   (c) 9·2 kg   (d) 0·632 kg   (e) 6·42 kg

9 Write each volume in ml.

(a) 3 litres   (b) 24 cm³   (c) 143 cm³   (d) 9·6 litres   (e) 3·125 litres

10 Copy each sentence below and choose the most sensible estimate.

(a) A baby weighs (*400 g/4 kg*).

(b) A bottle of wine contains (*7 ml/0·7 l*).

(c) A woman weighs (*6 kg/60 kg*).

(d) The height of the door is (*100 cm/2 m*).

(e) The length of a toothbrush is (*16 mm/16 cm*).

(f) A can of lemonade contains (*330 ml/33 l*).

11 Roy buys 1 kg of potatoes. 700 g are eaten. What is the weight of the potatoes that are left?

12 Gemma has a 2 litre bottle of cola. She pours out 4 glasses of cola each of 200 ml. What volume of cola is left in the bottle?

13 Nazim cuts 27 cm of a 2 m metal rod. What is the length of the metal rod now?

14 A lorry and its load weigh 3·1 tonnes. If the load weighs 600 kg, how much does the lorry weigh?

Can you still?

Drawing graphs

1 (a) Draw an x-axis from 0 to 5 and a y-axis from 0 to 10.

     (b) Draw the graph of the line $y = 3x + 2$.

     (c) Find the gradient of $y = 3x + 2$.

2 (a) Draw an x-axis from -3 to 3 and a y-axis from -6 to 10.

     (b) Copy and complete the table below then draw the curve $y = x^2 - 5$.

x	-3	-2	-1	0	1	2	3
y							

     (c) Read off the x-values when $y = 1$.

Copy and complete the following:

1 28 cm = ☐ m   **2** 1 cm = ☐ m   **3** 320 cm = ☐ m

4 9 cm = ☐ m   **5** 60 mm = ☐ cm   **6** 200 mm = ☐ cm

7 8 mm = ☐ cm   **8** 2500 m = ☐ km   **9** 350 m = ☐ km

10 9000 m = ☐ km   **11** 3 kg = ☐ g   **12** 9·5 kg = ☐ g

13 0·375 kg = ☐ g   **14** 575 g = ☐ kg   **15** 1849 g = ☐ kg

16 6 tonnes = ☐ kg   **17** 530 ml = ☐ litres   **18** 1832 ml = ☐ litres

19 5500 ml = ☐ litres   **20** 4·5 litres = ☐ ml   **21** 65 ml = ☐ litres

22 One tin of baked beans weighs 270 g. How many *kilograms* do 9 tins weigh?

23

The weight of a bag of flour is shown opposite. 1350 g is used. What is the weight of the flour left in the bag?

24 There are 48 tiles in a stack. Each tile is 7 mm thick. How high is the stack in centimetres?

25 How many 400 ml plastic beakers can be filled from an 88 litre barrel of beer?

26 Al has a 5·4 m piece of wood. He cuts it into small lengths of 45 cm. How many small pieces of wood will he have?

27 14 people have the following weights:

78 kg   69 kg   81 kg   83 kg   81 kg   77 kg   60 kg
52 kg   63 kg   50 kg   71 kg   51 kg   86 kg   81 kg

They get into a lift. The lift is *not* safe if the total weight of the people is more than 1 tonne. Will these 14 people be safe in this lift? Show your working out.

28 Write down the larger amount from each pair below.

(a) 19 m or 0·19 km   (b) 6 cm or 71 mm

(c) 2·3 tonnes or 285 kg   (d) 9200 ml or 9·4 litres

(e) 5·7 m or 569 cm   (f) 38 g or 0·04 kg

(g) 620 mm or 70 cm   (h) 700 mg or 0·8 g

(i) 65 cl or 0·6 litres   (j) 380 ml or 0·35 litres

Time

1 year = 12 months = 365 days = 52 weeks
3:20 a.m. (before midday) = 03:20. 3:20 p.m. (after midday) = 15:20

M9.5

1 Change these times into 24-hour clock time.
  (a) 11:15 a.m.   (b) 2:45 p.m.   (c) 5:30 p.m.
  (d) 9:40 a.m.   (e) 6:50 p.m.   (f) 9:32 p.m.

2 Change these times into 12-hour clock time.
  (a) 10:40   (b) 16:20   (c) 19:35
  (d) 21:10   (e) 02:05   (f) 08:05

3 Calli gets on a bus at 08:20. The bus journey is 45 minutes. What time does Calli get off the bus?

4 Ravi leaves for work at 7:50 a.m. His journey to work takes 50 minutes. What time does he arrive at work?

5 Karen spends a day shopping in London. She leaves home at 08:10 and arrives home at 17:00. How many hours and minutes is she out shopping?

6 A meeting at work begins at 2:30 p.m. and ends at 4:15 p.m. How long did the meeting last for?

7 Copy and complete the following:
  (a) 1 year = ☐ weeks   (b) 5 years = ☐ weeks
  (c) 2 years = ☐ months   (d) 10 years = ☐ months
  (e) 2 years = ☐ days   (f) 3 years = ☐ days

8 Dom borrows some money from a bank. He must pay some money back each month for 3 years. For how many months must he pay back money?

9

Bus leaves

Bus arrives

How long was the Bus journey?

10

Train leaves   Train arrives

How long was the train journey?

11 Copy and complete the table below.

Old time	Add on	New time
15:25	1 hour 40 minutes	
16:24	1 hour 45 minutes	
11:38	2 hours 50 minutes	

12 Simone arrives at the Gym at 16:25 and works out for 1 hour 40 minutes. At what time does she leave the Gym?

13 Carol goes out to a party at 19:50. She arrives home 3 hours 35 minutes later. At what time does she arrive home?

14

Plane leaves

A plane journey lasts for 3 hours 45 minutes. At what time does the plane journey end?

15 Phil drives from Reading up to Bromsgrove. He leaves at 08:45 and the journey takes one quarter of 11 hours. When does he arrive at Bromsgrove?

16 Copy and complete this train timetable. Each train takes the same time between stations.

	Train 1	Train 2	Train 3	Train 4	Train 5	Train 6
Henton	09:00	09:57	10:30	11:23	12:15	13:12
Oldhill	09:08					
Eastham	09:23			11:46		
Colston	09:40					
Todwick	09:55		11:25			

Key Facts

Speed can be measured in km per hour (km/h)

$$\text{Speed} = \frac{\text{Distance}}{\text{Time}}$$

we also have $\text{Time} = \dfrac{\text{Distance}}{\text{Speed}}$

$\text{Distance} = \text{speed} \times \text{time}$

These three important formulas can be remembered using a triangle as shown.

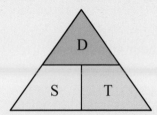

To find S: cover S and you have $\dfrac{D}{T}$

To find T: cover T and you have $\dfrac{D}{S}$

To find D: cover D and you have $S \times T$

These formulas can only be used for objects moving at a *constant* speed.

Be careful!

- If the speed is in miles per hour, the distance must be in miles and the time must be in hours.

A car travels 100 miles in 2 hours 30 minutes. Find the speed in mph

Time must be in hours only: 2 hours 30minutes = 2·5 hours.

     $S = \dfrac{D}{T} = \dfrac{100}{2 \cdot 5} = 40 \text{ mph}$

M9.6

1. A person cycles for 3 hours at a speed of 12 mph. How far does he travel?

2. Eurostar travels 420 km from London to Paris in 3 hours. Find the average speed of the train.

3. Charlie drives from Wells to Bristol at 40 mph in 30 minutes. How far is it from Wells to Bristol?

4. A hiker walks 28·5 miles at 3 mph. How long does the hiker walk for?

5 A plane flies 480 km at 320 km/h. How long does the journey take?

6 Mark runs at a speed of 6·5 m/s for 3 seconds. How far does he run?

7 A train travels 250 km at a speed of 100 km/h. How long does the train take to travel this distance?

8 Terry cycles at 16 mph for 30 minutes then slows down to 12 mph for 15 minutes. How far does he travel in total?

9 A car travels 100 km at a speed of 80 km/h. How long does the car take to travel this distance?

10 A lorry leaves Cardiff at 09:30 and arrives in London at 12:00. The journey is 130 miles. What was the average speed of the lorry?

Sometimes the units of speed must be changed.

Change the speed 72 km/h into metres per second.

72 km/h = 72 000 metres/hour

$$= \frac{72\,000}{60} \text{ metres/minute}$$

$$= \frac{72\,000}{60 \times 60} \text{ metres/second} = 20 \text{ m/s}$$

E9.1

1 Change the following speeds into the units indicated.

   (a) 54 km/h into m/s   (b) 90 km/h into m/s

   (c) 20 km/h into m/s   (d) 60 m/s into km/h

   (e) 10 m/s into km/h   (f) 126 km/h into m/s

2 Janine walks at 6 km/hr for 1 hour 30 minutes then 4 km/hr for 2 hours 15 minutes. How far does she walk in total?

3 Find the speed in mph for each of the following.

Distance	Time	Speed (mph)
30 miles	30 minutes	
9 miles	15 minutes	
15 miles	20 minutes	
6 miles	5 minutes	
30 miles	45 minutes	

4 A magpie flies 2 miles in 10 minutes. What is its speed in mph?

5 Sima drives 50 miles from Leeds to Manchester at an average speed of 40 mph. If she left Leeds at 10:20, when did she arrive at Manchester?

6 Sofia travels at 45 km/h. How far does she travel in 8 seconds? Give the answer in metres.

7 Patrick travels 60 m in 12 seconds. What is his speed in km/h?

8 The speed of light is 300 000 000 m/s. How long will it take light to travel 6 000 000 km?

9 Filip travels 75 km at 30 km/h and then 60 km at 40 km/h. Find (a) the total time taken, (b) the speed for the whole journey.

Can you still?

Number work

Do not use a calculator

1 Write down all the factors of 18 which are square numbers.

2 Find the difference between $(-2)^3$ and $(-2)^2$.

3 A coach can carry 52 people. How many coaches are needed for 340 people?

4 Write 52 000 as a number in standard form.

5 Jan says that $6 + 3 \times 4 - 2$ gives the answer 16. Is Jan correct? Explain your answer fully.

6 The sum of 2 prime numbers is a multiple of 4. What could the 2 prime numbers be?

7 Work out $782 \div 23$

Perimeter

The perimeter of a shape is the distance around its edges.

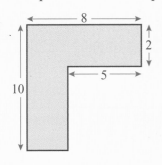

Find the perimeter of this shape.

Work out all missing lengths first.

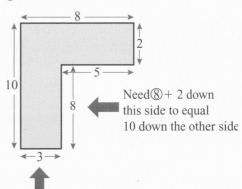

Need ⑧ + 2 down this side to equal 10 down the other side

Need ③ + 5 along the bottom to equal 8 along the top

Perimeter = 8 + 2 + 5 + 8 + 3 + 10 = 36.
If the lengths are in cm, the perimeter = 36 cm.

M9.7

1. Draw 3 different rectangles with a perimeter of 18 cm.

2. Find the perimeter of a rectangle with a length of 12 cm and a width of 7 cm.

3. For each triangle below you are given the perimeter. Find the missing value x. All lengths are in cm.

(a)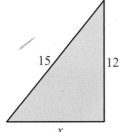

perimeter = 36 cm

(b)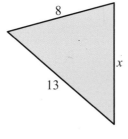

perimeter = 40 cm

(c)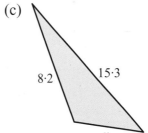

perimeter = 34 cm

4.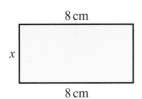

The perimeter of this rectangle is 26 cm.

Find the missing value x.

5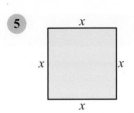

The perimeter of this square is 36 cm.

Find the missing value of x.

6 The perimeter of a square is 48 cm. How long is one of the sides of the square?

7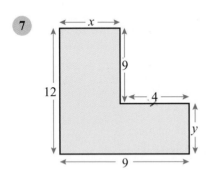

All lengths are in cm. Find the length of

(a) x

(b) y

(c) Find the perimeter of this shape.

In questions **8** to **13**, find the perimeter of each shape. All lengths are in cm.

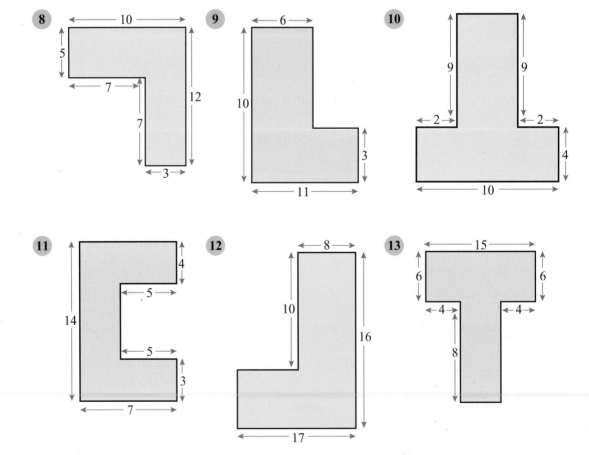

14

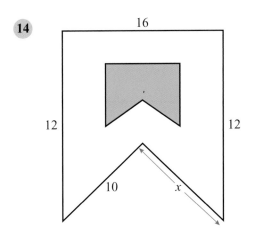

The perimeter of the large shape is twice the perimeter of the inside shape. All lengths are in cm.

The perimeter of the inside shape is 32 cm. Find the missing value of x.

Area of triangles and rectangles

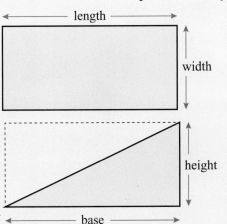

Key Facts

Area is measured in squares, usually square metres (m^2) or square centimetres (cm^2).

$$\text{Area of rectangle} = \text{length} \times \text{width}$$

$$\text{Area of triangle} = \tfrac{1}{2} \text{ area of rectangle}$$

$$\text{Area of triangle} = \tfrac{1}{2} (\text{base} \times \text{height})$$

Find the area of this shape.

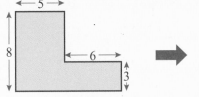 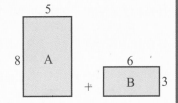

Area rectangle $A = 8 \times 5 = 40$

Area rectangle $B = 6 \times 3 = 18$

Total area $= 40 + 18 = 58 \text{ cm}^2$ if each length is given in cm.

Find the area of each shape below. All lengths are in cm.

1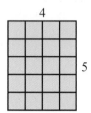

2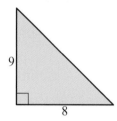

3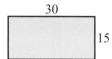

4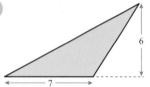

5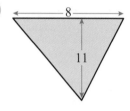

6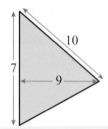

7 Find the area of this triangle.

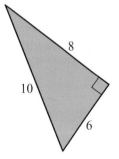

8 The ratio of the area of rectangle A to the area of rectangle B is 3 : 2. Find the value of x.

Can you still?

Mixed algebra

1 Aidan has n bikes. How many wheels is that in total?

2 $W = mg$. Find the value of W if $m = 7$ and $g = 10$.

3  Find the perimeter of this isosceles triangle. Simpify the answer.

4 Simplify $9n \times 3n$

5 Simplify $\dfrac{(m^4)^3}{m^4 \times m^3}$

6 Expand $6m(2m - n)$

7 Factorise $10n + 15$

Find the area of each shape in questions **9** to **14** by splitting them into rectangles.

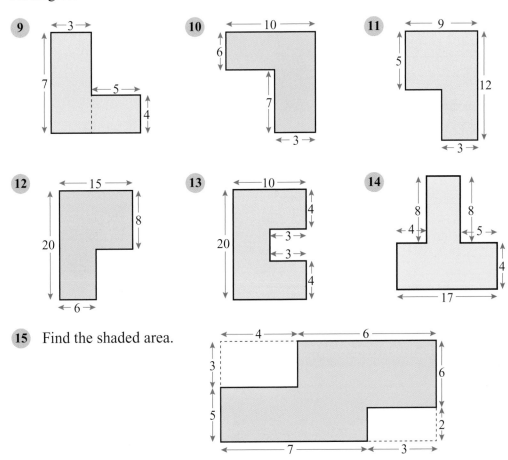

15 Find the shaded area.

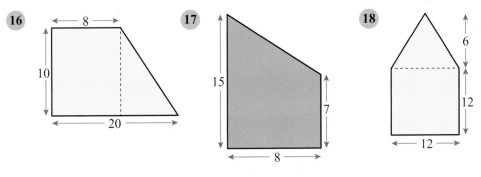

Find the area of each shape in questions **16** to **18** by splitting them into rectangles and triangles.

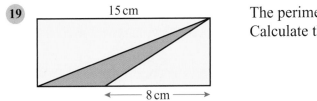

19

The perimeter of the rectangle is 50 cm.
Calculate the area of the red triangle.

285

20

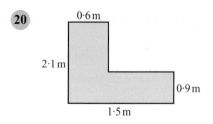

This section of a wall is to be covered with tiles.
Each tile is 30 cm by 30 cm.
How many tiles are needed to cover the entire wall?

In questions **21** to **23**, find the pink area.

21

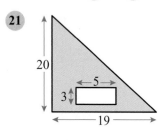

22

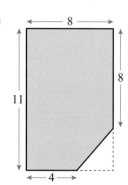

23

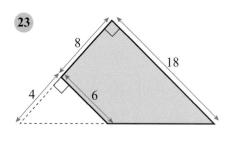

Areas of trapeziums and parallelograms

Parallelogram

height

base

$$\text{Area} = \text{base} \times \text{height}$$
$$\text{Area} = b \times h$$

Trapezium (2 parallel sides)

a

height

b

$$\text{Area} = \frac{1}{2}(a + b) \times h$$

(a)

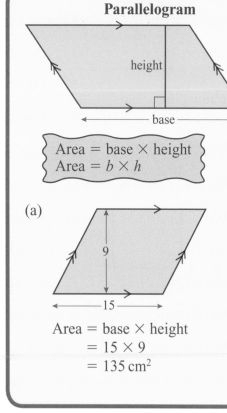

$$\text{Area} = \text{base} \times \text{height}$$
$$= 15 \times 9$$
$$= 135 \, \text{cm}^2$$

(b)

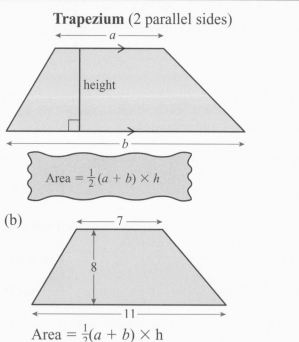

$$\text{Area} = \frac{1}{2}(a + b) \times h$$
$$= \frac{1}{2}(7 + 11) \times 8$$
$$= \frac{1}{2}(18) \times 8$$
$$= 9 \times 8 = 72 \, \text{cm}^2$$

286

Find the area of each shape below. All lengths are in cm.

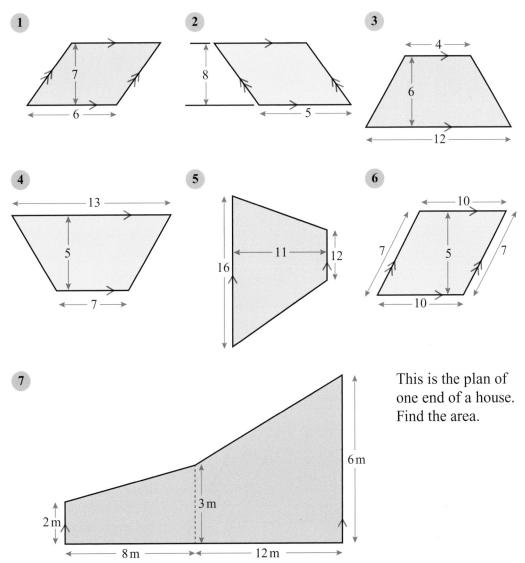

7

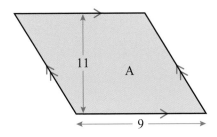

This is the plan of
one end of a house.
Find the area.

8 Find the ratio of the area of shape A to the area of shape B. Give the answer
in its simplest form.

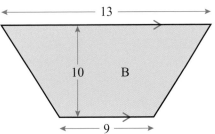

287

9 Find the pink area.

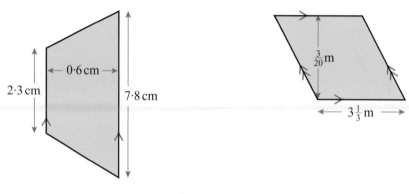

10 Find the area of the trapezium.

11 Find the area of the parallelogram.

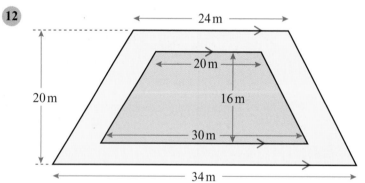

12

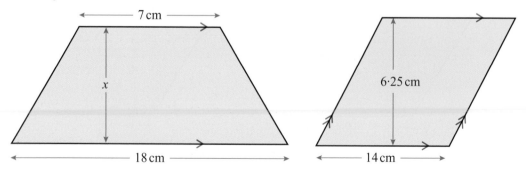

A garden is in the shape of a trapezium. It has a lawn also in the shape of a trapezium. The yellow area is a path around the lawn. Find the area of the path.

13 The area of the trapezium is equal to the area of the parallelogram. Find the missing value x

14 Wayne wants to grass an area in his garden (the green area). If it costs him £13 to grass every 30 m², how much will it cost him to grass the green area? (Give your answer to the nearest pound.)

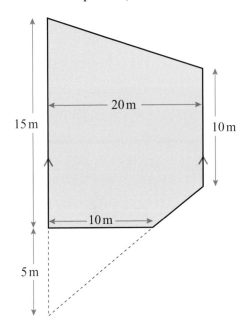

Can you still?

Finding angles

1
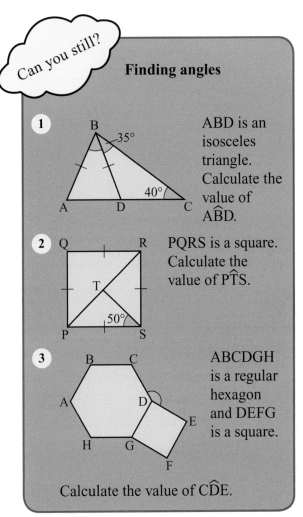

ABD is an isosceles triangle. Calculate the value of AB̂D.

2 PQRS is a square. Calculate the value of PT̂S.

3 ABCDGH is a regular hexagon and DEFG is a square.

Calculate the value of CD̂E.

Circumference of a circle

The perimeter of a circle is called the *circumference*.

diameter

radius

If you divide the circumference of a circle by its diameter the number you obtain is always just over 3,

in fact   3·14159265…

This number has many digits so it is more convenient to give the number a name. We call it 'pi'. This is the Greek letter π.

$$\pi = 3\cdot14159265\ldots$$

Key Facts

$$\left\{\frac{\text{circumference}}{\text{diameter}} = \pi\right\}$$ so circumference $= \pi \times$ diameter

$$\left\{C = \pi d\right\}$$ *Learn* this formula.

radius is 3 cm so diameter $= 6$ cm

$C = \pi d$

$C = \pi \times 6 = 18\cdot8$ cm.

Note. Sometimes π is not worked out and the answer is left as 6π so the circumference $= 6\pi$ cm.

M9.10

When necessary, give answers to 1 decimal place.

1 *Use a calculator* to find the circumference of each circle below.

(a) 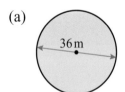   (b) 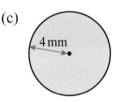   (c)   (d)

2 Which shape below has the larger perimeter – the square or the circle? Explain your answer fully.

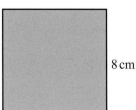   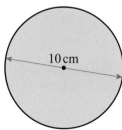

3 Kris walks around the edge of a circular lake of radius 250 m. If Kris walks once around the lake, how far does he walk? (Give your answer to the nearest metre.)

290

Find the perimeter of this shape (give the answer to 1 decimal place).

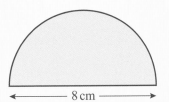

8 cm

The curved part is a semi-circle.

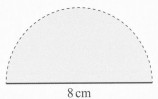

8 cm

$C = \pi d$ (whole circle)

$C = \pi \times 8 = 25 \cdot 13$

We want half the circumference
$= 25 \cdot 13 \div 2 = 12 \cdot 57$

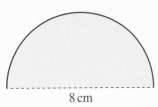

8 cm

Add on the straight line 8 cm

Perimeter of shape $= 12 \cdot 57 + 8 = 20 \cdot 57$

Perimeter $= 20 \cdot 6$ cm (to 1 decimal place)

E9.2

Calculate the perimeter of each shape. All arcs are either semi-circles or quarter circles. Give answers correct to 1 decimal place.

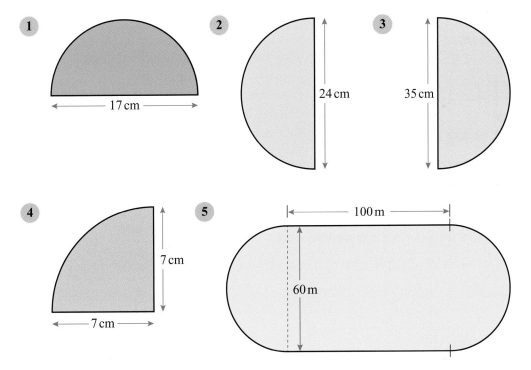

1 17 cm

2 24 cm

3 35 cm

4 7 cm, 7 cm

5 100 m, 60 m

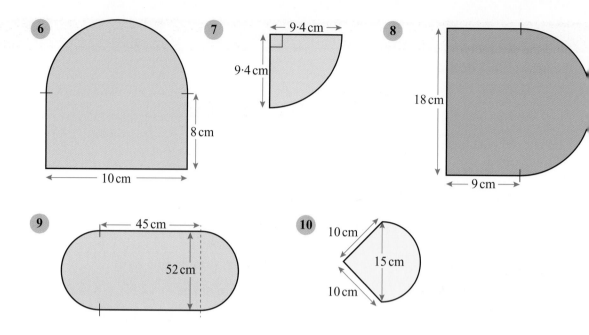

11 The wheels on Inzaman's bike have a diameter of 65 cm. He travels so that the wheels go round completely 10 times. What distance does Inzaman travel?
(Give your answer to the nearest cm).

12 Dan kicks a football down the side of a steep hill and it rolls 80 metres. If the diameter of the football is 27 cm, how many *complete* revolutions did the football make before it stopped?

13

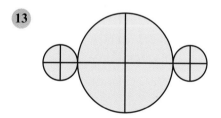

The metal frame for a stained glass window is shown opposite.
The large circle has diameter 40 cm and the two small circles each have radius 8 cm.
Calculate the total length of metal needed for the metal frame shown.

14 A car tyre has a radius of 41 cm.

(a) How long is its circumference in cm?

(b) How many complete revolutions will the tyre make if the car travels 5 km?

15 The circumference of a circular plate is 91 cm. Calculate the diameter of the plate to the nearest cm.

Key Facts

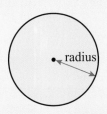

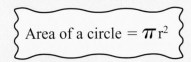

Learn this formula.

Area of a circle = πr^2

Note: πr^2 means 'r^2 then multiply by π'

Note. A line joining 2 points
on the circumference of a
circle is called a *chord*.

chord

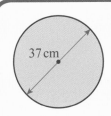

37 cm

diameter = 37 cm

so radius = 37 ÷ 2 = 18·5 cm

area   = πr^2

= $\pi \times 18\cdot5^2$

= $\pi \times 342\cdot25$

= 1075·2 cm²

M9.10

1 (a) Copy the diagram opposite.
O is the centre of the circle.

(b) Write down the special name
for the line RS.

(c) Write down the special name
for the line PQ.

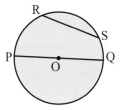

2 Calculate the area of each circle correct to 1 decimal place.

(a)
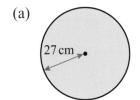
27 cm

(b)
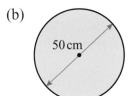
50 cm

(c)
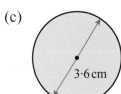
3·6 cm

3 (a) Draw any circle.

(b) Draw any two chords which are perpendicular to each other.

4 Tania creates a circular flower bed of radius 1·5 m. What is the area of this flower bed in m²?

5 Which shape below has the larger area – the rectangle or the circle?

Write down the difference between the two areas.

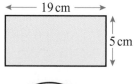

6 Do *not* use a calculator in this question.

Find the area of each circle, leaving π in your answer (for example, 18π).

(a)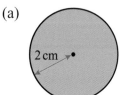

(b)

(c)

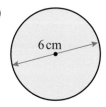

Can you still?

Sequences/rearranging

1 Write down the next two numbers in the sequence 1, 3, 6, 10, …

2 Here is a sequence:

7, 10, 13, 16, …

Write down (a) the common difference, (b) the nth term

3 The nth term in a sequence is $27 - 4n$. Find the 5th term.

In questions **4** to **7**, make x the subject of the formula.

4 $y = x - 4$

5 $m = 8x$

6 $m = 5x + 9$

7 $a = 2x - 6$

Find the area of this shape (give the answer correct to 1 decimal place).

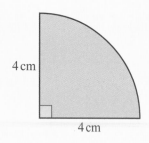

Area of circle $= \pi r^2$

$= \pi \times 4^2$

$= \pi \times 16 = 50\cdot27$ cm

Area of the quarter circle $= 50\cdot27 \div 4$

$= 12\cdot6$ cm²

(to 1 decimal place)

In questions 1 to 6 find the area of each shape. All arcs are either semi-circles or quarter circles and the units are cm. Give answers correct to 1 decimal place.

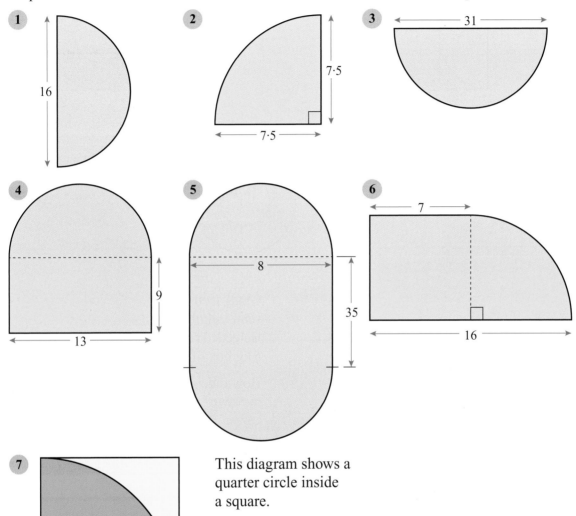

7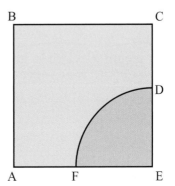

This diagram shows a quarter circle inside a square.

Calculate the yellow area.

8 The area of square ABCE is 81 cm².

AF = FE and CD = DE.

Calculate the area of the quarter circle DEF.

In questions ⑨ to ⑭ find the blue area. Lengths are in cm. Give answers correct to 1 decimal place

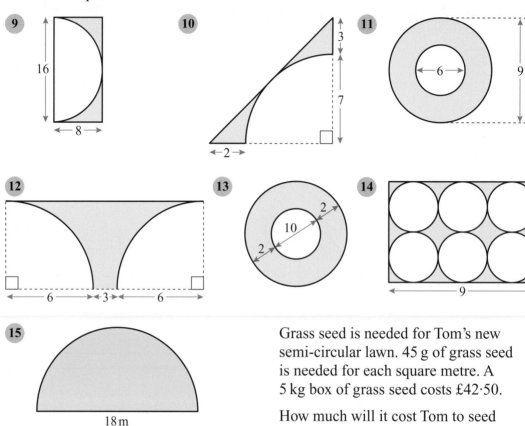

⑨ 16, 8

⑩ 3, 7, 2

⑪ 6, 9

⑫ 6, 3, 6

⑬ 10, 2, 2

⑭ 9

⑮

18 m

Grass seed is needed for Tom's new semi-circular lawn. 45 g of grass seed is needed for each square metre. A 5 kg box of grass seed costs £42·50.

How much will it cost Tom to seed his lawn?

Surface areas and volumes of cuboids

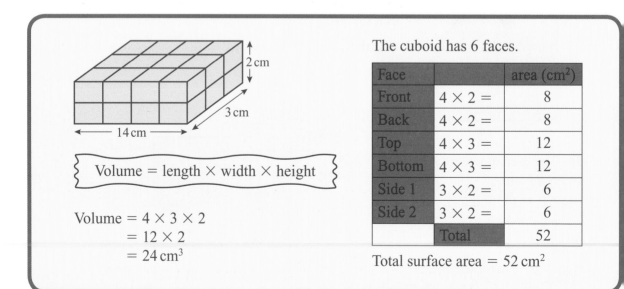

The cuboid has 6 faces.

Face		area (cm²)
Front	4 × 2 =	8
Back	4 × 2 =	8
Top	4 × 3 =	12
Bottom	4 × 3 =	12
Side 1	3 × 2 =	6
Side 2	3 × 2 =	6
	Total	52

Total surface area = 52 cm²

Volume = length × width × height

Volume = 4 × 3 × 2
= 12 × 2
= 24 cm³

1   Copy and complete the tables below to find the total surface area of each cuboid.

(a)

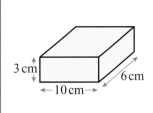

Face	Area (cm²)
Front	
Back	
Top	
Bottom	
Side 1	
Side 2	
Total =	

(b)

Face	Area (cm²)
Front	
Back	
Top	
Bottom	
Side 1	
Side 2	
Total =	

2   Find the volume of each cuboid in question 1 . The units for each answer will be cm³.

3   Which of these 3 cuboids has the largest surface area?

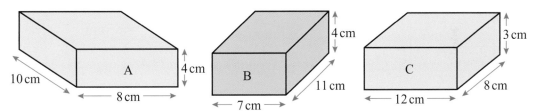

4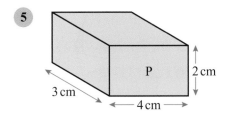

A breakfast cereal packet measures 30 cm × 20 cm × 7 cm.

The cereal packets are packed into large boxes which measure 1·2 m × 1 m × 0·42 m

How many cereal packets can be packed into 1 large box?

5

Find the ratio of the total surface area of cuboid P to the total surface area of cuboid Q. Give the answer in its simplest form.

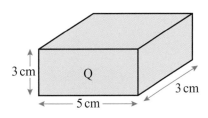

6   How many 2 cm × 2 cm × 2 cm cubes will fit into a box which measures 30 cm × 12 cm × 18 cm?

Prisms

A prism has the same cross section throughout its length.

Volume of prism = (Area of cross section) × (length)

Any cuboid is a prism since it has the same cross section throughout its length.

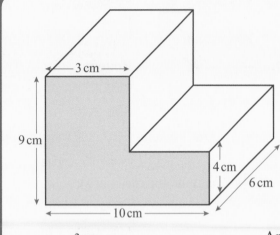

Find the volume of this prism.

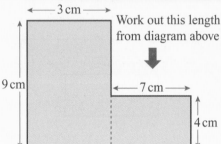

Work out this length from diagram above

Area of cross section = (9 × 3) + (7 × 4)

$$= 27 + 28$$

$$= 55 \text{ cm}^2$$

Volume of prism = Area of cross section × length

$$= 55 × 6$$

$$= 330 \text{ cm}^3$$

M9.12

1   Which of the solids below are prisms?

(a)
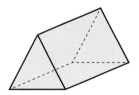

(b)
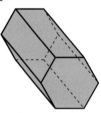

(c)

(d)

(e)
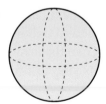

(f)

(g)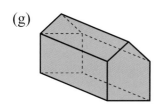

(h)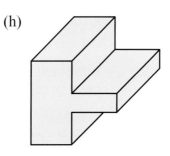

In questions ② to ⑦ find the volume of each prism.

2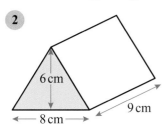

6 cm
8 cm
9 cm

3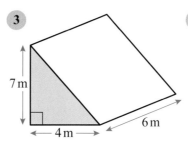

7 m
4 m
6 m

4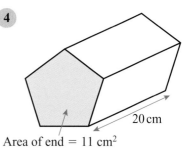

20 cm
Area of end = 11 cm²

5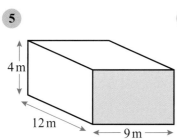

4 m
12 m
9 m

6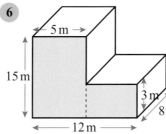

5 m
15 m
12 m
3 m
8 m

7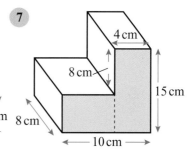

4 cm
8 cm
15 cm
8 cm
10 cm

8 A garden shed is shown opposite.

Calculate the volume of this shed.

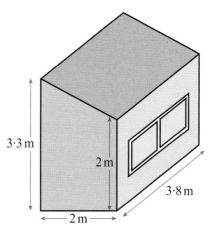

3·3 m
2 m
2 m
3·8 m

9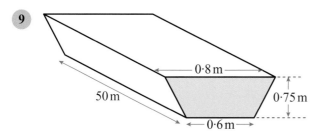

0·8 m
50 m
0·75 m
0·6 m

A trench is dug in a field. Calculate the mass of soil removed if 1 m³ of soil weighs 0·9 tonnes.

10 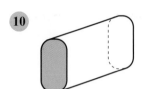 A piece of metal is in the shape of a prism. It has a volume of 6400 cm³.

If the area of the cross section is 32 cm², how long is the piece of metal?

In questions **11** and **12** find the *total surface area* of each prism.

11

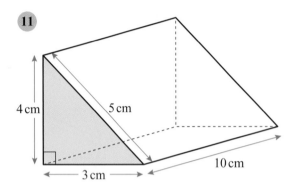

4 cm   5 cm   3 cm   10 cm

12

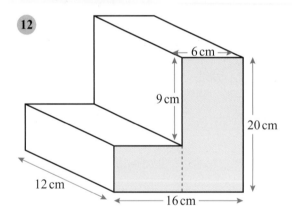

 6 cm   9 cm   20 cm   12 cm   16 cm

Can you still?

Probability

1 Rena has 19 pencils. 9 are red, 3 are blue and the rest are black.

Rena takes out a pencil at random. What is the probability that she takes out: (a) red? (b) black? (c) blue or black?

2 $\mathcal{E}$

A   B   7   2   9   3

$\mathcal{E}$ = {some people who play football}

A = {people who play for team A}
B = {people who play for team B}

If one person is chosen at random, what is the probability that this person does not play for team B?

3 A dice is thrown 240 times. How many times would you expect to get:
(a) a 5?   (b) a square number?

🔑 # Key Facts

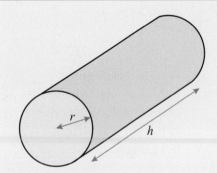

A cylinder is a prism because it has the same cross section throughout its length.

Volume = (area of cross section) × (length)

Volume = $\pi r^2 \times h$

$$V = \pi r^2 h$$ *Learn* this formula.

A cylinder has radius 0·5 m and length 1·2 m. Find the volume of the cylinder.

$V = \pi r^2 h$

$V = \pi \times 0·5^2 \times 1·2$

$V = 0·942 \text{ m}^3$ (to 3 decimal places)

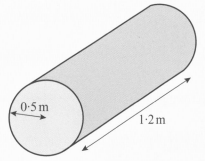

0·5 m

1·2 m

If the cylinder is full of water, how many litres does it hold?

$1\text{m}^3 = 1000$ litres

↑

Learn this!

$V = 0·942 \text{ m}^3$
Number of litres = 0·942 × 1000
= 942
The cylinder holds 942 litres.

M9.13

Use a calculator and give answers to 1 decimal place where necessary.

In questions **1** and **3** find the volume of each cylinder.

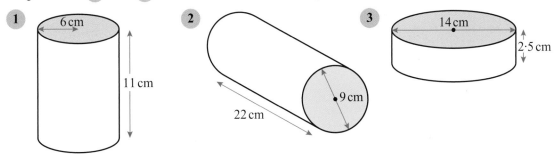

1 6 cm
11 cm

2 22 cm
9 cm

3 14 cm
2·5 cm

4 Find the volume in *litres* of a cylindrical tank of diameter 2·4 m and height 1·9 m.

5 A cylindrical can of cat food has a radius of 3·5 cm and a height of 11 cm. If the can contains 400 cm³ of cat food, how much empty space is there inside the can?

6 Find the volume of a cylindrical container of radius 2 m and height 10 m. Leave π in your answer (for example, 24π).

301

7 Which of the cylinders below has the larger volume and by how much?

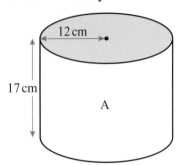
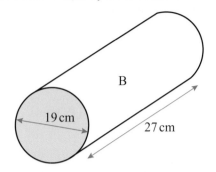

8 Cylinders are cut along the axis of symmetry. Find the volume of each object. (Give answers correct to 1 decimal place.)

(a)
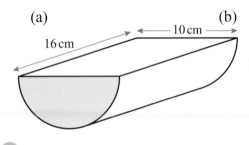

(b)

(c)
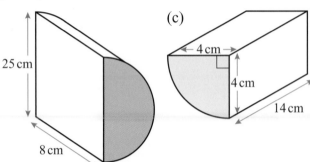

9

2 litres of lemonade is 2000 cm³.

How many glasses of radius 2·5 cm and height 10 cm can be completely filled from the bottle of lemonade?

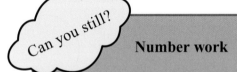

Number work

1 £2000 is shared between Lucy and Andy in the ratio 5 : 3. Lucy then spends 20% of her money. She invests the rest of her money at 4% per annum simple interest. How much interest does she make in 2 years?

2 Work out $0.6^2 - 0.19$

3 Pat weights 110 kg. He loses 7% of his body weight. How much does he weigh now?

4 Work out $\dfrac{1}{2} \times \dfrac{1}{2} + \dfrac{1}{3} \times \dfrac{1}{3}$

10

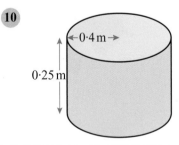

This cylindrical tank is filled with water at a rate of 0·3 litres per second. How long does it take to fill the tank completely? Give the answer to the nearest second.

11 A 300 m tunnel is dug. It forms a prism with the cross section shown.

    (a) Calculate the area of the cross section.

    (b) Calculate the volume of earth which is dug out for the tunnel.

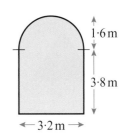

12

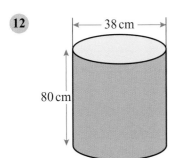

A cylindrical barrel is full of water. The water is poured into a trough as shown.

Will all the water go in without the trough overflowing? Show all your working out.

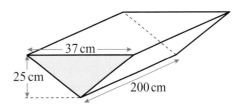

Identifying similar shapes

Two shapes are *similar* if they have the same angles.

Corresponding sides must be in the same proportion.

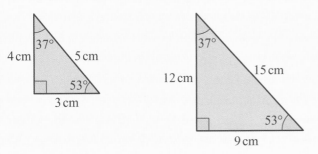

The triangles are similar because all 3 angles are the same.

Each side in the larger triangle is 3 times the corresponding side in the smaller triangle.

M9.14

1 Which shapes below are similar to shape A?

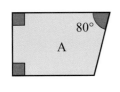

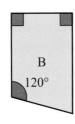

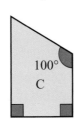

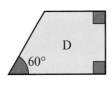

2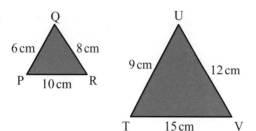

Explain why these triangles are similar.

3 For each part of the question below, the shapes are similar. Find *x*.

(a)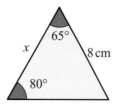

(b)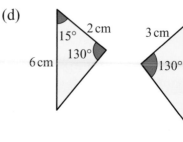

(c)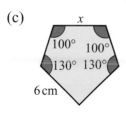

(d)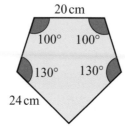

USE YOUR MATHS! – Which is better value?

How do you spot the best value in a shop?

A pack of 2 kitchen rolls £1.20	A pack of 3 kitchen rolls £1.71

To compare the cost, find the cost of 1 kitchen roll (the *unit* cost) for each pack.

2 rolls for £1·20 gives 60p per roll

3 rolls for £1·71 gives 57p per roll

The pack of 3 rolls is the best value (obviously you would only buy the pack of 3 kitchen rolls if you do not mind having that many rolls or have enough money to buy that pack at that particular moment).

Marshmallows £2.25 750 g	Which packet of Marshmallows is the best value?	Marshmallows £1.60 500 g

750 g costs 225 p, so 1 g costs $\frac{225}{750} = 0{\cdot}3$ p

500 g costs 160 p, so 1 g costs $\frac{160}{500} = 0{\cdot}32$ p

so the 750 g box is the best value.

OR

500 g costs 160 p, so 250 g costs 80 p

At this price, 3×250 g $= 750$ g costs 3×80 p $= £2{\cdot}40$

This is more expensive than the 750 g box.

Task

For each of questions **1** to **4**, decide which is the better value.

1

A pack of 2 light bulbs 92 p	or	A pack of 5 light bulbs £2.40
A		B

2

1 can of cola 45 p	or	A pack of 6 cans of cola £2.34
A		B

3

150 g tin of baked beans 33 p	or	400 g tin of baked beans 56 p
A		B

4

500 g punnet of strawberries £1.89 BUY ONE AND GET ONE FREE	or	1 kg punnet of strawberries £3.82
A		B

5 Carl is buying paper plates and plastic cups for a party. Paper plates cost 80 p for a pack of 20 or £1·50 for a pack of 50.

Plastic cups cost 78 p for a pack of 12 or £1·80 for a pack of 30.

Carl needs 60 plates and 75 cups. What is the cheapest way of buying them?

305

6 Jordan buys some tomato ketchup from the local supermarket. There are 3 different sized bottles.

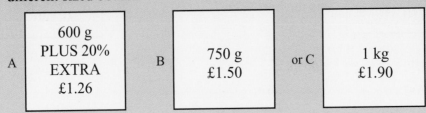

A
```
600 g
PLUS 20%
EXTRA
£1.26
```

B
```
750 g
£1.50
```

or C
```
1 kg
£1.90
```

Which bottle gives the best value for money?

7 Which box of washing powder below is the best value?

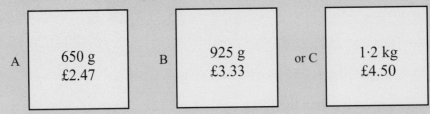

A
```
650 g
£2.47
```

B
```
925 g
£3.33
```

or C
```
1·2 kg
£4.50
```

TEST YOURSELF ON UNIT 9

1. Reading scales

For each of the scales below, write down the measurement indicated by the arrow.

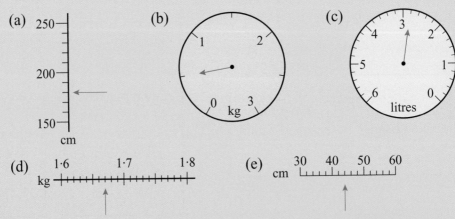

(a)
(b)
(c)
(d)
(e)

2. Using and converting metric units

(a) Chas has 1·4 kg of flour and uses 638 g. How much flour does he have left?

(b) Sarah knocks over a 2 litre bottle of water and spills 735 ml. How much water is left in the bottle?

3. Dealing with 'time' problems

    (a) Shanta catches a train at 14:45. Is this in the morning or the afternoon?

    (b)

        Plane leaves   Plane arrives

      How long was the plane journey?

    (c) Ravi and Bella start watching a DVD at 7:40 p.m. The DVD lasts for 2 hours 25 minutes. At what time do they stop watching the DVD.

    (d) A game of football starts at 12:30. The game finishes 1 hour 40 minutes later. At what time does the game finish?

    (e) Joey gets up at 07:45 and goes to bed at 23:30. How long is he up for?

4. Using speed, distance and time

    (a) Sharon walks for 3 hours at a speed of 5 km/hr. How far does Sharon walk?

    (b) Greg cycles 63 km at a speed of 14 km/hr. How long does the journey take him?

    (c) A lorry travels at 51 mph for 20 minutes. How far does the lorry travel?

    (d) Change 45 km/h into m/s.

    (e) Change 20 m/s into km/h.

5. Finding perimeters of shapes

Find the perimeter of each shape below. All lengths are in cm.

(a)   (b)   (c) Find x if the perimeter of the shape below is 64 cm.

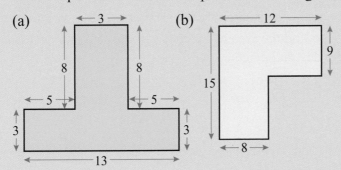
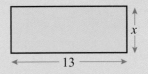

307

6. Finding areas of triangles and rectangles

Find the area of each shape below. All lengths are in cm.

(a) 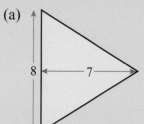 (b) 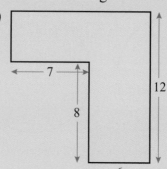 (c)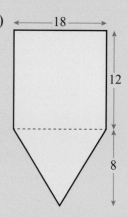

7. Finding areas of trapeziums and parallelograms

Find the area of each shape below. All lengths are in cm.

(a) 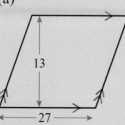 (b) 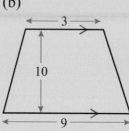 (c)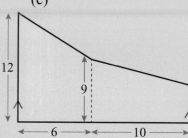

8. Finding circumferences of circles

Use a calculator to find the circumference or perimeter of each shape below. When necessary, give answers to 1 decimal place.

(a) (b) 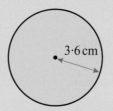 (c)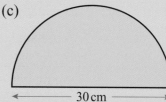

9. Finding areas of circles

Use a calculator to find the area of each shape below. When necessary, give answers to 1 decimal place.

(a) 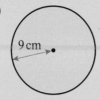 (b) (c)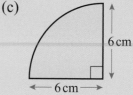

308

(d) Find the blue area.

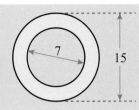

---

10. Finding surface areas and volumes of cuboids

Find (i) the volume and (ii) the total surface area of each cuboid below.

(a)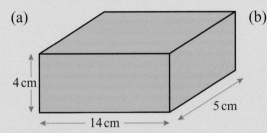

(b)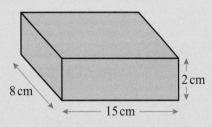

(c) A cuboid has a length of 20 cm and a width of 5 cm. What is the height of the cuboid if the volume is 320 cm³?

---

11. Finding surface areas and volumes of prisms

(a) Find the volume of the triangular prism.

(b) Find the total surface area of the triangular prism.

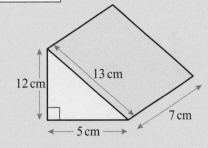

---

12. Finding volumes of cylinders

Find the volume of each prism below. When necessary, give answers to 1 decimal place.

(a)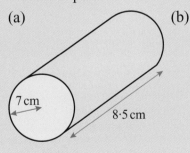

(b)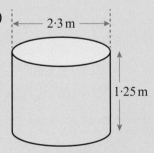

(c) The cylinder in part (b) is filled with water at a rate of 140 litres per minute.
How long does it take to completely fill the cylinder?

---

13. Identifying similar shapes

Which triangles are similar to triangle P?

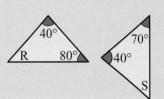

Mixed examination questions

1 *ABCD* is a trapezium.

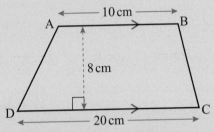

Calculate the area of *ABCD*.
State the units of your answer.

(AQA)

2 Three identical rectangles, each 10 cm by 2 cm, are place to make the shape shown in the diagram.

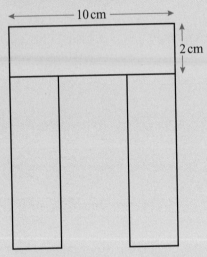

diagram not drawn to scale

(a) Calculate the perimeter of the shape.

(b) Calculate the area of the shape.
   Write down the units of your answer.

(WJEC)

3 Parvinder has a bicycle.
Each wheel has a diameter of 65·5 cm.

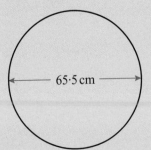

On one journey each wheel rotated 3509 times.

Calculate the distance Parvinder cycled.
Give your answer in kilometres.

(OCR)

4 Write down the quantity that is the appropriate estimate for each of the following.

Weight of a woman	50 g	500 kg	50 mg	50 kg
Volume of a glass of water	27 litres	270 ml	2·7 cm^3	270 litres
Height of a man	180 cm	18 m	180 mm	1800 cm
Distance from Calais to Paris	266 mm	266 cm	266 m	266 km

(WJEC)

5 Mr Weaver's garden is in the shape of a rectangle.

In the garden there is a patio in the shape of a rectangle and two ponds in the shape of circles with diameter 3·8 m.

The rest of the garden is grass.

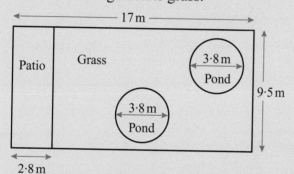

Mr Weaver is going to spread fertiliser over all the grass.
One box of fertiliser will cover 25 m^2 of grass.

How many boxes of fertiliser does Mr Weaver need?
You must show your working.

(EDEXCEL)

6 This is the bus timetable from Norford to Wenton.

Norford	8:05	9:05	11:35	13:05	15:35	17:05	18:35	20:05
End lane	8:17	9:17	11:47	13:17	15:47	17:17	18:47	20:17
Church Street	8:31	9:31		13:31		17:31		20:31
Village Hall	8:39	9:39	12:06	13:39	16:06	17:39	19:06	20:39
Queens Road	8:47	9:47		13:47		17:47		20:47
Wenton	8:51	9:51	12:15	13:51	16:15	17:51	19:51	20:51

(a) Oliver is going from End Lane to Queens Road.
He catches the bus at 9:17.

At what time should the bus get to Queens Raod?

(b) Katie is travelling to Wenton. She catches the bus from Norford at 11:35.
How long should it take her?

(c) Charlie must be at the Village Hall by 6 o'clock in the evening.
It takes him 18 minutes to walk from his home to the bus stop at Norford.
What is the latest time he can leave home?

(OCR)

7 The radius, r, of the cylinder is 10 cm.
The height, h, is 4 cm.

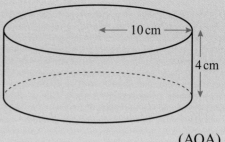

Work out the volume of the cylinder. (AQA)

8 Ellie drives 169 miles from Sheffield to London.

She drives at an average speed of 65 miles per hour.
She leaves Sheffield at 6:30 a.m.

Does she arrive in London before 9:00 a.m.?
You **must** show your working. (AQA)

9 The diagram shows a prism.

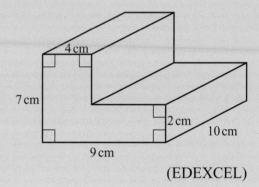

Work out the volume of the prism. (EDEXCEL)

10 The radius of the base of a cylindrical oil tank is 60 cm.

(a) Calculate the area of the base of the oil tank.

The height of the oil tank is 70 cm.

(b) Calculate the volume of the oil tank. Give your answer in **litres**. (CEA)

11 One quarter of the tank is filled
with water.

1 cubic metre holds 1000 litres
of water.

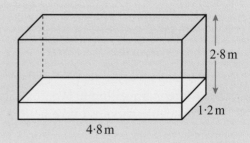

Work out how many **more** litres of water are needed to fill the tank. (AQA)

In this unit you will learn how to:

- find the mean, median, mode and range for sets of numbers
- use charts and graphs
- use stem and leaf diagrams
- use pie charts
- use two-way tables
- draw scatter diagrams and describe correlation
- recognise misrepresentation of data
- find the median and mode from tables of information
- find mean averages from tables of information (including grouped data)
- compare sets of data
- USE YOUR MATHS! – feed the dogs

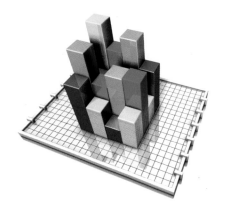

Averages and range

 **Key Facts**

mean – add up the data then divide by the number of items

median – put numbers in order of size then choose middle item

mode – the item which occurs most often

range – largest value – smallest value

The shoes sizes of 6 people were:

6, 2, 8, 5, 8, 7

(a) *mean* shoe size $= \dfrac{6 + 2 + 8 + 5 + 8 + 7}{6}$

> add up all the numbers

$= \dfrac{36}{6} = 6$

> the total number of people

(b) arrange the shoe sizes in order:

$$2\ 5\ 6\ 7\ 8\ 8$$

↑

the median is the $\frac{1}{2}$-way number

$median = \dfrac{6 + 7}{2} = 6{\cdot}5$

(c) *mode* = 8 because there are more 8s than any other number.

(d) *range* = highest number − lowest number

$= 8 - 2$

$= 6$

M10.1

1 Copy and fill the empty boxes.
The marks scored by 7 students in a test are:

5   2   8   5   9   7   6

(a) The range is the highest mark ☐ − the lowest mark ☐ = ☐

(b) The mode is the most common value, which is ☐

(c) The median is the middle value when the numbers are arranged in size order:

median = ☐

(d) The *mean* is the total marks ☐ ÷ 7 = ☐

2 The parents of 5 children were asked how much money they spent on each child last Christmas. The money is shown below:

£200   £300   £160   £280   £260

Find the mean average amount of money spent on each child last Christmas.

314

3 The heights of some Russian dolls were recorded as:

5·6 cm, 2·1 cm, 7·8 cm, 6·3 cm, 4·9 cm

Find the median height.

4 Find the mode of the set of numbers:

12, 13, 18, 13, 12, 19, 17, 13, 18, 12, 17, 13

5 The temperature was recorded at midnight in nine towns. The readings were:

$2°, -3°, 0°, 1°, -1°, -2°, 0°, -4°, -2°$

What was the range of the temperatures?

6 On a school trip, the ages of the boys were 14, 14, 12, 15, 12, 11 and the ages of the girls were 13, 16, 15, 12.

(a) Find the mean age for the boys.

(b) Find the mean age for the girls.

(c) Find the mean age for all the children.

7 | 2 | 9 | 5 | 3 | 5 | 8 | 9 | 7 |

For the set of numbers above, find

(a) the mean   (b) the median   (c) the mode   (d) the range

8

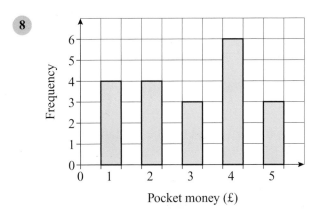

The bar chart above shows the pocket money received by some young children. Work out the mean amount of pocket money.

Mean, median or mode?

When working out an average, how do I choose which one to use?

Look at the numbers 1, 1, 1, 1, 66

$$\text{mean} = \frac{70}{5} = 14 \qquad\qquad \text{median} = 1$$

Since each number is 1 except the last number, the median gives a more sensible idea of the average.

The mean average is distorted by the one high value 66.

Key Facts

If a set of numbers has extreme values, the mean average can be distorted so it is often better to use the median.

The median and mode are not calculated using all the numbers in the list but the mode is good for finding the most likely value and for data which are not numbers.

The mean average is better for numbers which are spread out in a balanced way.

E10.1

You may *use a calculator* for this exercise.

1 The shoe sizes of the students in a year 11 class were:

7, 8, 8, 5, 7, 7, 5, 7, 6, 7
5, 10, 7, 11, 9, 7, 7, 6, 8, 10

Find (a) the mode (b) the mean. Which average best describes these shoe sizes, the mode or the mean? Explain why.

2 For the set of numbers below, find (a) the mean and (b) the median.

| 0 | 1 | 1 | 1 | 2 | 2 | 70 |

(c) Which average best describes this set of numbers? Explain why.

3 Write down 3 *different* numbers with a mean of 7.

4 Write down 7 numbers with a median of 6.

5 Jenny has 5 cards. The 5 cards have a mean of 9 and a range of 6.

| | 8 | 9 | 10 | |

What are the missing 2 numbers?

6 A theatre needs a mean average of 220 people to attend each show if it is to make enough money to stay open.

The mean average for the first 23 shows is 216.

How many people must attend the next show so that the mean average will become 220?

7 The list below shows the yearly salaries of all the people who work at 'Easiprint'.

£7000	£6900	£6900	£138 000
£7500	£5600	£5900	£7100
£7000	£7700	£7900	£7200

(a) Which kind of average would be the most sensible to use? Explain why.

(b) Work out this average.

8 The mean average pocket money received by 6 children is £5 each week.

(a) What is the total amount of pocket money received by the 6 children each week?

(b) Rowan joins the 6 children. Rowan gets £12 pocket money each week. What is the mean average pocket money for all 7 children?

9 Owen does exams in six subjects.
His results in five of the exams are shown below:

48%   57%   41%   69%   58%

His mean mark for all six exams was 58%.

What was Owen's mark in the sixth subject?

10 In 3 cricket innings, Tariq has a median score of 42 and a mean score of 38.

The range of the 3 scores is 14.

What are the three scores?

11 The mean average of the four numbers shown below is 3. Find the value of x.

12 The 6 numbers below have a mean of 9. What is the value of x?

| 12 | 3 | 8 | x | 17 | 6 |

13 The mean height of 20 people is 160 cm.

(a) What is the total height of all 20 people?

(b) One person of height 179 cm leaves the group. Find the mean height of the remaining 19 people.

14 In one football game, the mean age of the England team was equal to the mean age of the France team. 21 of the ages are shown below.

| England | 33 | 24 | 26 | 26 | 28 | 31 | 29 | 32 | 35 | 27 | 28 |
| France | 24 | 27 | x | 27 | 34 | 29 | 33 | 22 | 33 | 29 | 30 |

Find the value of x.

15 Maya takes 8 shots in an archery competition and has a mean average score of 35.

She then takes another 12 shots and has a mean average score of 30.

Calculate her mean average score for all 20 shots.

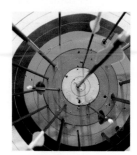

16 Luke wants to know if his salary puts him in the top half of the country for how much money is earned by people. Which type of average should he look at?

Can you still?

Number work

Copy the crossnumber puzzle onto squared paper. Use the clues to complete the crossnumber puzzle.

1		2		3
		4		
	5		6	
7			8	

Clues across

1. $157 + 394$

4. $831 - 236$

5. 201×4

7. $-3 + 17$

8. -8×-4

Clues down

1. $712 - 187$

2. 130×12

3. $1575 \div 35$

5. $504 \div 6$

6. $602 \div 14$

1 The pictogram below shows how many year 10 students were absent from school during one week.

How many students were absent on:

(a) Friday?

(b) Wednesday?

(c) Thursday?

(d) How many *more* students were absent on Thursday than on Tuesday?

(e) What percentage of the absences took place on Wednesday?

Monday	☺ ☺
Tuesday	☺ ☾
Wednesday	☺ ☺ ☾
Thursday	☺ ☺ ☺ ☾
Friday	☺ ☺ ☺

☺ means 10 students

2 In Hart High School, students choose their year 10 options. 60 students choose History, 70 choose Geography, 30 choose Business Studies, 15 choose Spanish and 45 choose Art. Copy and complete the pictogram below:

History	
Geography	⊠ ⊠ ⊠ ◹
Business Studies	
Spanish	
Art	

⊠ means 20 students

3

Day	Number of people
Monday	6
Tuesday	8
Wednesday	4
Thursday	9
Friday	3
Saturday	5

A Shopping Centre is looking for new workers. The table shows how many people are interviewed each day during one week.

Draw a bar chart to show the information in the table.

319

4 Two bands, 'Inferno' and 'Hotplay', tour part of the UK. The bar chart below shows how many people watched each concert.

How many people watched 'Inferno' in:

(a) Exeter?

(b) Swindon?

(c) Reading?

(d) Where did 310 people watch 'Hotplay'?

(e) In which place did more people watch 'Inferno' than 'Hotplay'?

(f) How many *more* people watched 'Hotplay' than 'Inferno' in Bristol?

(g) How many *more* people watched 'Hotplay' than 'Inferno' in Reading?

(h) What is the total number of people who watched 'Hotplay' in all 5 venues?

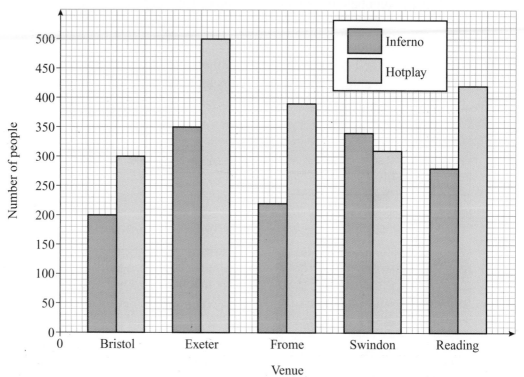

5 Twenty Year 10 students are asked how many text messages they have sent in the previous 4 hours.

The number of messages is shown below:

2 4 0 3 3 5 6 1 5 1

5 1 5 4 6 3 5 0 5 6

Draw any suitable chart to display this information.

6 The graph opposite shows the percentage of adults who smoke cigarettes in Great Britain.

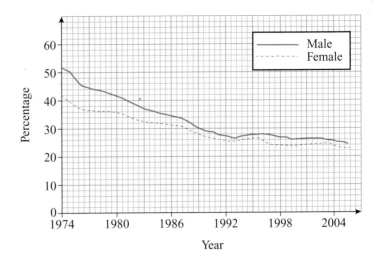

What percentage of males smoked in:

(a) 1980

(b) 1986

(c) 1998

(d) What was the *drop* in the percentage of male smokers between 1974 and 2004?

(e) What was the *drop* in the percentage of female smokers between 1980 and 1998?

(f) What was the *difference* in the percentage of male smokers compared to female smokers in 1980?

7 Some young people were asked how many computer games they have.
The results are below:

8	3	13	7	15	5	11	18	23	2	0	1	16	8
26	9	8	24	12	0	28	13	9	15	13	21	19	4
12	8	11	21	17	7	16	22	18	6	0	14	22	12

(a) Copy and complete the tally chart below:

Number of games	Tally	Total (Frequency)
0–4	ЖĦ ‖	7
5–9		
10–14		
15–19		
20–24		
25–29		

(b) Copy and complete this frequency diagram:

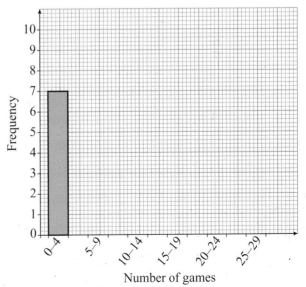

(c) How many people had 15 or more computer games?

(d) Write down the group which gives the modal number of games.

321

Stem and leaf diagrams

Here are the marks of 20 girls in a science test.

47	53	71	55	28	40	45	62	57	64
33	48	59	61	73	37	75	26	68	39

We will put the marks into groups 20–29, 30–39… 70–79.

We will choose the tens digit as the 'stem' and the units as the 'leaf'.

The first four marks are shown opposite [47, 53, 71, 55].

Stem (tens)	Leaf (units)
2	
3	
4	7
5	3 5
6	
7	1

The complete diagram is below. This is an *unordered* stem and leaf diagram.

Stem	Leaf
2	8 6
3	3 7 9
4	7 0 5 8
5	3 5 7 9
6	2 4 1 8
7	1 3 5

An *ordered* stem and leaf diagram has the leaves in numerical order.

Stem	Leaf
2	6 8
3	3 7 9
4	0 5 7 8
5	3 5 7 9
6	1 2 4 8
7	1 3 5

We write a key next to the stem and leaf diagram to explain what the stem digit means and what the leaf digit means.

In this example Key 4|7 = 47

The diagram shows the shape of the distribution. It is also easy to find the mode, the median and the range.

M10.3

1 The heights of 26 pupils were recorded to the nearest cm.

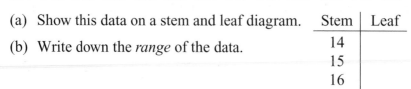

162 153 155 146 149 161 155 163 146 155 153 162 148

157 146 148 162 153 151 164 147 149 152 158 149 157

(a) Show this data on a stem and leaf diagram.

(b) Write down the *range* of the data.

Stem	Leaf
14	
15	
16	

2 The number of children in each class in Holland Bank School is recorded below:

28	31	27	28	30	24	23	32	29
29	29	30	26	27	31	27	26	31
25	27	30	28	27	29	30	28	27

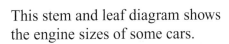

(a) Draw a stem and leaf diagram to show this data.

(b) How many classes were there?

(c) What is the median number of children in a class?

(d) Find the range for the number of children in each class.

(e) If one class is chosen at random, what is the probability that there are less than 30 children in it?

3

Stem	Leaf
1	1 1 3 3 3 4 5 7 7 8
2	1 1 1 2 3 4 4 5

Key 2|3 = 2·3 litres

This stem and leaf diagram shows the engine sizes of some cars.

(a) What is the median engine size?

(b) What is the range of the engine sizes?

4 Dan, Simon, Darryl and Julian try to play golf. The stem and leaf diagram shows the scores for each of their last 5 rounds of golf.

Stem	Leaf
7	8 9
8	1 2 2 4 5 5 5 7 9 9
9	0 1 1 3 3 4 6
10	1

Key 8|2 = 82

(a) What was their median score?

(b) Find the range of the scores.

(c) What percentage of their scores were 90 or over?

Can you still?

Number work

1 Write out the numbers below in order of size, starting with the smallest:

0·73, 0·37, 0·703, 0·4, 0·137

2 Work out

(a) $\dfrac{2}{3} - \dfrac{3}{7}$ (b) $\dfrac{8}{15} \div \dfrac{2}{3}$

(c) $2\dfrac{3}{4} \times 1\dfrac{1}{5}$ (d) $\dfrac{3}{4} \times 24$

3 The angles in a triangle are in the ratio $7:4:9$. If the smallest angle is $36°$, find the size of the other angles.

4 The price of a £44 train ticket is increased by 12%. What is the new price?

5 The ages of the teachers in Holland Bank School and Grindley High School are shown in the back-to-back stem and leaf diagram.

Holland Bank school		Grindley High school
9 6 6 4	2	2 3 3 5 7 7 7 8
9 8 5 5 4 2	3	0 0 1 3 4 4 6
9 8 8 6 6 6 5 5 0	4	1 2 2 5 7 7 8 8 8
7 7 7 5 5 5 3 2 2	5	0 6 6 7
3 2 2 1	6	0

Key 6|2 = 26   Key 4|5 = 45

Compare the ages of teachers in each school.

Pie charts

Drawing pie charts

Some people were asked what they had for breakfast. The data is recorded below:

Breakfast	Frequency (number of people)
cereal	18
toast	8
egg	4
nothing	15

To draw a pie chart:

(a) Add up the number of people.
Total frequency = 18 + 8 + 4 + 15 = 45

(b) Whole angle in a pie chart = 360°
This must be split between 45 people.
Angle for each person = 360° ÷ 45 = 8°

(c) Angle for 'cereal'   = 18 × 8° = 144°
Angle for 'toast'   = 8 × 8° = 64°
Angle for 'egg'   = 4 × 8° = 32°
Angle for 'nothing' = 15 × 8° = 120°

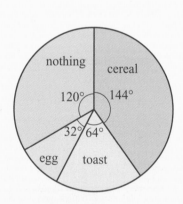

Remember

Always find the total frequency then divide it into 360° to find out what angle is needed for each item in the pie chart.

1 Some people were asked where they were going to spend their Summer holiday. The table below shows the information.

Country	Frequency
France	7
Spain	8
USA	4
Greece	6
UK	15

(a) Find the total frequency.

(b) Work out the angle for each person to help draw a pie chart.

(c) Work out the angle for each country and draw a pie chart.

2 120 children were asked who their favourite 'Simpsons' character was. The information is shown below.

Character	Frequency	Angle
Homer	52	
Bart	32	
Mr. Burns	17	
Lisa	12	
Marge	7	

Copy and complete the table then draw an accurate pie chart to show this information.

3

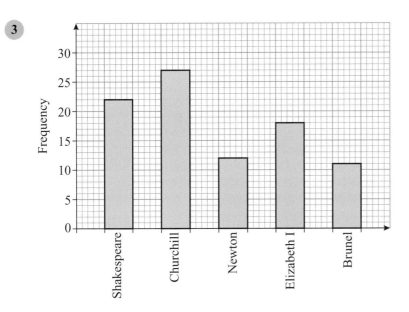

Some people were asked who their favourite British person was.
The information is shown in this bar chart.
Draw a pie chart to display this information

325

4 Hal carries out a survey of 60 year 10 students. He asks them what their favourite cartoon is. He draws this accurate pie chart.

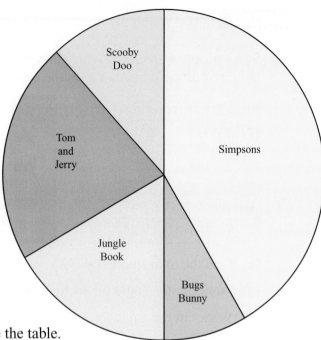

Measure the angles and complete the table.

Cartoon	Frequency	Angle
Simpsons	25	
Bugs Bunny		
Jungle Book	10	60°
Tom and Jerry		
Scooby Doo		
Total	60	

Reading from pie charts

Marilyn has £120 to spend each week. The pie chart shows what she spends her money on. How much does she spend on rent?

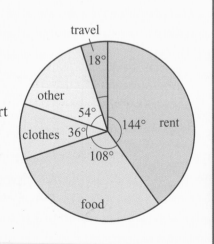

fraction of pie chart $= \dfrac{144}{360}$ ← angle for 'rent'
← total angle for pie chart

$\qquad\qquad = \dfrac{72}{180} = \dfrac{36}{90} = \dfrac{4}{10} = \dfrac{2}{5}$

money spent on rent $= \dfrac{2}{5}$ of £120

$\qquad\qquad = (120 \div 5) \times 2$

$\qquad\qquad = 24 \times 2$

$\qquad\qquad = £48$

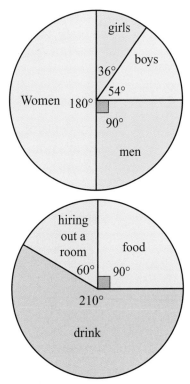

1. The pie chart shows the 80 passengers travelling on a train. How many of the passengers were:

   (a) men   (b) women

   (c) girls   (d) boys

2. Jack Jones runs a pub. He makes his money from 3 main things: food, drink and hiring out rooms. The pie chart shows what fraction of his money he gets from each of these things.

   If Jack makes £900 one week, how much did he make from:

   (a) food

   (b) hiring out a room

   (c) drink

3. Penny delivers 240 newspapers each Sunday.

   The pie chart shows the different newspapers which Penny delivers.

   How many of the newspapers were:

   (a) Sunday Express   (b) Sunday Mirror

   (c) Sunday Telegraph   (d) Sunday Times

   (e) Mail on Sunday   (f) Others

4. Neil draws a pie chart to show what he does during a typical day (24 hours).

   How many hours does he do the following?

   (a) exercise   (b) school

   (c) sleep   (d) eat

   (e) watch TV   (f) other things

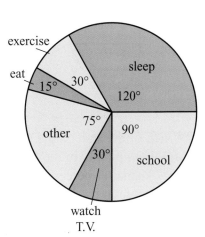

5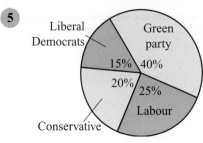

Some young people were asked who they would vote for at the next general election. The information is shown on the pie chart.

Find the angle on the pie chart for:

(a) Labour   (b) the Green party

(c) Conservative   (d) the Liberal Democrats

6 The students of 2 different schools were asked to state their favourite children's film. Here are the results.

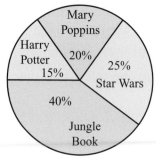

Holland Bank School

There were 800 students

Hatton Green School

There were 1000 students

(a) Carl says 'More students in Holland Bank School like Star Wars than the students in Hatton Green School.'
Use both charts to explain whether or not Carl is right.

(b) Yasmin says 'Less students in Holland Bank School like Harry Potter than the students in Hatton Green School.'
Use both charts to explain whether or not Yasmin is right.

7 People in the North and South of England were asked how many hours of exercise they took each week. The information is shown in the pie charts below.

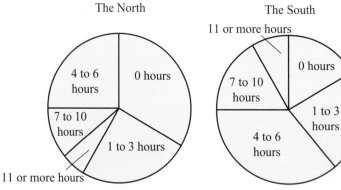

Which of the statements below is correct?

(a) 'Less people in the North do some exercise than people in the South'.

(b) 'A smaller percentage of people in the North do some exercise than people in the South.'

(c) 'More people in the North do some exercise than people in the South.'
Explain why you chose your answer.

8

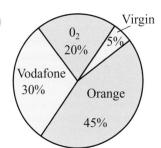

Over 2000 people were asked who their phone providers were. The results are shown in the pie chart.

Find the angle on the pie chart for:

(a) Vodafone   (b) O_2

(c) Virgin   (d) Orange

9 The pie charts below show the ages in years of people in the UK and Kenya.

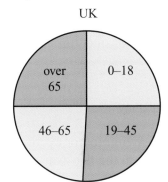

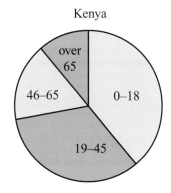

Which of the statements below are correct.

(a) 'There are more 0 to 18 year-olds in Kenya than in the UK.'

(b) 'There are less 0 to 18 year-olds in Kenya than in the UK.'

(c) 'A greater percentage of the people in Kenya are 0 to 18 year-olds than in the UK.'

Explain why you chose your answer.

Can you still?

Cuboids – volume and surface area

1 Which of these 3 cuboids has the *smallest* surface area?

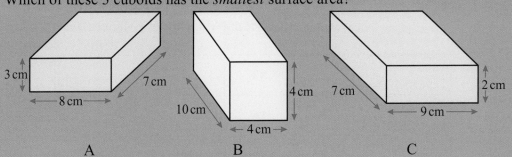

         A   B   C

2 Write down the ratio of the volume of cuboid A to the volume of cuboid B. Give the answer in its simplest form.

3 The volume of a cuboid is 420 cm^3. Find its length if its height is 5 cm and it is 6 cm wide.

Two-way tables

70 students from years 10 and 11 were asked what sport they played in their last games lesson. The information is shown below in a two-way table.

	Football	Rugby	Badminton	Total
Year 10	18	14	2	34
Year 11	14	16	6	36
Total	32	30	8	70

Totals can be found in two ways (add numbers in rows across or in columns down).

M10.6

1. 80 children were asked if they went to the cinema, swimming or cycling one day in the Easter holidays. The information is shown in the two-way table below.

	Cinema	Swimming	Cycling	Total
Boys	18	17		47
Girls	15		8	
Total				80

   (a) Copy and complete the two-way table.

   (b) How many children went swimming in total?

   (c) One child is picked at random. What is the probability that this child went swimming?

2. 500 football fans from Liverpool and Manchester were asked which football team they supported. The two-way table below shows the information.

	Liverpool	Everton	Manchester United	Manchester City	Total
Fans from Liverpool		83	15		210
Fans from Manchester	12	16			
Total	119		156		500

   (a) Copy and complete the two-way table.

   (b) *Use a calculator* to find what percentage of the fans supported Manchester City (reminder: 'number of Manchester City fans ÷ 500 then multiply by 100').

3 1800 people were asked if they had been in a car accident. The information is shown in the two-way table according to different age groups.

	Car accident	No car accident	Total
17 to 25	123	481	
26 to 60	65		702
over 60			
Total	286		1800

(a) Copy and complete the two-way table.

(b) *Use a calculator* to find what percentage of the people had been in a car accident.

4 200 pupils were asked what their favourite school subjects were.
53 boys chose PE and 28 chose Maths.
The only other subjects chosen were Art and Science.
28 girls chose PE.
32 pupils chose Science of which 14 were girls.
51 pupils chose Art.
How many girls chose Maths if there were 119 boys in total?
(Hint: draw a two-way table.)

5 100 people were asked what their favourite watersport was. They all chose surfing, sailing or water skiing. 5 out of 43 women chose water skiing. 46 people chose sailing and 21 men chose surfing. How many women chose sailing if 14 people chose water skiing?

6 150 students in Birmingham or Nottingham are asked if they go to school by car, bike or walk.
80 students live in Birmingham. 20% of the 45 students who walk come from Nottingham.
One quarter of the 32 students who go by bike live in Birmingham.
How many students in Nottingham go to school by car?

- Here is a scatter diagram showing the number of hours without sleep for a group of people and their reaction time.

- We can see a connection. The longer people went without sleep, the greater their reaction time (ie. people reacted more slowly as they went without sleep).

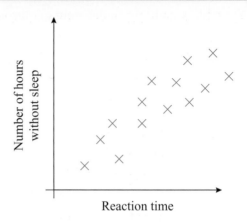

Correlation

The word 'correlation' describes how things *co-relate*. There is 'correlation' between 2 sets of data if there is a connection or relationship.

The correlation between 2 sets of data can be positive or negative and it can be strong or weak. This can be shown on scatter diagrams.

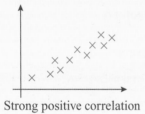
Strong positive correlation

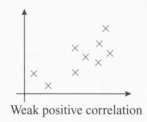
Weak positive correlation

When the points are around a line which slopes *upwards* to the right, the *correlation* is *positive* (as the values for one set of data increases, the values for the other set of data also increases).

Strong correlation – the points are bunched close to a line through their midst.

Weak correlation – the points are more scattered.

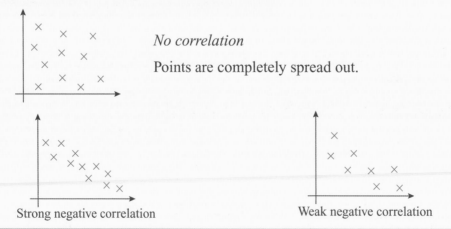

No correlation

Points are completely spread out.

Strong negative correlation

Weak negative correlation

1 The table below shows the number of days absence for fifteen year 10 pupils and their maths test results.

Number of days absent	5	9	0	1	10	7	0	5	2	9	10	2	6	8	4
Test score	7	3	10	9	2	5	9	6	8	4	3	9	6	4	7

(a) Copy and complete this scatter graph to show the data in the table (the first point (5, 7) is done for you).

(b) Describe the correlation in this scatter graph.

(c) What proportion of the test scores were 4 or less?

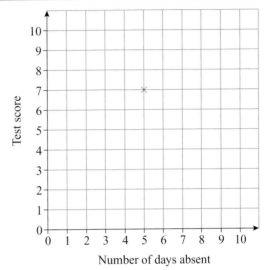

2 The table below shows the heights and weights of 12 people.

Weight (kg)	72	60	66	55	80	63	70	79	57	60	77	65
Height (cm)	175	167	177	168	184	173	180	188	171	173	178	170

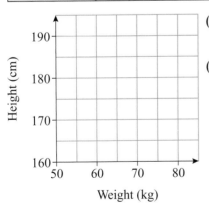

(a) Copy and complete this scatter graph to show the data in the table.

(b) Describe the correlation in this scatter graph.

3 Describe the correlation, if any, in these scatter graphs.

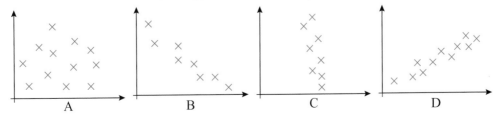

333

4 The table below shows the age and value of 12 used cars.

Age (years)	4	8	1	7	2	6	5	7	1	4	7	5
Value (£1000's)	7	2	8	3	7	2	6	5	9	5	4	4

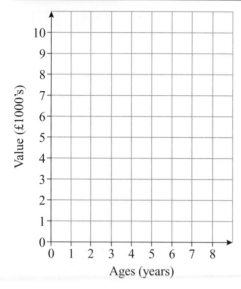

(a) Copy and complete this scatter diagram to show the data in the table.

(b) Describe the correlation in this scatter graph.

5 **Whole class activity**

(a) *If your teacher allows,* each person in your class must do as many step-ups onto a chair as possible in one minute. When a person finishes, that person must find his/her pulse rate by counting how many beats in one minute.

Also each person needs to find out his/her height (to the nearest cm) and record his/her shoe size.

Enter all the data in a table, either on the board or on a sheet of paper.

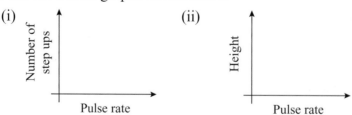

height	shoe size	number of step-ups	pulse rate

(b) Draw the scatter graphs shown below.

(i) [Scatter graph with "Number of step ups" on vertical axis and "Pulse rate" on horizontal axis]

(ii) [Scatter graph with "Height" on vertical axis and "Pulse rate" on horizontal axis]

(c) Describe the correlation, if any, in the scatter graph you drew in part (b).

(d) (i) Draw a scattergram of 2 sets of data where you think there might be positive correlation.

(ii) Was there indeed a positive correlation?

Misrepresenting data

In the following exercise you will look at some ways in which data can be misleading.

M10.8

1 The number of girls in five year 10 classes in Hatton High School is recorded.

Class	10A	10B	10C	10D	10E
Number of girls	10	13	11	9	12

A bar chart is drawn to show this information.

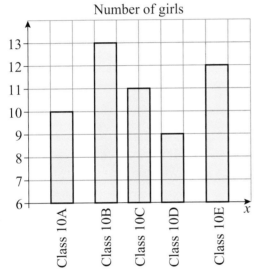

Write down 3 mistakes that have been made with this bar chart.

2 'Tel scored 1500 runs during the cricket season and Pat scored only 90 runs. Tel is the better batsman.' Why might this be misleading? Discuss.

3 '9 out of 10 dentists recommend MegaClean toothpaste.' Why might this be misleading? Discuss.

Mixed algebra

1 $v = u + at$. Find the value of v when $u = 6$, $a = 4$ and $t = 3$.

2 Expand $5(a + 3b)$

3 Solve $2x + 5 = 6$

4 Simplify $4a + 3ab - a$

5 Factorise $4n - 7mn$

6 Simplify $3(2m + 4) + 4(5m + 1)$

7 Simplify $(a^2)^4 \times a^6$

4. The bar chart opposite shows how many cards each of companies A, B and C have sold. Why is it not a good representation? Discuss.

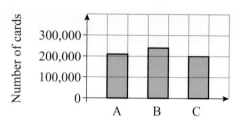

5.

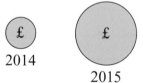

The graph opposite shows how many cups of tea are sold during a nine day period.

Give two reasons why this graph is misleading.

6. 'Shopping at the Big Deal store can save you up to £80 a month.' Why might this statement be misleading? Discuss.

7.

£ 2014

£ 2015

The diagram opposite shows that the sales for a company doubled in 2015 compared to 2014. Why is the diagram misleading? Discuss.

8.

The bar chart opposite shows the number of tickets sold for each night of a play.

Give a reason why this graph is misleading.

9 The value of Emily's house is shown opposite. Criticise the graph.

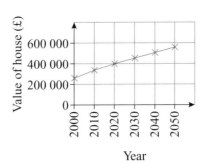

Median and mode from tables of information

The table below shows the ages of some children.

Age	7	8	9	10
Frequency	4	2	1	2

Find (a) the modal age

(b) The median age

(a) 'Frequency' is 'how many'. There are 4 ages of 7.
7 occurs the most, so the mode = 7 (modal age)

(b) The table shows
   7 7 7 7   8 8   9   10 10
   ⎵⎵⎵⎵⎵⎵   ⎵⎵   ⎵   ⎵⎵⎵
   4 lots   2 lots 1 lot 2 lots

The numbers are in order of size. The middle number is the median which is 8.

This is the 5th number in the list.

We do not want to have to write out all the numbers.

> If you have n numbers, the middle number is always at position $\dfrac{n+1}{2}$

There are 9 numbers in the list so the median is at position $\dfrac{9+1}{2} = 5$ so the 5th largest number.

M10.9

1 Some people were asked how many holidays abroad they had taken in the last 2 years. The information is shown in the table below.

Number of holidays	0	1	2	3	4
Frequency		28	37	21	12	6

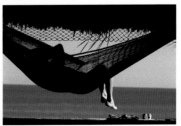

Find

(a) the modal number of holidays

(b) the median number of holidays

2 The 2 tables below show the number of visits made to the doctor during last year.

Number of visits	0	1	2	3	4
Frequency	32	29	15	9	3

14 to 21 year-olds

Number of visits	0	1	2	3	4
Frequency	8	19	42	35	31

Over 65 year-olds

(a) Find the median number of visits for *each* age group.

(b) Which age group has the higher median number of visits?

3 The table below shows the weights of some newborn babies at the local hospital.

Weight (in pounds)	4 to 6	6 to 7	8 to 9	10 or more
Frequency	26	27	31	4

Find (a) the modal interval

  (b) the interval which contains the median.

4 The tables below show the salaries earned by workers in 2 firms.

EASITECH	
Salary (£1000's)	Frequency
4 to 6	7
7 to 10	15
11 to 15	29
16 to 25	36
26 or more	12

COMPFIX PLC	
Salary (£1000's)	Frequency
4 to 6	29
7 to 10	43
11 to 15	19
16 to 25	16
26 or more	13

(a) For each firm, find the interval which contains the median.

(b) For which firm do you think people generally earn more money?
Explain why you think this.

Can you still?

Mixed shape

1  Find the size of B$\hat{D}$C. Give reasons for your answer.

2 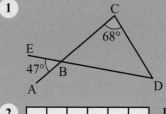 Draw a different rectangle which has the same area as this rectangle.

3 Which shapes below have rotational symmetry of order 2 – square, kite, parallelogram?

4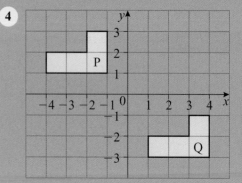

Describe fully how shape P is transformed into shape Q.

5 This table shows how many goals were scored by the football teams in the Premiership one season.

Number of goals	Frequency
20 to 29	1
30 to 39	2
40 to 49	8
50 to 59	4
60 to 69	3
69 to 70	2

Find (a) the modal interval

(b) the interval which contains the median.

Mean averages from tables of information

Some students are asked how many pairs of shoes they have. The table shows the information.

Find the mean average.

Number of pairs of shoes	Frequency
1	5
2	3
3	3
4	5
5	4

$$\text{mean average} = \frac{\text{total number of pairs of shoes}}{\text{total number of people}}$$

total number of pairs of shoes

$= (5 \times 1) + (3 \times 2) + (3 \times 3) + (4 \times 5) + (4 \times 5)$

$= 5 + 6 + 9 + 20 + 20 = 60$

total number of people = total frequency $= 5 + 3 + 3 + 5 + 4 = 20$

so mean average $= \dfrac{60}{20} = 3$ pairs of shoes.

M10.10

Use a calculator if you need to.

1 This table shows the number of cars owned by people who live in Beech Grove.

Number of cars	Frequency
0	1
1	4
2	4
3	6

(a) Find the total number of cars.

(b) Find the mean average.

2 Some people were asked how many portions of fruit and vegetables they ate each day.

The information is shown in the table below.

Number of portions	0	1	2	3	4	5	6	7
Frequency	17	20	16	28	11	4	3	1

(a) Find the total number of portions eaten.

(b) Find the mean average.

3 Three different hotels are rated by guests using a points score out of 20. The scores are shown in the table below.

HOTEL PARADISE		HOTEL DE VERE		TROPIC HOTEL	
Score	Frequency	Score	Frequency	Score	Frequency
14	21	14	31	14	86
15	38	15	21	15	91
16	33	16	49	16	33
17	49	17	42	17	75
18	17	18	21	18	61
19	24	19	17	19	47
20	6	20	9	20	18

(a) Work out the mean average for each hotel, giving your answers to 2 decimal places.

(b) Which hotel had the highest points score?

4

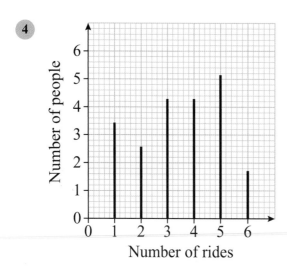

A group of young people visited Alton Towers theme park. The number of major rides they had is shown in the chart opposite.

(a) Work out the mean average number of rides for this group of people.

(b) Which number of rides is the mode?

Mixed algebra

1. Write down the next two numbers in the sequence 5, 2, −1, −4, …
2. Draw the graph of $y = 3x − 1$.
3. Make x the subject of the formula $y = 4x + 3$.
4. Find the nth term formula for the sequence 7, 12, 17, 22, …
5. Complete the table then draw the curve $y = x^2 − 4$.

x	−3	−2	−1	0	1	2	3
y							

Mean averages for grouped data

Some Year 11 students take a Maths test. The table shows their marks.

Estimate the mean average test mark.

We need to find the total number of marks.

The problem is we do not know exactly how many marks each person has.

Number of Marks	Frequency
0–9	28
10–19	18
20–29	33
30–39	21

We will get a reasonable answer if we take the mid-value of each interval and assume that is how many marks each person has.

To find the mid-value of an interval, add the first and last values then halve the answer.

For the 10–19 interval,

mid-value $= \dfrac{10 + 19}{2} = 14\cdot5$

Number of Marks	Frequency	Mid-value
0–9	28	4·5
10–19	18	14·5
20–29	33	24·5
30–39	21	34·5

We now use the mid-value and the frequency to find the total number of marks.

Mean average $= \dfrac{(28 \times 4\cdot5) + (18 \times 14\cdot5) + (33 \times 24\cdot5) + (21 \times 34\cdot5)}{28 + 18 + 33 + 21}$

Mean average $= \dfrac{1920}{100} = 19\cdot2$

This is an *estimate* because we used the mid-values not the exact number of marks.

Note

Sometimes the interval 10–19 might be written as $10 \leqslant n \leqslant 19$ where n is the number of marks. ($n \leqslant 19$ means n is less than or equal to 19).

1

Number of trips abroad	Frequency	Mid-value
0–2	6	
3–5	8	
6–10	5	8
11–15	1	

Some teenagers were asked how often they had been abroad in their lifetime. The information is shown in the table.

(a) Copy and complete the table.

(b) Estimate the total number of trips abroad.

(c) Estimate the mean average.

2 The table below shows how many days off work were taken by staff at a hospital during the last year.

Number of days off work	0 to 9	10 to 19	20 to 29	30 or 39	40 or 59
Frequency	88	57	31	18	6
Mid-value					

(a) Copy and complete the table.

(b) Estimate the total number of days off work.

(c) Estimate the mean average.

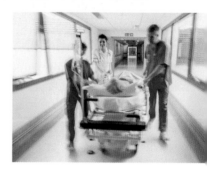

3 The tables below show the salaries earned by people in 2 different firms.

JETBUILD	
Salary(s) (£1000's)	Frequency
$4 \leqslant s < 6$	6
$6 \leqslant s < 10$	15
$10 \leqslant s < 15$	18
$15 \leqslant s < 25$	8
$25 \leqslant s < 70$	3

KABINSEAL	
Salary(s) (£1000's)	Frequency
$4 \leqslant s < 6$	8
$6 \leqslant s < 10$	21
$10 \leqslant s < 15$	24
$15 \leqslant s < 25$	17
$25 \leqslant s < 70$	5

(a) Which firm offers the higher mean average salary?

(b) Write down an estimate of this mean average salary.

4 The table below shows how many DVDs were owned by 250 families.

Number of DVD's (n)	$0 \leqslant n < 10$	$10 \leqslant n < 20$	$20 \leqslant n < 30$	$30 \leqslant n < 40$	$40 \leqslant n < 50$	$50 \leqslant n < 60$
Frequency	21	23	91	74	32	9
Mid-value						

(a) Estimate the total number of DVD's.

(b) Estimate the mean average.

5 The table below shows how many hours of TV were watched by 500 people last week.

Hours of TV (h)	$0 \leqslant h < 10$	$10 \leqslant h < 20$	$20 \leqslant h < 35$	$35 \leqslant h < 50$	$50 \leqslant h < 60$	$60 \leqslant h < 80$
Frequency	83	112	155	102	36	12

Estimate the mean average number of hours of TV watched.

6

Number of lengths swum (n)	Frequency
0 to 20	25
21 to 30	65
31 to 40	32
41 to 60	46
61 to 80	24
81 to 100	8

200 people took part in a sponsored swim. The table shows how many lengths they swam.

Estimate the mean number of lengths swum.

Can you still?

Speed, distance, time and metric units

1 A car travels 70 miles in $1\frac{1}{4}$ hours. What is the car's average speed?

2 Tom's watch is 5 minutes slow. It takes him 22 minutes to walk to school which starts at 08:45. At what time by his watch must he leave for school if he is to arrive there exactly on time?

3 Change 16 m/s into km/h.

4 Olivia wants to fill 6 glasses with 270 ml lemonade each and 3 glasses with 350 ml lemonade each. She has 2·5 litres of lemonade. Is this enough? Explain your answer fully.

Key Facts

To compare 2 sets of data, always write at least 2 things:

1. Compare an *average* (i.e. mean, median or mode).

2. Compare the *range* of each set of data (this shows how spread out the data is).

Six members of the Harris family weigh 40 kg, 53 kg, 71 kg, 75 kg, 79 kg and 90 kg.

Five members of the Collins family weigh 61 kg, 62 kg, 84 kg, 86 kg and 87 kg.

Harris family: median = 73 kg (half way between 71 kg and 75 kg)
                 range = 90 − 40 = 50 kg

Collins family: median = 84 kg
                 range = 87 − 61 = 26 kg.

Compare the weights of the Harris family and the Collins family.

Answer

The *median* for the Harris family is less than the median for the Collins family but the *range* for the Harris family is greater than the range for the Collins family (i.e. the weights are more spread out).

M10.12

1   7 members of the Truman family weigh 46 kg, 51 kg, 52 kg, 67 kg, 74 kg, 79 kg and 82 kg.

4 members of the Jenkins family weigh 42 kg, 68 kg, 70 kg and 86 kg.

Copy and complete the statements below to compare the weights of the Truman family and the Jenkins family.

Truman family: median = _____ kg   range = _____ kg

Jenkins family: median = _____ kg   range = _____ kg

'The median for the Truman family is (*greater/smaller*) than the median for the Jenkins family and the range for the Truman family is (*greater/smaller*) than the range for the Jenkins family (i.e. weights for the Truman family are (*more/less*) spread out).'

2 Some 16 year-olds and 17 year-olds are asked how much they earn per hour in their part-time jobs. The information is shown below.

16 year-olds:			
£5	£4·50	£4·30	£4·80
£5·20	£5·75	£6·10	£5·15
£4·70	£4·60		

17 year-olds:			
£4·90	£5·30	£5	£5·25
£4·95	£6·20	£5·06	£5·50

Copy and complete the statements below to compare the hourly rate of pay for these 16 year-olds and 17 year-olds.

16 year-olds: mean = £ _____   range = £ _____

17 year-olds: mean = £ _____   range = £ _____

'The mean for the 16 year-olds is (*greater*/*smaller*) than the mean for the 17 year-olds and the range for the 16 year-olds is (*greater*/*smaller*) than the range for the 17 year-olds (i.e. the hourly rate of pay for the 16 year-olds is (*more*/*less*) spread out).'

Can you still?

Prisms

1 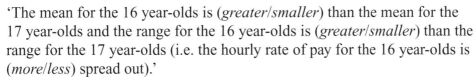 Calculate the volume of this prism.

5 cm
8 cm
15 cm
15 cm

2 A cylinder has volume 63 cm³ and a length of 9 cm. What is the area of the circular cross section?

3 Calculate the total surface area of this prism.

25 cm
24 cm
20 cm
7 cm

3 The Wolves and the Sentinels are 2 basketball teams. The ages (in years) of the players in each team are listed below:

The Wolves:	23	18	19	25	20
	27	23	22	20	26
The Sentinels:	22	28	19	27	21
	21	29	21	25	22

Copy and complete the statements below to compare the ages of the players for the Wolves and the Sentinels.

The Wolves: median = _____   range = _____

The Sentinels: median = _____   range = _____

'The median for the Wolves is (*greater*/*smaller*) than the median for the Sentinels and the range for the Wolves is (*greater*/*smaller*) than the range for the Sentinels (i.e. the ages for the Wolves are (*more*/*less*) spread out).'

345

1 The marks obtained by 2 classes in a maths test are shown in the back-to-back stem and leaf diagram.

Class 10A		Class 10B
9 6	4	3 3 7 8
7 7 7 3 2	5	0 1 4 6 6 6 8
9 9 8 8 4 1	6	2 5 5 8 9
6 6 5 2	7	4 5 7 7 9 9
8 7 4 0	8	1 3 6
1 1	9	2 4

Key 4|6 = 64   Key 6|5 = 65

(a) Find the median and range for each class.

(b) Write a sentence to compare the test marks for the two classes.

2 Ten students from Year 10 and ten students from Year 11 were asked how often they had their hair cut each year. The information is shown below:

Year 10

Year 11

(a) Work out the mean and range for Year 10.

(b) Work out the mean and range for Year 11.

(c) Write a sentence to compare the number of hair cuts for the students in Year 10 and Year 11.

3 The scatter graph shows the weights and heights of some boys. A group of girls has a mean weight of 68 kg and a range for weights of 52 kg. Write a statement to compare the weights of the boys with the weights of the girls.

4 The tables below show how many televisions are owned by families living in 2 streets.

Ash Lane	
Number of TVs	Frequency
0	3
1	5
2	7
3	4
4	1

Tibbs Drive	
Number of TVs	Frequency
0	1
1	2
2	4
3	1
4	2

(a) Work out the mean and range for Ash Lane.

(b) Compare the number of televisions owned by families in Ash Lane and Tibbs Drive.

5 The scattergraph shows the ages of members of Climbing Team A and the number of climbs they have done so far this year.

The vertical line graph shows the number of climbs so far this year which have been made by members of Climbing Team B.

Compare the number of climbs made by members of Team A and Team B.

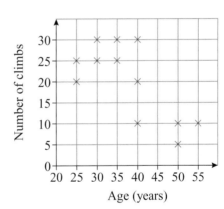

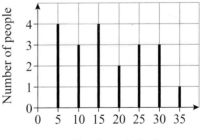

Alex and Kate own 9 dogs. They have worked out that it costs about £50 each per week to deal with the dogs.

Use all the information provided to find out if Alex and Kate are correct. Make sure you show all your working out.

The dogs		
Breed	Age (years)	Weight (kg)
Scottish Terrier	3	9·1
Chihuahua	7	2·7
Labrador	6	29·5
Springer Spaniel	2	19·1
Beagle	2	15·9
Yorkshire Terrier	3	3·6
Labrador	11	31·8
Great Dane	6	50·9
Golden Retriever	9	31·4

Each dog must have a booster once each year which costs £32.

Each dog must be wormed and have flea drops which costs £11·45 each month.

Alex and Kate insure each dog against unexpected illness or injury. The total cost for all the dogs is £76 each month.

The dogs are fed either with dry food only or with dry food mixed with can food.

The amount of food given each day depends on the weight of the dog as shown in the table below.

Weight of dog (kg)	Dry food	Dry food mixed with can food
Up to 4·5	$\frac{1}{2}$ cup	$\frac{1}{4}$ can and $\frac{1}{2}$ cup
4·5 to 11	2 cups	$\frac{1}{2}$ can and $1\frac{1}{4}$ cups
11 to 23	$3\frac{1}{2}$ cups	1 can and 2 cups
23 to 34	$4\frac{1}{2}$ cups	$1\frac{1}{2}$ cans and 3 cups
Over 34	8 cups	2 cans and 5 cups

The Scottish Terrier, Yorkshire Terrier, Chihuahua, Beagle and Great Dane each have dry food only. The other four dogs have dry food mixed with can food.

The costs of the food are:

packet of dry food £4·50

(36 cups)

can food 42p

TEST YOURSELF ON UNIT 10

1. Finding the mean, median, mode and range for sets of numbers

(a) 9, 7, 3, 7, 4, 8, 2, 7, 1, 6, 1

For the set of numbers above, find the (i) mode (ii) median (iii) mean (iv) range

(b) 8, 6, 5, 9, 8, 6

For the set of numbers above, which is larger – the mean or the median?

2. Using charts and graphs

The chart below shows the percentage of people in the USA who are obese (*very* overweight).

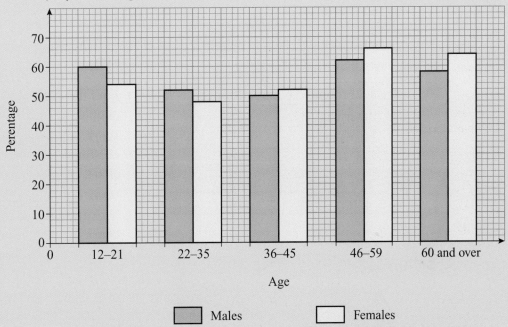

(a) In which age groups were the percentage of obese males greater than the percentage of obese females?

(b) What percentage of 46–59 year-old females are obese?

(c) What percentage of 22–35 year-old males are obese?

(d) What is the *difference* in the percentage of 46–59 year-old obese females compared to 46–59 year-old obese males?

349

3. Using stem and leaf diagrams

The ages of 25 people who work for a local newspaper are recorded below.

31	42	27	50	21
26	19	19	62	35
32	23	53	27	46
48	43	28	53	58
37	51	36	47	20

(a) Draw an ordered stem and leaf diagram to show this data.

(b) What is the median age?

(c) Find the range of the ages.

4. Using pie charts

(a) In a list of the richest people in a country, their backgrounds are listed below.

Background	Number of people
inherited	15
business	28
music	20
sport	17
other	10

(i) Find the total number of people.

(ii) Work out the angle for each person to help draw a pie chart.

(iii) Work out the angle for each background and draw a pie chart.

(b)

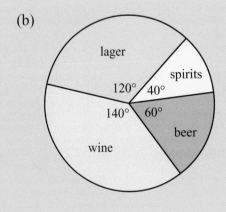

108 people were asked what their favourite drink is. The results are shown in the pie chart. How many people said:

(i) beer

(ii) lager

(iii) spirits

(iv) wine?

5. Using two-way tables

120 people went on holiday to Australia, India or the USA.
32 out of the 71 females went to India.
47 people went to Australia of which 24 were male.
33 people went to the USA.

(a) One of these people is picked at random. Write down the *probability* that the person has chosen India.

(b) *Use a calculator* to work out what percentage of the people who went to the USA were male?

6. Drawing scatter diagrams and describing correlation

Describe the correlation, if any, in these scatter graphs.

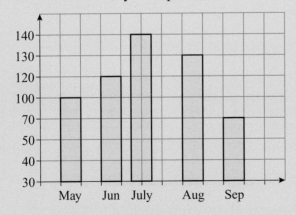

(a) (b) (c)

7. Recognising misrepresentation of data

The bar chart below shows the number of guests who stay in a hotel in the months of May to September.

Write down *at least* 3 mistakes on this bar chart.

8. Finding the median and mode from tables of information

Some 16 year-olds were asked how many dental fillings they had been given during their lifetimes. The table shows the information.

Number of fillings	0	1	2	3	4	5
Frequency	12	17	24	18	7	3

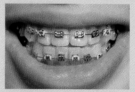

Find (a) the modal number of fillings

(b) the median number of fillings

9. Finding mean averages from tables of information (including grouped data)

The table below shows how many hours were spent using a computer by 200 people last week.

Hours using a computer (h)	$0 \leqslant h < 5$	$5 \leqslant h < 10$	$10 \leqslant h < 20$	$20 \leqslant h < 30$	$30 \leqslant h < 40$	$40 \leqslant h < 60$
Frequency	49	68	36	23	17	7

Estimate the mean number of hours spent using a computer.

10. Comparing sets of data

30 young people were asked how many cards they received on their last birthday (10 nine year-olds and 20 nineteen year-olds). The information is shown below:

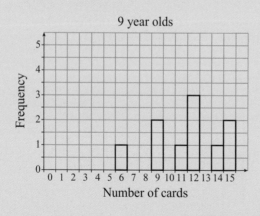

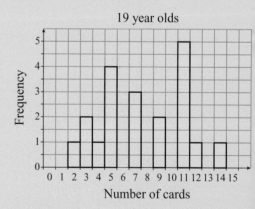

(a) Work out the mean and range for the 9 year-olds.

(b) Compare the number of birthday cards received by 9 year-olds and 19 year-olds.

Mixed examination questions

1 A rugby team played six games.

Here is the number of points they scored in each game.

    24   8   18   6   12   19

(a) Work out the median score for these six games.

(b) Work out the mean score for these six games.

The rugby team played one more game.
The mean score for all seven games is 16

(c) Work out the number of points the team scored in the seventh game.

(EDEXCEL)

2 Every Friday for 6 weeks, the number of customers entering a sandwich shop and the takings of the shop were recorded.
The takings were recorded correct to the nearest £10.
The table below shows the results.

Number of customers	104	82	120	64	70	118
Takings, in £	510	420	590	320	340	560

(a) Draw a scatter diagram of these results.

(b) Write down the type of correlation that is shown by the scatter diagram.

(WJEC)

3 Caroline and Marc are in a darts team.

The pie charts show information about the number of games Caroline and Marc each won last year.
They also show information about the number of games Caroline and Marc each lost last year.

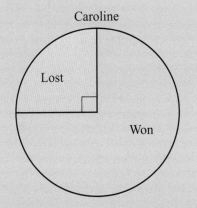
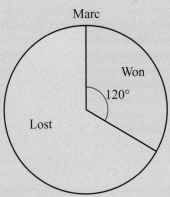

Caroline played 52 games. Marc played 150 games.
Marc won more games than Caroline.
How many more?

(EDEXCEL)

4 Lizzie and Megan are competing to swim for the school team in the 50 m freestyle. They both complete some trial swims and record their times.

Lizzie swims 5 trials and these are her times (in seconds).

   26·3   26·2   26·7   26·3   26·5

Megan swims 6 trials and these are her times (in seconds).

   26·5   26·7   26·1   26·3   26·9   26·5

Who should the girls' teacher select?
State clearly the figures that you use for your calculations.   (OCR)

5 One morning Sam records the number of people in each car passing his house. Here are his results.

Number of people in a car	Frequency	
1	26	
2	38	
3	24	
4	16	
5	8	

Calculate the mean number of people in the cars passing Sam's house. (OCR)

6 Seven **single digit numbers** have a median of 6 and a range of 8.
The mode of the seven numbers is 3.
Find the seven numbers.
Write your single digit numbers in order in the boxes.

[ ] [ ] [ ] [ ] [ ] [ ] [ ]   (WJEC)

7 Here is a pictogram.
It shows the number of boxes of chocolates Mr Fenn sold last week from Monday to Friday.

What fraction of the total number of these boxes of chocolates did Mr Fenn sell on Tuesday?   (EDEXCEL)

354

8 80 patients give information about how long they waited to see the doctor.

Time, T (minutes)	Frequency		
$0 \leqslant T < 10$	5		
$10 \leqslant T < 20$	22		
$20 \leqslant T < 30$	28		
$30 \leqslant T < 40$	21		
$40 \leqslant T < 50$	4		

(a) Work out an estimate of the mean time that the patients waited.

(b) The doctor says, "70% of our patients wait less than 30 minutes to be seen."

   Is she correct?

   You **must** show your working.   (AQA)

9 The table shows the number of different types of birds on a lake.

BIRD	TERNS	WADERS	GEESE	DUCKS	SWANS
NUMBER	50	20	30	10	10
ANGLE					

Draw a clearly labelled pie chart to show the number of different types of birds.   (CEA)

10 Kitty and George sell cars.

The table shows the numbers of cars sold by Kitty and by George in the first four months of 2013

	January	February	March	April
Kitty	2	5	13	10
George	4	7	9	10

Show this information in a suitable diagram.   (EDEXCEL)

11 The number of letters delivered to the houses in a street were recorded in this frequency table.

Number of letters	Frequency
1	9
2	4
3	7
4	5
5	1
6	3

(a) Write down the modal number of letters delivered.

(b) Write down the range of the number of letters delivered.

(c) How many houses are there in the street?   (CEA)

GEOMETRY 3

In this unit you will learn how to:
- measure lengths and angles
- construct triangles
- make scale drawings
- draw nets
- draw 3-D objects
- interpret plans and elevations
- use map scales
- use bearings
- solve problems with shapes and lines using co-ordinates
- (USE YOUR MATHS!) – car insurance

Measuring lengths and angles

M11.1

1. Read the measurements shown on the ruler.

Measure these lines to the nearest tenth of a centimetre.

2.

3.

4 Measure the perimeter of each shape below to the nearest tenth of a centimetre.

(a) 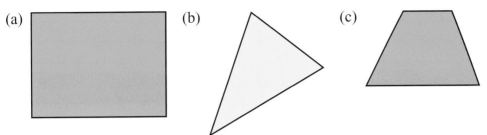 (b) (c)

Using a protractor, measure the following angles.

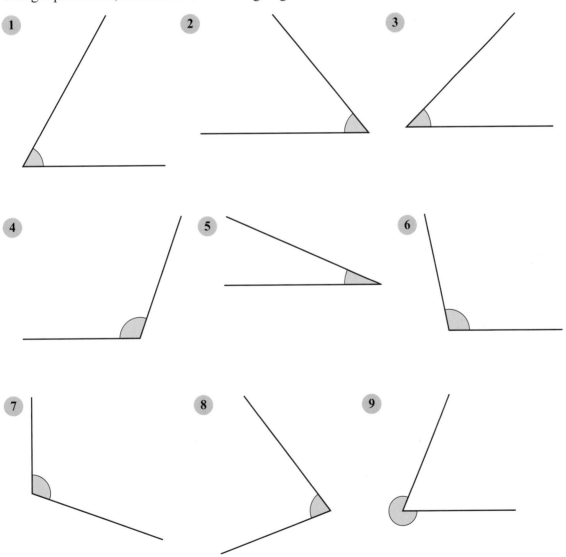

1

2

3

4

5

6

7

8

9

10 Use a protractor to draw the following angles. Label each angle acute, obtuse or reflex.

    (a) 70°   (b) 25°   (c) 54°   (d) 31°

    (e) 165°   (f) 108°   (g) 172°   (h) 15°

    (i) 310°   (j) 230°   (k) 126°   (l) 283°

Constructing triangles

M11.3

The questions below deal with triangles where 2 sides and an angle are known or 2 angles and a side are known.

Use a ruler and protractor to draw:

1

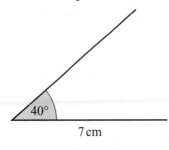

2

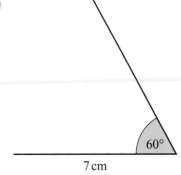

Now draw both of these on the same diagram like below:

3

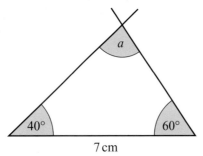

Measure angle a. It should be 80°.

4 Use a ruler and protractor to draw:

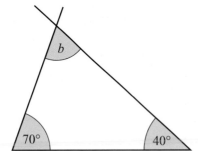

Measure and write down angle b.

5 Draw accurately:

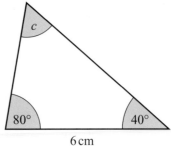

Measure and write down angle c.

6 Use a ruler and protractor to draw:

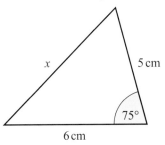

Measure the length of the side marked x.

In questions **7** to **11**, construct the triangles and measure the lengths of the sides marked x.

7

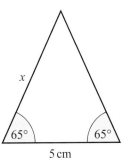

8

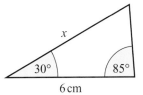

9

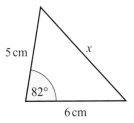

10

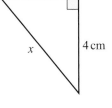

11

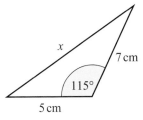

Can you still?

Mixed Shape Work

1

(a) Copy the diagram above.

(b) Reflect △P in the line $y = 1$. Label the image Q.

(c) Rotate △P 90° anticlockwise about (0, 0). Label the image R.

(d) Translate △P with $\begin{pmatrix} -4 \\ -3 \end{pmatrix}$. Label the image S.

2

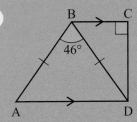

BC is parallel to AD. ABD is an isosceles triangle. Calculate BD̂C. Give reasons for your answer.

3 Draw any shape with order of rotational symmetry 3.

4 The exterior angle of a regular polygon is 36°. How many sides does the polygon have?

If we know all 3 sides, a triangle can be drawn with a ruler and a pair of compasses only.

Draw accurately

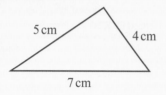

(a) Draw one side with a ruler.

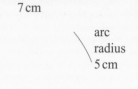

7 cm

(b) Set your pair of compasses to 5 cm. Put the point of the pair of compasses on one end of the line and draw an arc of radius 5 cm.

arc
radius
5 cm

7 cm

(c) Set your pair of compasses to 4 cm. Put the point of the pair of compasses on the other end of the line and draw an arc of radius 4 cm.

Join the point where the 2 arcs cross to each end of the 7 cm line to make a *perfect* triangle.

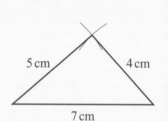

M11.4

In questions **1** to **3**, use a ruler and compasses only to draw each triangle.
Use a protractor to measure each angle *x*.

1
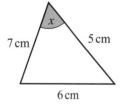

2
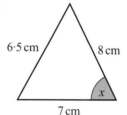

3
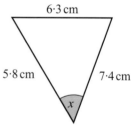

4 Construct an equilateral triangle with each side equal to 6 cm.
Measure the angles to check that each one is 60°.

5
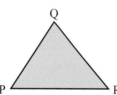

Draw a triangle PQR, where PR = 7·5 cm, QP̂R = 55° and PQ = 5 cm.

Measure the length of QR.

6 Draw a triangle XYZ, where XY = 4·8 cm, YZ = 6·1 cm and XZ = 7 cm.
Measure XŶZ, YẐX and ZX̂Y.

7
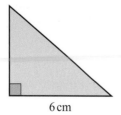

Construct a triangle with base 6 cm and area 12 cm².

360

8 Construct any triangle which has area 20 cm² and a base length which is a prime number. Write the base length clearly on your diagram.

Draw accurately the diagrams in questions **9** to **12**.

9

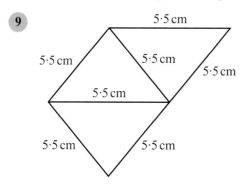

10

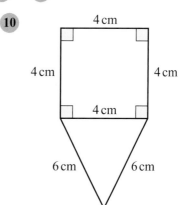

11

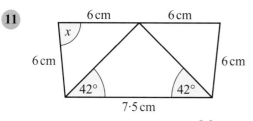

Measure *x*.

12

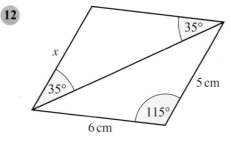

Measure *x*.

Scale drawings

M11.5

Draw an accurate scale drawing of each shape below using the scale shown.

1

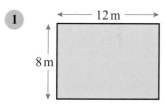

Scale: 1 cm for every 4 m

2

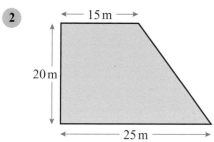

Scale: 1 cm for every 5 m.

3

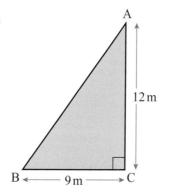

Scale: 1 cm for every 3 m. Measure (in cm) then write down the actual length of AB (in m).

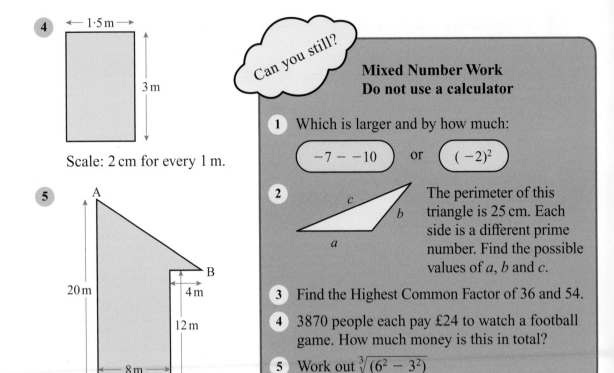

4

← 1·5 m →

3 m

Scale: 2 cm for every 1 m.

5

A

20 m

4 m

12 m

8 m

4 m

B

Scale: 1 cm for every 4 m.
Measure in cm the length of AB.

Can you still?

Mixed Number Work
Do not use a calculator

1 Which is larger and by how much:

$-7 - -10$ or $(-2)^2$

2 *c*   *b*   *a*   The perimeter of this triangle is 25 cm. Each side is a different prime number. Find the possible values of *a*, *b* and *c*.

3 Find the Highest Common Factor of 36 and 54.

4 3870 people each pay £24 to watch a football game. How much money is this in total?

5 Work out $\sqrt[3]{(6^2 - 3^2)}$

Nets

Key Facts

A shape which folds up to make a solid is called a *net*.

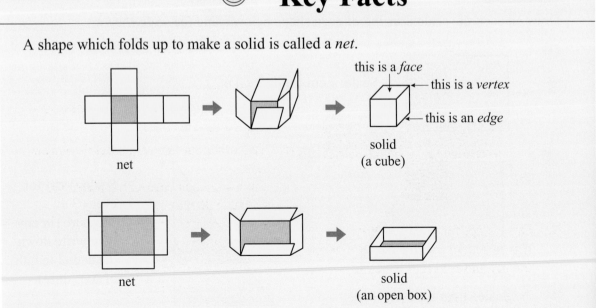

this is a *face*

this is a *vertex*

this is an *edge*

net

solid
(a cube)

net

solid
(an open box)

1

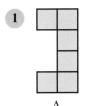 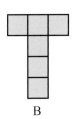 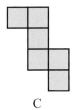 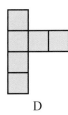 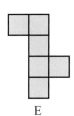

A   B   C   D   E

Which of these nets will fold to make a cube?
If your teacher wants you to, draw the nets on squared paper, cut them out
and fold them to see which ones do make cubes.

2   Draw an accurate *net* for this cube.

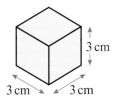

3

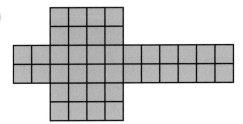

This net makes a cuboid.
Each small square is 1 cm long.
(a) How long will the cuboid be?
(b) How wide will it be?
(c) How high will it be?
(d) What is the volume of the cuboid?

4

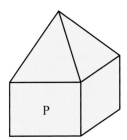

How many more edges
does solid P have
than solid Q?

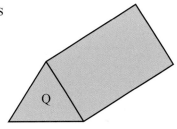

5

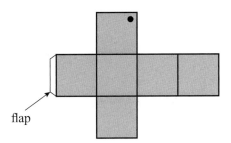

flap

(a) Sketch this net.
(b) Which edge will the flap be stuck to?
    Put a ✓ on this edge.
(c) Two other corners will meet the corner
    with a •
    Put a • in each corner that meets the
    corner with a •

6   Draw a net for this *open* box.
If your teacher wants you to, cut out
the net and fold it to check it is right.

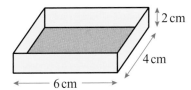

7   Draw any solid which has
10 *vertices* only.

8 The dots on opposite faces of a die add up to seven. There must be 4 dots on the bottom of this die.

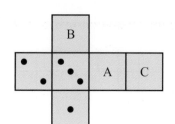 This is a net of a die. How many dots are on faces A, B and C?

9 Which of the nets below will make a closed box?

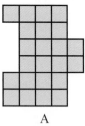

A

B

Can you still?

Mixed Algebra Work

1 Simplify $6ab + 3ab - 7ab$

2 Solve $4(n - 2) = 20$

3

Write down an expression for
(i) the perimeter of the rectangle
(ii) the area of the rectangle

4 Henry has £n. Izzy has £7 less than Henry. Sonny has three times more money than Izzy. Write down an expression for how much money Sonny has.

5 Factorise (i) $3a + 12$ (ii) $6a^2 - 10ab$

E11.1

1 This diagram shows the net of a solid.
  (a) Use *compasses* and a *ruler* to draw the net accurately on paper or card.
  (b) Draw on some flaps.
  (c) Cut out the net, fold and glue it to make the solid.
  (d) What is the name of the solid?

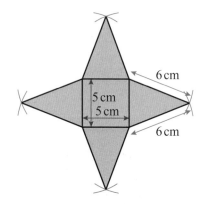

2 The diagram shows a triangular prism.

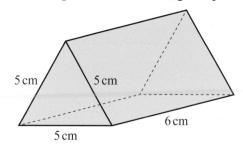

  (a) Use *compasses* and a *ruler* to construct the net for this prism on paper or card.
  (b) Draw on some flaps.
  (c) Cut out the net, fold and glue it to make the solid.

3 Here is another triangular prism (a wedge).

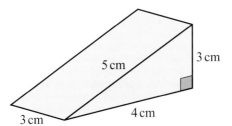

(a) Use *compasses* and a *ruler* to construct the net for this prism on paper or card.

(b) Draw on some flaps.

(c) Cut out the net, fold and glue it to make the solid.

4 Draw an *accurate net* for this square-based pyramid.

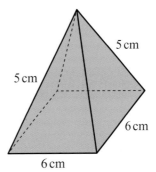

3-D objects

M11.7

You will need isometric dot paper.

1

Here is a cube made from eight 1 cm cubes.

Draw a cuboid with a volume of 18 cm³.

2 Draw a cuboid with a volume of 20 cm³.

3 Make a copy of each object below. For each drawing state the number of 'multilink' cubes needed to make the object.

(a)

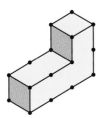

(b)

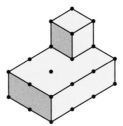

4

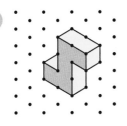

This shape falls over onto the shaded face.

Draw the shape after it has fallen over.

5 Using four cubes, you can make several different shapes. A and B are different shapes but C is the same as A.

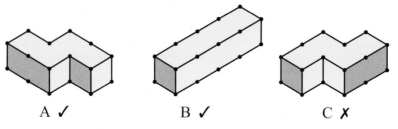

A ✓   B ✓   C ✗

Make as many *different* shapes as possible, using four cubes, and draw them all (including shapes A and B above) on isometric paper.

Plans and elevations

Key Facts

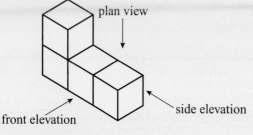

Here is a 3-D object made from centimetre cubes.

A plan view is when the object is looked at from above.

plan view

A front elevation is when the object is viewed from the front.

front elevation

A side elevation is when the object is viewed from the side.

side elevation

M11.8

1

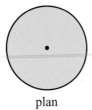

plan

elevation

Name the solid with the plan and elevation shown opposite.

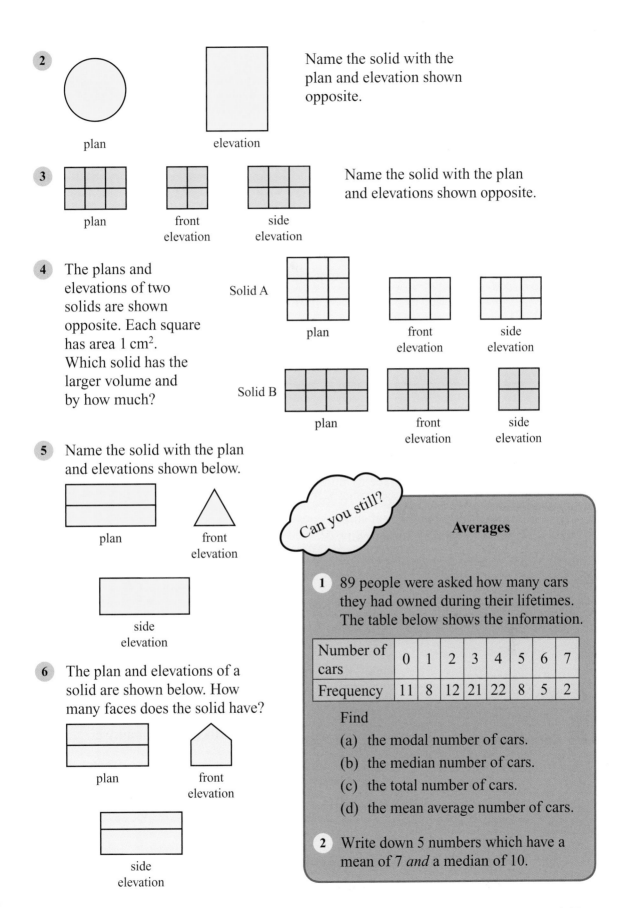

2 Name the solid with the plan and elevation shown opposite.

plan

elevation

3 Name the solid with the plan and elevations shown opposite.

plan

front elevation

side elevation

4 The plans and elevations of two solids are shown opposite. Each square has area 1 cm². Which solid has the larger volume and by how much?

Solid A

plan

front elevation

side elevation

Solid B

plan

front elevation

side elevation

5 Name the solid with the plan and elevations shown below.

plan

front elevation

side elevation

6 The plan and elevations of a solid are shown below. How many faces does the solid have?

plan

front elevation

side elevation

Can you still?

Averages

1 89 people were asked how many cars they had owned during their lifetimes. The table below shows the information.

Number of cars	0	1	2	3	4	5	6	7
Frequency	11	8	12	21	22	8	5	2

Find

(a) the modal number of cars.

(b) the median number of cars.

(c) the total number of cars.

(d) the mean average number of cars.

2 Write down 5 numbers which have a mean of 7 *and* a median of 10.

On a map of scale 1 : 3000 000 cm, Leeds and Manchester are 2 cm apart. What is the actual distance between the cities?

1 cm on map   = 3000 000 cm for real

2 cm on map   = 2 × 3000 000 cm for real

                = 6000 000 cm   (÷100 to change cm into m)

                = 60000 m   (÷1000 to change m into km)

                = 60 km

The actual distance between Leeds and Manchester is 60 km.

M11.9

You may use a calculator.

1   A model of a ship is made using a scale of 1 : 50. The model is 16 cm long. How long is the real ship? (Give your answer in metres.)

2

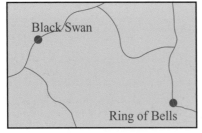

Scale is 1:50000

Measure the shortest distance between the Black Swan and the Ring of Bells (give your answer in km).

3   Two towns are 3 cm apart on a map whose scale is 1 : 5000 000. Find the actual distance (in km) between the two towns.

4 A lake is 5 cm long on a map whose scale is 1 : 50 000. Find the actual length (in km) of the lake.

5 Copy and complete the table below.

Map length	Scale	Real length
6 cm	1 : 80	m
4 cm	1 : 5000	m
9 cm	1 : 200 000	km
cm	1 : 2000	160 m
cm	1 : 3000 000	120 km
cm	1 : 1000 000	35 km

6 The length of part of a railway track is 18 km. How long will it be on a map of scale 1 : 200 000?

7

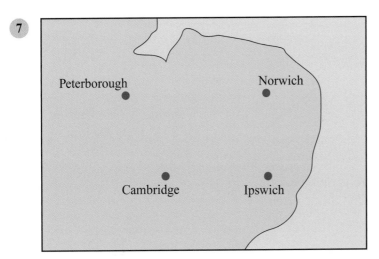

Scale is 1:3000 000

Measure then write down the actual distances (in km) between:

(a) Norwich and Ipswich

(b) Peterborough and Norwich

(c) Cambridge and Ipswich

8 The distance between two cities is 110 km. How far apart will they be on a map of scale 1 : 2000 000?

9 The length of a house is 8·4 m. A plan of the house is drawn using a scale of 1 : 70. How long will the house be on the plan?

Key Facts

Bearings are used by navigators on ships and aircraft and by people travelling in open country.

> Bearings are measured from the *North* line in a *clockwise* direction.
> A bearing is always given as a *three-figure number*.

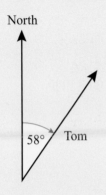

Tom is walking on
a bearing of 058°.

↑

3-figures used

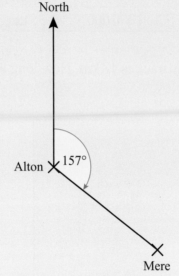

Mere is on a bearing
of 157° from *Alton*.

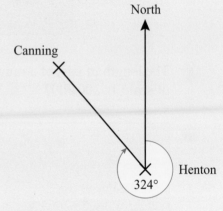

Canning is on a bearing
of 324° from *Henton*.

M11.10

1

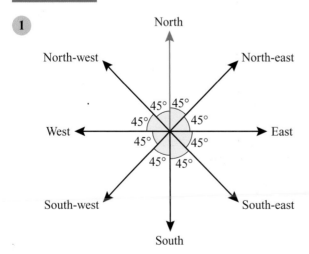

Write down the bearing for each
compass direction below:

(a) East

(b) South-east

(c) West

(d) North-east

(e) South-west

(f) North-west

(g) South

(h) North

2 Peter hits 6 golf balls, aiming north, with his usual precision. The golf balls travel in the directions shown. On what bearing does each golf ball fly?

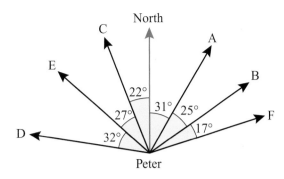

3

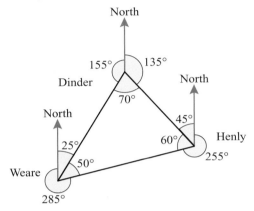

Write down the bearing of:

(a) Henly *from Dinder*

(b) Dinder *from Weare*

(c) Weare *from Dinder*

(d) Weare *from Henly*

(e) Dinder *from Henly*

(f) Henly *from Weare*

4 Seven travellers head off from camp on their search for the 'meaning of life'. They begin walking in the directions shown. On what bearing is each traveller walking?

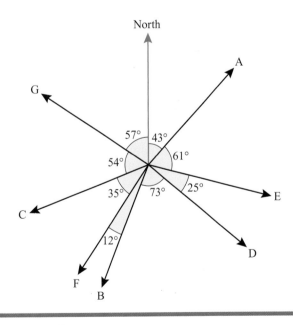

---

1 North

Copy a point to show Alan's position as shown opposite.
Bevan is 300 m from Alan on a bearing of 125°.
Draw Bevan's position using a scale of 1 cm for every 50 m.

•
Alan

2

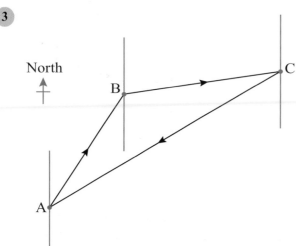

Use a protractor to measure the bearing of:

(a) Carling *from Pinton*

(b) Otley *from Carling*

(c) Pinton *from Otley*

(d) Carling *from Otley*

3

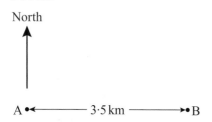

A hiker walks from A to B then B to C and finally from C to A.

Use a protractor to measure the bearing of the walk from

(a) *A to B*

(b) *B to C*

(c) *C to A*

4 Draw two points A and B which are 3·5 km apart as shown below. Use a scale where 1 cm represents 500 m.

North

A •◄——— 3·5 km ———►• B

A hang glider is on a bearing of 035° from A and on a bearing of 295° from B.

(a) Draw the position of the hang glider.

(b) How far is the hang glider from B at this moment?

(c) Write down the bearing of B *from* the hang glider.

5 Yasmin goes on a sponsored walk. Her route is shown opposite.

Work out the bearing of the journey from:

(a) Start to Jam Hill

(b) Jam Hill to Pilling Mount

(c) Pilling Mount to the White Swan.

(d) The White Swan back to the Finish.

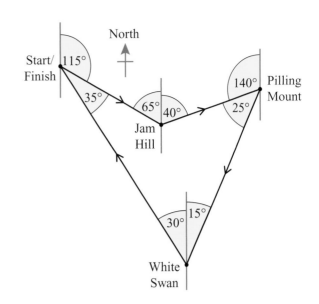

6 A ship sails 6 km due north and then a further 8 km on a bearing of 070°.

Use a scale of 1 cm for every 1 km to draw the ship's journey. How far is the ship now from its starting point?

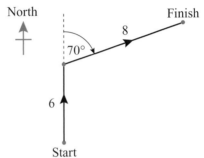

7 A ship sails 7 km due south and then a further 5 km on a bearing of 120°. Use a scale of 1 cm for every 1 km to draw the ship's journey. How far is the ship from its starting point?

8

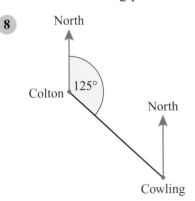

Find the bearing of:

(a) Cowling *from Colton*

(b) Colton *from Cowling*

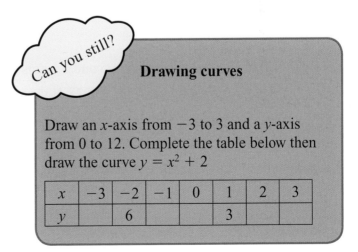

Can you still?

Drawing curves

Draw an x-axis from -3 to 3 and a y-axis from 0 to 12. Complete the table below then draw the curve $y = x^2 + 2$

x	-3	-2	-1	0	1	2	3
y		6			3		

Shapes and lines using co-ordinates

M11.12

1 Draw an x-axis from -5 to 5 and a y-axis from -5 to 5.

ABCD is a square. A is $(-3, 2)$, B is $(-3, -4)$, C is $(3, -4)$.

(a) Draw the square.

(b) Write down the co-ordinates of D.

(c) Write down the co-ordinates of the centre of the square.

(d) E has co-ordinates $(5, -4)$.
Work out the area of the triangle ADE.

(e) The point E is translated with $\begin{pmatrix}-4\\0\end{pmatrix}$.

Explain what happens to the area of triangle ADE.

2

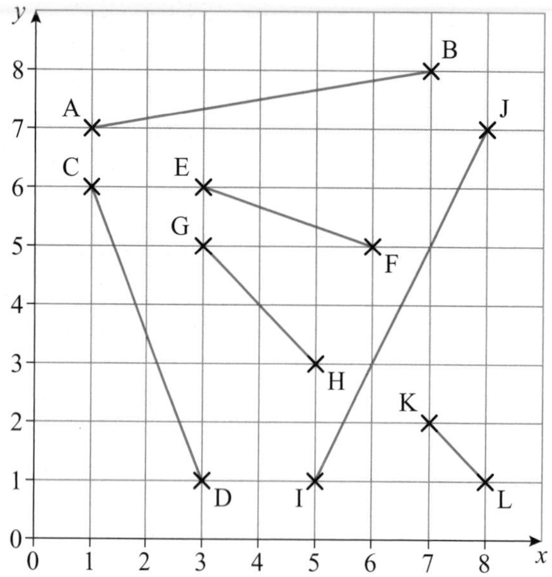

(a) Write down the co-ordinates of the midpoint of each line.

(b) Work out the area of triangle GHD.

(c) Write down the co-ordinates of a point M such that shape KLIM is a parallelogram.

3 Draw an x-axis from -5 to 5 and a y-axis from -5 to 5.

ABCD is a rhombus. A is $(-4, 2)$, B is $(1, 2)$, C is $(4, -2)$.

(a) Draw the rhombus.

(b) Write down the co-ordinates of D.

(c) Write down the co-ordinates of the midpoint of diagonal BD.

(d) Work out the area of the rhombus.

(e) On the same axes, draw a rectangle which has an area equal to the area of the rhombus and a perimeter of 24 units.

4 Copy the graph shown.

(a) A, B and F are three corners of a square. Write down the coordinates of the other corner.

(b) B, C and D are three corners of another square. Write down the co-ordinates of the other corner.

(c) D, E and F are three corners of a rectangle. Write down the co-ordinates of the other corner.

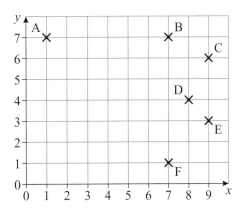

5 The diagram below shows one side of an isosceles triangle.

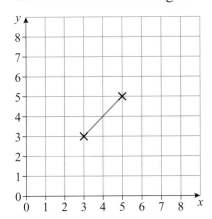

(a) Complete an isosceles triangle using the given side.

(b) Find the area of your isosceles triangle.

6 Copy the diagram below which shows part of a kite.

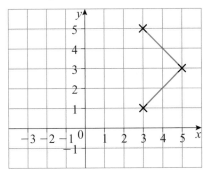

(a) Draw the complete kite so that it has an area of 16 square units.

(b) Write down the co-ordinates of all 4 vertices of the kite.

Can you still?

Mixed

1 Write 21 300 in standard form.

2

$2n + 30$

$n + 30$ $3n$

Write down an equation and solve it to find the value of n.

3 £30 000 is shared between Molly and Felix in the ratio 3 : 7. Felix invests his money and receives 5% per annum simple interest. After how many years will he have made £4200 interest?

4 The Venn diagram shows 100 people on a cold day and whether they wear a hat or gloves.

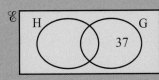

H = {people wearing a hat}
G = {people wearing gloves}
64 people wear gloves and 16 people do not wear a hat or gloves. If one person is chosen at random, find the probability that this person wears a hat but no gloves.

375

The law says you must have car insurance if you drive on public roads.

The car insurance will pay out money if you injure or kill somebody or damage another person's property.

The two main types of car insurance are:

Third party, fire and theft

This does not provide much cover for your own vehicle but will deal with the other person if you are responsible for the damage.

Fully comprehensive

This provides full cover for your own vehicle and any other vehicle involved.

Cost

The amount you pay for car insurance depends on several factors:

- the value of your car
- where you live
- your age
- if you have made a claim on the car insurance in recent years.

No claims bonus

The amount you pay is reduced by 10% each year you do not claim on your car insurance. The biggest discount you can usually have is 60% which is a considerable saving. This percentage reduction is called the 'no claims bonus'.

The bonus is lost if you make a claim on your car insurance then you build up the bonus again over the next few years. Some people pay extra to protect their 'no claims bonus'.

Payments

Some people pay the annual (yearly) cost of their car insurance in one payment but many people spread the cost over 12 equal monthly instalments.

This year Karen's fully comprehensive car insurance quote is £700. She gets a 60% no claims bonus and wants to pay 12 equal monthly instalments. How much is each monthly payment (to the nearest penny)?

No claims bonus	= 60% of £700 = £420
Amount to pay	= £700 − £420 = £280
Monthly payment	= £280 ÷ 12 = £23·33 (to the nearest penny)

---

1 Warren is given a quote of £620 this year for third party, fire and theft insurance on his Nissan Micra. He gets a 60% no claims bonus and wants to pay 12 equal monthly instalments. How much is each monthly payment (to the nearest penny)?

2 Helen's fully comprehensive car insurance quote this year for her Astra is £1154. She has a 40% no claims bonus. If she pays 12 equal monthly instalments, how much is each payment (to the nearest penny)?

Copy and complete the table below to work out the monthly insurance payments for each car.

	Car	Annual car insurance (£)	No claims bonus	Annual insurance to pay (£)	Monthly payment (£)
3	Corsa	950	60%	380	
4	Lexus	1260	60%		
5	Shogun	1530	30%		
6	Ford Escort	1125	50%		
7	Saab 900S	935	20%		
8	Ford Fiesta	870	60%		
9	VW Golf	1060	20%		

10 Sally bumps her car and has to claim on her car insurance. Her annual insurance is £1280. Before her claim she had a 60% no claims bonus. After the claim, her no claims bonus is reduced by 20% (i.e. she has a 40% no claims bonus).

(a) What was her monthly payment before the claim?

(b) What is her monthly payment after the claim?

(c) How much more does she have to pay each month?

11 David is involved in a car accident and puts in a claim on his car insurance. His annual insurance is £1370. Before the accident he had a 50% no claims bonus. After the claim, his no claims bonus is reduced *to* 20%. How much more will he have to pay each month for his car insurance?

12 There are many other insurances that people are advised to take out, for example: life insurance, medical insurance, buildings insurance, contents insurance, critical illness insurance and income protection insurance.

(a) Find out what these insurances cover you for.

(b) **Discuss with your teacher** the advantages and disadvantages of taking out these types of insurance.

1. Measuring lengths and angles

(a) Measure AB to the nearest tenth of a centimetre.

A —————————————————————— B

(b) Measure the perimeter of this trapezium to the nearest tenth of a centimetre.

(c) Using a protractor, measure each angle stated below:

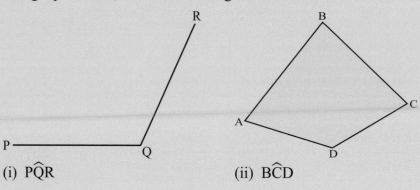

(i) PQ̂R   (ii) BĈD

2. Constructing triangles

(a) Use a ruler and protractor to draw the triangle below.

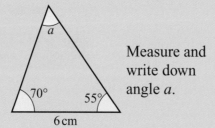

Measure and write down angle *a*.

(b) Use a ruler and compasses only to construct the triangle below.

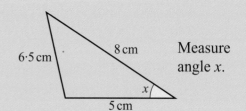

Measure angle *x*.

3. Making scale drawings

Draw an accurate scale drawing of each shape below using the scale shown.

(a)

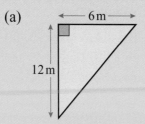

Scale: 1 cm for every 3 m

(b)

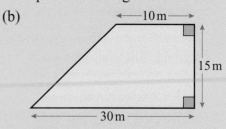

Scale: 1 cm for every 5 m

4. Drawing nets

(a)

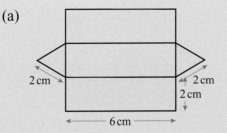

This diagram shows the net of a solid.

Name the solid.

(b)

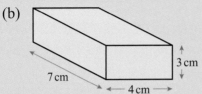

Draw an accurate net for this cuboid.

5. Drawing 3-D objects

(a) On isometric dot paper, draw any solid with a volume of 10 cm³.

(b)

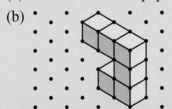

This shape falls over onto the red face.

Draw the shape after it has fallen over.

(c) Draw a hexagonal prism.

6. Interpreting plans and elevations

(a)

plan front elevation side elevation

Name the solid with the plan and elevations shown opposite.

(b) Work out the total surface area of the solid with the plan and elevations shown opposite.

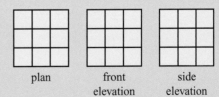

plan front elevation side elevation

7. Using map scales

(a) Cara is making a scale drawing of her garden using a scale of 1 : 50. If her pond has a diameter of 3 m, what is the diameter of the pond on the scale drawing (give the answer in cm)?

(b) The distance between two villages is 2·5 cm on a map. Find the real distance between the two villages if the map scale is 1 : 300 000.

8. Using bearings

(a) *Use a protractor* to measure the bearing of:

   (i) Ambleford from Cayton

   (ii) Berwick from Cayton

   (iii) Berwick from Ambleford

   (iv) Cayton from Ambleford

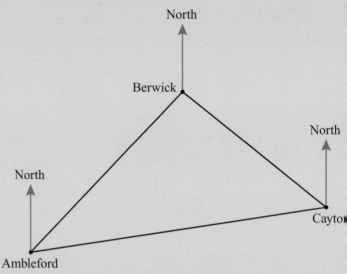

(b)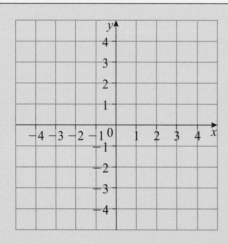

Copy the diagram opposite to show the position of Otley.

Caxton is 8 km from Otley on a bearing of 118°.

   (i) Draw the position of Caxton using a scale of 1 cm for every 2 km.

   (ii) Write down the bearing of Otley from Caxton.

9. Solving problems with shapes and lines using co-ordinates

(a) Copy this grid.

(b) ABCD is a rectangle. A is $(-3, 2)$, B is $(3, 2)$, C is $(3, -3)$.
Draw the rectangle.

(c) Write down the co-ordinates of D.

(d) Write down the co-ordinates of the midpoint of diagonal BD.

(e) Put a cross at a point, E, on the side AB so that the area of triangle AED is 5 square units. Write down the co-ordinates of point E.

(f) Join the point E to the point C. Write down the ratio of the area of triangle DCE to the area of triangle BCE. Give the answer in its simplest form.

Mixed examination questions

1 Match each net with a solid. The first one has been done.

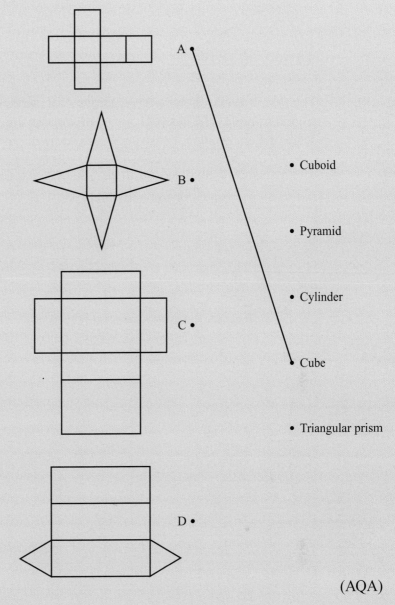

A •

B •

C •

D •

• Cuboid

• Pyramid

• Cylinder

• Cube

• Triangular prism

(AQA)

2 Here is a sketch of a quadrilateral.

Make an accurate drawing of the quadrilateral ABCD. The point A, marked with a cross (×), has been drawn for you.

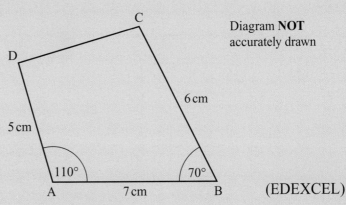

Diagram **NOT** accurately drawn

(EDEXCEL)

381

3

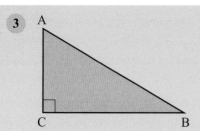

The sketch above shows a large garden ABC which is in the shape of a right-angled triangle. The side CB = 160 m and the side AC = 110 m. Using a scale of 1 cm = 20 m, construct a scale drawing to represent the garden.   (CEA

4 The map shows the positions of two ships A and B, and a port O.

Scale: 1 cm represents 10 km

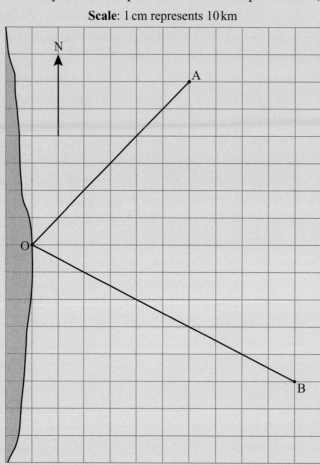

(a) Ship S is North-East of O. What is the **three-figure** bearing of North-East?

(b) Ship A sails directly to O. In which direction does it travel?

(c) Measure the bearing of ship B from O.

(d) How far is ship B from O?

(AQA

5

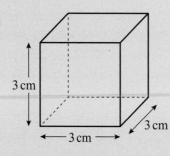

Draw a net of this cube.

(CEA

382

6

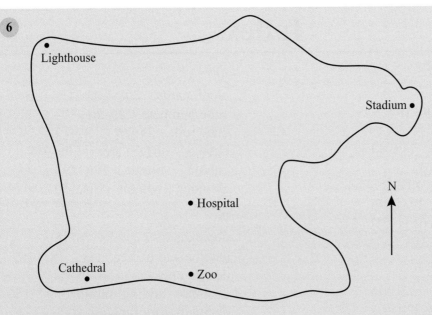

(a) What is South of the Hospital?

(b) What is South-East of the Lighthouse?

(c) Measure the three-figure bearing of the Stadium from the Hospital.　　(AQA)

7　The diagram opposite
shows two sides of a
parallelogram PQRS.

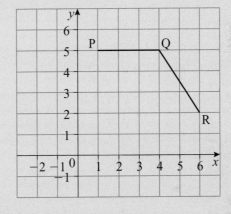

(a) Copy the diagram and
complete the parallelogram
PQRS. Write down the
co-ordinates of S.

(b) Draw a triangle PQT such
that the area of triangle
PQT is equal to the area
of the parallelogram PQRS.
Write down the co-ordinates of T.

8　The diagram below shows a rough sketch of a triangular plot of land.

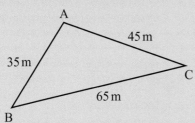

Using ruler and compasses only, make an accurate scale drawing below
of the plot of land.

Use a scale of 1 cm to represent 5 metres.　　　　　　　　　　(CEA)

Index

Can you still? sections page numbers

NIT 1

ge 1 M1·1

1. (a) 600 (b) 4 (c) 8 (d) 3000 (e) 6
   (f) 700 (g) 80 (h) 5000 (i) 10 (j) 600
   (k) 6 (l) 5000 (m) 100 (n) 700 (o) 5

2. (a) 863 (b) 368 **3.** (a) 8812 (b) 6598 (c) 4025

4. (a) 4080, 4089, 4158, 4163 (b) 7365, 7377, 7396, 7418, 7481, 7492

5. (a) 7641 (b) 1467 **6.** (a) 51 498 (b) less

7. 24 587 **8.** (a) 69 734 (b) 69 735 (c) b larger by 1

ge 2 M1·2

1. (a) $\dfrac{2}{100}$ (b) $\dfrac{9}{10}$ (c) $\dfrac{5}{10}$ (d) $\dfrac{7}{1000}$ (e) $\dfrac{9}{10}$

   (f) $\dfrac{7}{1000}$ (g) $\dfrac{8}{1000}$ (h) $\dfrac{2}{100}$ (i) 7 units (j) $\dfrac{2}{10}$

   (k) 8 units (l) 10 (m) $\dfrac{8}{10}$ (n) $\dfrac{8}{1000}$ (o) 30

2. correct **3.** 0·1 **4.** 0·5 **5.** $80 + 4 + \dfrac{7}{10} + \dfrac{3}{100}$

6. (a) 87·643 (b) 34·678 (c) 98·654 (d) 14·568

ge 3 M1·3

1. 60 **2.** 50 **3.** 310 **4.** 290 **5.** 1320 **6.** 6150 **7.** 200

8. 600 **9.** 700 **10.** 700 **11.** 900 **12.** 1400 **13.** 2700 **14.** 4600

15. 2200 **16.** 5400 **17.** £1700 **18.** 3000 **19.** 16000 **20.** 1000 **21.** £39000

22. 482 000 **23.** 8 **24.** 3 **25.** 3 **26.** 12 **27.** 8 **28.** £3

29. £3 **30.** £7 **31.** £13 **32.** £25 **33.** 7 kg **34.** 4 kg **35.** 14 kg

36. 9 kg **37.** 23 kg

ge 5 M1·4

1. (a) 2320 (b) 2300 (c) 2000 **2.** (a) 4630 (b) 4600 (c) 5000

3. (a) 6280 (b) 6300 (c) 6000 **4.** (a) 4190 (b) 4200 (c) 4000

5. (a) 1000 (b) 1000 (c) 1000 **6.** (a) 3280 (b) 3300 (c) 3000

7. (a) 8170 (b) 8200 (c) 8000 **8.** (a) 17 450 (b) 17 500 (c) 17 000

9. 550, 610, 619, 583

10. China 1100, India 900, USA 300, Brazil 200, Pakistan 100, Japan 100, Mexico 100 (All Millions)

11. 50,351 : 49,681 : 50,018 : 49,899 **12.** 1750

ge 6 M1·5

1. 248 **2.** 366 **3.** 4305 **4.** 308 **5.** 11 390 **6.** 843 **7.** 3669 **8.** 117 831

9.   **10.** 505 **11.** 1170 **12.** 79 **13.** 161 **14.** 368

9	2	4		2
5		2	4	3
8	8	4		2
	3		5	8
6	4	2	5	9

2

Page 6 M1·6

1. (a) £1262 (b) £263 (c) £138   2. £377   3. £39

6. 32 350

4.

+	38	87	245	66
109	147	196	254	175
326	364	413	571	392
163	201	250	408	229
446	484	533	691	512

5.

+	443	148	516	244
384	827	532	900	628
252	695	400	768	496
87	530	235	603	331
226	669	374	742	470

7. (a) 57 (b) 61 (c) 4 (d) 16   8. 15   9. 1880

Page 8 M1·7

1. 31 000   2. 8170   3. 5270   4. 316 000   5. 53 000   6. 2100   7. 4000
8. 3600   9. 27 000   10. 560 000   11. 2   12. 8   13. 8   14. 8
15. 60   16. 240 000   17. 30   18. 40   19. £5200   20. £1300   21. 110
22. 6000   23. 460   24. 49 000   25. 100   26. 5   27. 70   28. 1500
29. 35 000   30. 50   31. 30   32. £5000   33. Yes, £26 000 saved
34. 3160→316 000→31 600→316
35. 8640→8640→864
36. 800→24 000→40→4
37. 30→1500→45 000→500

Page 10 M1·8

1.

×	7	2	12	8	6	3	11	9	4	5
7	49	14	84	56	42	21	77	63	28	35
2	14	4	24	16	12	6	22	18	8	10
12	84	24	144	96	72	36	132	108	48	60
8	56	16	96	64	48	24	88	72	32	40
6	42	12	72	68	36	18	66	54	24	30
3	21	6	36	24	18	9	33	27	12	15
11	77	22	132	88	66	33	121	99	44	55
9	63	18	108	72	54	27	99	81	36	45
4	28	8	48	32	24	12	44	36	16	20
5	35	10	60	40	30	15	55	45	20	25

×	2	9	6	3	5	11	12	8	7	4
2	4	18	12	6	10	22	24	16	14	8
9	18	81	54	27	45	99	108	72	63	36
6	12	54	36	18	30	66	72	48	42	24
3	6	27	18	9	15	33	36	24	21	12
5	10	45	30	15	25	55	60	40	35	20
11	22	99	66	33	55	121	132	88	77	44
12	24	108	72	36	60	132	144	96	84	48
8	16	72	48	24	40	88	96	64	56	32
7	14	63	42	21	35	77	84	56	49	28
4	8	36	24	12	20	44	48	32	28	16

2. 1664   3. 1539   4. 1296   5. 3488   6. 1040   7. 2214   8. 18 912
9. 44 688   10. £511   11. £1304   12. 288   13. £2790   14. 1638

Page 11 M1·9

1. 368   2. 560   3. 2511   4. 3128   5. 3952   6. 2006   7. 1792
8. 31 692   9. 23 482   10. 27 812   11. 41 741   12. 22 274   13. 9464   14. 57 996
15. 395 304   16. £46 336   17. 5460   18. 9000 kg   19. £13 578   20. £22 060
21. total paid = £5046, total cost = £4954 so enough money   22. 272 short

Page 12 M1·10

1. 2   2. 2   3. 6   4. 8   5. 4   6. 9   7. 10
8. 8   9. 4   10. 2   11. 9   12. 10   13. 7   14. 5
15. 0   16. 1   17. 243   18. 145   19. 257   20. 232   21. 216

49   **23.** 729   **24.** 466   **25.** 257   **26.** 205   **27.** 1296   **28.** 726
305   **30.** 1387   **31.** 5457   **32.** 1754   **33.** 5231   **34.** 698   **35.** 3214
2234

ge 13   M1·11

64 r2   **2.** 41 r6   **3.** 528 r2   **4.** 3570 r1   **5.** 154 r1   **6.** 426 r2   **7.** 501 r6
39 r1   **9.** 6   **10.** 14   **11.** 118   **12.** 17   **13.** 13

ge 14   M1·12

36   **2.** 27   **3.** 25   **4.** 23   **5.** 43   **6.** 24   **7.** 32
25   **9.** 38   **10.** 29   **11.** 26   **12.** 23   **13.** 18   **14.** 36
18   **16.** Elaine 32 Carl 35 Maisy 11 Dan 9   **17.** 35

ge 15   M1·13

12 classes, 8 over   **2.** 42   **3.** 74   **4.** 423   **5.** 1 hour 30 minutes

3	8		5	2	8
1		4	7		6
6	8		2	4	3
	1	8		2	
4	9		3	7	2
3		7	3		4
6	2	6		8	3

ge 15   Can you still?

8000   **2.** 8000   **3.** 28 000   **4.** 54 000   **5.** 18   **6.** 56   **7.** 66   **8.** 560

ge 16   M1·14

(a) 2°   (b) 4°   (c) 5°   (d) 3°   (e) 7°   (f) 12°
−3, −2, −1, 0, 7, 9   **3.** −10, −8, −4, 4, 1   **4.** −6, −5, −3, 0, 2, 6   **5.** −1°
−1°, −5°, −1°, −9°, 3°, −3°, 8°, −7°, −5°, −4° (in order vertically)
4°   **8.** London   **9.** Belfast   **10.** 5°   **11.** 3°   **12.** 7° C   **13.** Liverpool
(a) −3   (b) −6   (c) −4   (d) 0   (e) −3   (f) −6
(g) −8   (h) −9   (i) −2   (j) −4   (k) −9   (l) −1

Old Temp. °C	Change °C	New Temp. °C
−2	Rises 7	5
−1	Rises 3	2
2	Falls 6	−4
−8	Falls 2	−10
−7	Rises 7	0
−6	Rises 4	−2
−12	Rises 8	−4
−4	Rises 3	−1
−2	Falls 5	−7
−10	Falls 4	−14

Page 18   M1·15

1. (a) 2   (b) 3   (c) −6   (d) −5   (e) 5   (f) 6   (g) −7   (h) −1
   (i) −3   (j) −2   (k) −9   (l) −4   (m) 8   (n) 9   (o) −7   (p) −7
2. (a) £37   (b) £12   (c) £79
3. Yes, £1 under overdraft limit   4. £438
5. (a) −1   (b) −10   (c) 11   (d) −6   (e) 2   (f) −11   (g) −6   (h) −4
   (i) −14   (j) −4   (k) 6   (l) −11   (m) −7   (n) −8   (o) 1   (p) −7
   (q) 1   (r) −10   (s) −5   (t) −8
6. B
7. $\boxed{-1} - 2 = -3,\ -8 - -7 = \boxed{-1},\ -6 + 1 = \boxed{-5},\ \boxed{5} - -2 = 7$
8. $7 + -3 = \boxed{4},\ 2 + -4 = -2,\ \boxed{-1} - 7 = -8,\ 6 - \boxed{7} = -1,\ -3 + \boxed{-6} = 1 - 10$

Page 19   *Can you still?*

1. 6376   2. 5318   3. 147   4. 218   5. 430   6. 286   7. 552   8. 571

Page 20   M1·16

1. (a) −15   (b) −18   (c) 24   (d) 21   2. (a) 32   (b) −42   (c) 12   (d) −36
3. (a) −30   (b) −3   (c) 45   (d) 16   4. (a) −2   (b) −7   (c) 5   (d) −5
5. (a) 6   (b) −6   (c) −3   (d) 6   6. (a) −6   (b) 6   (c) 5   (d) −7

7.

×	−3	−6	8	−2
7	−21	−42	56	−14
−5	15	30	−40	10
−4	12	24	−32	8
9	−27	−54	72	−18

8.

×	−7	4	−3	−8
4	−28	16	−12	−32
−6	42	−24	18	48
−5	35	−20	15	40
7	−49	28	−21	−56

9. (a) −5   (b) 12   (c) 9   (d) −9   10. (a) −132   (b) 384   (c) −238   (d) 782
11. (a) 4   (b) −8   (c) 16   12. (a) −27   (b) 32   (c) −60

Page 21   M1·17

1.

20	÷	−4	→	−5
÷		×		
−10	×	−3	→	30
↓		↓		
−2	×	12	→	−24

2.

−30	×	−2	→	60
÷		÷		
−5	×	4	→	−20
↓		↓		
6	×	−8	→	−48

3.
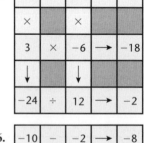

−8	÷	−2	→	4
×		×		
3	×	−6	→	−18
↓		↓		
−24	÷	12	→	−2

4.

−8	+	−4	→	−12
−		+		
2	−	12	→	−10
↓		↓		
−10	+	8	→	−2

5.

−11	−	−1	→	−10
+		+		
6	−	8	→	−2
↓		↓		
−5	−	7	→	−12

6.

−10	−	−2	→	−8
−		−		
−4	+	7	→	3
↓		↓		
−6	−	−9	→	3

−10	÷	5	→	−2
×		−		
−2	×	9	→	−18
↓		↓		
20	÷	−4	→	−5

8.

30	÷	−5	→	−6
−		−		
40	÷	−8	→	−5
↓		↓		
−10	×	3	→	−30

9.

−16	+	4	→	−12
÷		×		
−8	−	−6	→	−2
↓		↓		
2	×	−24	→	−48

---

ge 22 M1·18 _____

11	**2.** 23	**3.** 10	**4.** 10	**5.** 24	**6.** 40	**7.** 6	**8.** 5	**9.** 14
9	**11.** 56	**12.** 34	**13.** 4	**14.** 33	**15.** 55	**16.** 17	**17.** 56	**18.** 35
8	**20.** 13	**21.** 5	**22.** 20	**23.** 22	**24.** 5	**25.** 11	**26.** 18	**27.** 38

---

ge 23 M1·19 _____

16   **2.** 6   **3.** 20   **4.** 4   **5.** 20   **6.** 7   **7.** 55   **8.** 17

4   **10.** 34   **11.** 56   **12.** 16   **13.** 14   **14.** 11   **15.** 8   **16.** 26

78   **18.** 100   **19.** 11   **20.** 2   **21.** 57   **22.** C, D, F

$(3 + 2) \times 5 = 25$ **24.** $(7 + 4) \times 4 = 44$ **25.** $5 \times (2 + 3) = 25$ **26.** $8 + (3 \times 6) = 26$

$5 \times (9 − 4) = 25$ **28.** $6 \times (15 − 6) = 54$ **29.** $(40 − 25) \times 3 = 45$ **30.** $(63 − 7) \div 8 = 7$

$42 \div (6 + 1) = 6$ **32.** $(18 − 12) \div (12 \div 4) = 2$ **33.** $(16 + 14) \div 2 = 15$

$(7 + 25) \div 4 = 8$ **35.** $(7 + 3) \times (8 − 5) = 30$ **36.** $(13 + 2) \times 4 = 60$

$(3 + 8 + 19) \div 3 = 10$ **38.** $(5 + 6) \times (10 − 4) = 66$ **39.** $(6 + 4) \times 7 − 3$

---

ge 24 M1·20 _____

1, 4, 9, 16, 25, 36, 49, 64, 81, 100, 121, 144   **2.** 149   **3.** 39   **4.** 28   **5.** 65

34   **7.** 16   **8.** 84   **9.** 81   **10.** 30   **11.** 10 cm   **12.** 8   **13.** 7 cm

(a) 1   (b) 5   (c) 16   (d) 6

(a) 289   (b) 784   (c) 12 996   (d) 0·16   (e) 14·44   (f) 0·01

(a) 17   (b) 24   (c) 50   (d) 41   (e) 2·9   (f) 0·3

Peyton is correct (13 × 13)   **18.** (a) 4 cm   (b) 128 cm

49, 16 or 1, 64   (b) 9,1   (c) 25,4   (d) 64,9   (e) 25, 36

---

ge 26 M1·21 _____

1, 8, 27, 64, 125, 216, 343, 512, 729, 1000   **2.** Yes   **3.** No   **4.** 3

(a) 3   (b) 5   (c) 4   (d) 6

(a) 2744   (b) 9261   (c) 3·375   (d) 0·008

(a) 15   (b) 24   (c) 40   (d) 0·3   (e) 0·4

(a) 6   (b) 8   (c) 125

Page 26   **Can you still?**

1. (a) 31°C

2. (a) −7   (b) 2   (c) −5   (d) −3   (e) 6   (f) −2   (g) −2   (h) −5   (i) −7

3. (a) −2   (b) −2

Page 27   **M1·22**

1. $8 \times 8 \times 8 \times 8$ **2.** $6 \times 6 \times 6 \times 6 \times 6$ **3.** $10 \times 10 \times 10 \times 10$ **4.** 12×12

5. $7 \times 7 \times 7 \times 7 \times 7$ **6.** $3 \times 3 \times 3 \times 3 \times 3 \times 3 \times 3$ **7.** $8 \times 8 \times 8 \times 8 \times 8 \times 8$

8. $2 \times 2 \times 2 \times 2 \times 2 \times 2 \times 2 \times 2$ **9.** 4^5 **10.** 2^6 **11.** 5^3 **12.** 3^8 **13.** 10^5 **14.** 6^4

15. (a) 50 cm, 30 cm, 25 cm   (b) 105 cm

16. 3^3 **17.** same   **18.** 24   **19.** 48   **20.** 100   **21.** 128

22. (b) 2^5, 32   (c) $7 \times 7 \times 7$, 343   (d) 8^4, 4096   (e) 16 384   (f) 9^5, 59 049   (g) 10^6, 1 000 000

23. £8192   **24.** 9 765 625   **25.** 90

Page 28   **Can you still?**

1. 18 142   **2.** 67   **3.** 112   **4.** £466

Page 29   **M1·23**

1. 1, 2, 4, 8   **2.** 1, 2, 4, 8, 16   **3.** 1, 11   **4.** 1, 3, 5, 15   **5.** 1, 2, 3, 4, 6, 8, 12, 24
6. 1, 19   **7.** 1, 5, 7, 35   **8.** 1, 2, 4, 7, 14, 28   **9.** 1, 2, 4, 5, 8, 10, 20, 40
10. 1, 23   **11.** 1, 2, 3, 5, 15, 30   **12.** 1, 2, 3, 6, 7, 14, 21, 42   **13.** 1, 17
14. 1, 2, 13, 26   **15.** 1, 2, 5, 10, 25, 50   **16.** 11, 15, 17, 19, 23, 35   **17.** 8, 16, 24, 26, 28, 30, 40, 42, 50
18. 11, 17, 19, 23   **19.** No   **20.** 20   **21.** 22   **22.** 21, 28
23. 51, 53, 55, 57   **24.** 77   **25.** 2, 4, 8, 16   **26.** 81, 90, 99   **27.** No. These are 4 numbers

Page 31   **M1·24**

1. 21, 28, 35, 42, 49, 56, 63, 70   **2.** 16, 32, 48, 64, 80, 96, 112, 128, 144, 160
3. 30, 60, 90, 120, 150, 180, 210, 240, 270, 300   **4.** 11, 54   **5.** 22, 38, 91   **6.** 23   **7.** 72   **8.**
9. (a) 30   (b) 21   (c) 45   (d) 70   (e) 6   (f) 40   (g) 60   (h) 60   (i) 60
10. 15, 30   **11.** (a) 60   (b) 4

Page 31   **Can you still?**

1. (a) −6   (b) −20   (c) 12   (d) −30   (e) −4   (f) −5
2. (a) −4   (b) −9   (c) −2   **3.** (a) 9   (b) 81   (c) −1   (d) 60

Page 32   **M1·25**

1. (a) 1, 3, ⑤, ⑮   (b) 1, 2, 3, ⑥, ⑨, ⑱   (c) 3

2. (a) 1, 2, ④, ⑤, ⑩, ⑳   (b) 1, 2, ③, ⑤, ⑥, ⑩, ⑮, ㉚   (c) 10

3. (a) 1, 2, 4, 8, 16, 32   (b) 1, 2, 4, 5, 8, 10, 20 40   (c) 8
4. (a) 1, 2, 3, 4, 6, 8, 12, 24   (b) 1, 2, 3, 4, 6, 9, 12, 18, 36   (c) 12
5. (a) 2   (b) 10   (c) 5   (d) 5   (e) 4   (f) 8   (g) 1   (h) 16
6. (a) 2   (b) 5   (c) 12

ge 34 M1·26

(a) 20   (b) 30   (c) 45   (d) 42   (e) 165   (f) 100

(a) $70 = \boxed{2} \times \boxed{5} \times \boxed{7}$ (b) $72 = \boxed{3} \times \boxed{3} \times \boxed{2} \times \boxed{2} \times \boxed{2}$

(a) $24 = \boxed{2} \times \boxed{2} \times \boxed{2} \times \boxed{3}$ (b) $84 = \boxed{2} \times \boxed{2} \times \boxed{3} \times \boxed{7}$

(a) $2 \times 3 \times 3$ (b) $2 \times 2 \times 7$ (c) 2×11 (d) $2 \times 2 \times 2 \times 2 \times 2$

(e) $2 \times 2 \times 2 \times 2 \times 3$ (f) $2 \times 5 \times 5$ (g) $3 \times 3 \times 3 \times 3$ (h) $2 \times 2 \times 2 \times 2 \times 2 \times 3$

(i) $2 \times 2 \times 2 \times 5 \times 5$ (j) $2 \times 2 \times 2 \times 3 \times 5$ (k) $2 \times 2 \times 7 \times 7$ (l) $2 \times 2 \times 2 \times 7 \times 7$

(a) 60   (b) 120   (c) 70

ge 35 E1·1

(a) 7×10^4 (b) $6·4 \times 10^4$ (c) $3·5 \times 10^3$ (d) $9·84 \times 10^5$ (e) 4×10^{-2}

(f) $3·6 \times 10^{-2}$ (g) $8·7 \times 10^{-4}$ (h) $5·9 \times 10^5$ (i) $9·3 \times 10^{-3}$

$3·84 \times 10^5$ **3.** $1·5 \times 10^5$

(a) 8×10^5 (b) 7×10^2 (c) $3·9 \times 10^3$ (d) $4·82 \times 10^4$

(e) $7·9 \times 10^4$ (f) $9·2 \times 10^{-3}$ (g) $6·8 \times 10^{-1}$ (h) $1·6 \times 10^{-5}$

(i) $6·83 \times 10^{-1}$ (j) $5·4 \times 10^7$ (k) $8·7 \times 10^{-3}$ (l) $5·96 \times 10^{-2}$

$3·5 \times 10^6$ **6.** 7×10^{-6} **7.** b, c, d and f

(a) 6000   (b) 590   (c) 47 000   (d) 0·003   (e) 7150

(f) 0·000 26   (g) 0·035   (h) 0·568   (i) 193 000   (j) 0·000 846

(a) 9×10^{-3} (b) $5·16 \times 10^2$ (c) $5·28 \times 10^4$ (d) $6·14 \times 10^5$ (e) $7·6 \times 10^{-2}$

(f) 8×10^{-4} (g) 7×10^{-5} (h) $5·28 \times 10^3$ (i) $1·67 \times 10^7$ (j) $1·2 \times 10^{-2}$

ge 36 Can you still?

(a) true   (b) true   (c) true   (d) true

(a) 288   (b) 100   (c) 80   (d) 72

(a) 5   (b) 4   (c) 5   (d) 2

ge 37 E1·2

(a) $1·5 \times 10^8$ (b) $4·14 \times 10^{20}$ (c) 3×10^{11}

(d) $3·09 \times 10^{-10}$ (e) $1·2 \times 10^{26}$ (f) $1·84 \times 10^{10}$

(a) $2·05 \times 10^5$ (b) St. Davids   (c) 3600

(d) St. Davids, Wells, Chester, Norwich, Aberdeen, Swansea, Liverpool, London

(a) 2×10^{11} (b) $7·4 \times 10^{21}$ (c) 9×10^{-17}

(d) $5·49 \times 10^{-17}$ (e) $3·25 \times 10^8$ (f) $6·25 \times 10^{-25}$

375 times   **5.** (a) $(8·4664 \times 10^6)$ (b) Kuchar   (c) $(2·22766 \times 10^7)$

ge 39 Win the premiership

Task A

Team	P	W	D	L	F	A	Pts
Man Utd	38	27	5	6	90	32	86
Chelsea	38	25	10	3	85	30	85
Arsenal	38	23	11	4	68	30	80
Liverpool	38	24	7	7	75	35	79

Task B

Team	P	W	D	L	F	A	Pts
Chelsea	38	26	9	3	86	30	87
Man Utd	38	26	7	5	89	31	85
Arsenal	38	23	10	5	71	31	79
Liverpool	38	23	10	5	74	36	79

Page 40   **Test yourself on Unit 1**

1. (a) 400   (b) 20   (c) $\dfrac{9}{100}$ (d) $\dfrac{6}{10}$ (e) $\dfrac{7}{1000}$

2. (a) 4   (b) 8   (c) 8390, 7865, 7950

3. (a) 315   (b) 117   (c) 1315   (d) 246

4. (a) 5600   (b) 2304   (c) 328   (d) 326   (e) 3042
   (f) 19186   (g) 67   (h) 53   (i) 7   (j) £256

5. (a) 46°   (b) −3°C   (c) −3   (d) −4   (e) −4
   (f) 4   (g) −24   (h) 7   (i) −8   (j) −12

6. (a) 13   (b) 9   (c) 4   (d) 2   (e) 16
   (f) 45   (g) $7 \times (4 + 5)$ (h) $(10 − 7) \times (8 + 2)$

7. (a) (i) 1, 36, 81   (ii) 1, 8   (b) 8   (c) 4   (d) 4   (e) 7
   (f) 125   (g) 32   (h) 625   (i) 10 000   (j) 3

8. (a) 1, 2, 3, 6, 9, 18   (b) 1, 2, 4, 8, 16, 32   (c) 3, 5, 7, 17

9. (a) 42, 49   (b) 24   (c) 24   (d) 7   (e) 4

10. (a) $2^2 \times 3$ (b) $2^2 \times 3^2$ (c) 2×3^3 (d) $2^2 \times 5^2$ (e) $2^4 \times 3^2$

11. (a) 7×10^3 (b) $5 \cdot 84 \times 10^4$ (c) $9 \cdot 3 \times 10^{-2}$ (d) 4×10^{-3} (e) 50 000
    (f) 26 000   (g) 0·0048   (h) 350   (i) Q, R, T, P, U, S
    (j) $2 \cdot 16 \times 10^{34}$ (k) $4 \cdot 31 \times 10^{18}$ (l) $1 \cdot 4 \times 10^{14}$ (m) $1 \cdot 84 \times 10^{24}$

Page 43   **Mixed examination questions**

1. (a) 81   (b) 1·6   (c) 10·24

2. £1·20 each, £3·60   3. eg. $2 + 3 = 5$ 4. (a) −3°C   (b) 3°C

5. (a) 3   (b) 6   (c) 18   (d) 7

6. 11:00 am   7. (a) (i) 33   (ii) 8   (iii) 7   (b) (i) 36   (ii) 13

8. (a) 1   (b) 0·000 067   (c) $2 \cdot 7 \times 10^{14}$ 9. 125 and 216

10. (a) (i) $(4 + 3) \times 8 − 13 = 43$ (ii) $(5 + 3)^2 \times 2 \div 8 = 16$ (b) (i) 338·56   (ii) 56

11. (a) 240 miles   (b) 30 miles extra   12. (a) 4608   (b) 14·66

13. (i) −7 and 3   (ii) −5 and −2   14. 136

15. (a) $2^3 \times 3 \times 5^2$ (b) 16:20   16. 10 cm

17. (a) 5×10^5 (b) $3 \cdot 1 \times 10^{-5}$ 18. 52p change

UNIT 2

Page 48   **M2·1**

1. (a) $2n$ 2. (a) $x + 7$ (b) $x + 3$ (c) $3x + 10$ (d) $x + 14$

3. (a) £$5x$ (b) £$2y$ (c) £$(5x + 2y)$ 4. 11p

5. (a) £215   (b) £$(3m + 20)$ (c) £$(3n + 20)$ (d) £$(3m + 6n + 445)$

6. (a) Lillian : £$(n −8)$, Sheila : £$(3n −y)$, Pavel : £8, Jim : £y (b) £$4n$ 7. £$\left(\dfrac{x − y}{3}\right)$

Page 50   **M2·2**

1. 24	2. 12	3. 10	4. 4	5. 8	6. 7	7. 12	8. 22	9. 16	10. 36
11. 40	12. 24	13. 6	14. 20	15. 1	16. 12	17. 36	18. 16	19. 3	20. 4
21. 30	22. 9	23. 9	24. 9	25. 0	26. 0	27. 0	28. 73	29. 42	30. 24
31. 292	32. 2	33. 14	34. 23	35. 19	36. 40	37. 12	38. 19	39. 16	40. 9

Page 51   **E2·1**

1. 65	2. 25	3. 100	4. 400	5. 64	6. 98	7. 48	8. 140	9. 82	10. 23
11. 90	12. 34	13. 44	14. 196	15. 3	16. 54	17. 104	18. 50	19. 186	20. 10

46   **22.** 18   **23.** 3   **24.** 0   **25.** 16   **26.** -6 **27.** 14   **28.** -9 **29.** 6   **30.** 14

-11 **32.** -16 **33.** 4   **34.** 20   **35.** 18   **36.** -30 **37.** -2 **38.** 24   **39.** -27 **40.** 36

48   **42.** 27   **43.** -5 **44.** 11

---

ge 52   M2·3

17   **2.** 15   **3.** 10   **4.** 3   **5.** 33   **6.** 22   **7.** 26   **8.** 34   **9.** 44   **10.** 6

16   **12.** 12   **13.** 56   **14.** 752   **15.** 85   **16.** 761   **17.** 60   **18.** 30·38   **19.** 14   **20.** 5

---

ge 53   Can you still?

19   **2.** 4   **3.** 18   **4.** 10   **5.** 27   **6.** 13   **7.** 4   **8.** 26   **9.** 3   **10.** 15

15   **12.** 14   **13.** $(7 + 4) \times 3 = 33$ **14.** $(25 - 20) \times 4$ **15.** $(7 - 2) \times (5 + 1) = 30$

---

ge 54   E2·2

(a) 29   (b) 9   (c) 52   **2.** (a) 112   (b) 300   (c) 101

(a) 5   (b) 34   (c) 12   **4.** (a) $720°$ (b) $18\,000°$

(a) 29   (b) -6 (c) 2   **6.** (a) 39   (b) -33 (c) -27

(a) 75   (b) 300   (c) 12   (d) 192   **8.** (a) 600   (b) 300

(a) 72   (b) 931   **10.** (a) 13   (b) 125   (c) -1

52   **12.** (a) 3   (b) -5

---

ge 56   M2·4

$5a + 4b$ **2.** $12a$ **3.** $7a + 4b$ **4.** $7p + 8q$ **5.** $11p + 5q$

$7p + 9q$ **7.** $13p + 8q$ **8.** $4x + 5y$ **9.** $3y$ **10.** $5x + 3y$

$9a$ **12.** $15x + 4y$ **13.** $9x$ **14.** $4x + 2y$ **15.** $11a + 1$

$7x - 3$ **17.** $5p + 8q$ **18.** $14c - 2$ **19.** $18a + 4$ **20.** $4x + 9y$

$3c + 9$ **22.** $16c + 15$ **23.** $6a + 12b + 14$ **24.** $15a + 14$ **25.** $15x + 8y + 18$

$5m + 2n$ **27.** $3b$ **28.** $8a + 10$ **29.** $2p + q$ **30.** $5a + 3b - 2$

$5a + 8b$ **32.** $17x + 7y$ **33.** $11x + 4$

---

ge 57   Can you still?

64   **2.** 9   **3.** 20   **4.** 2   **5.** 1   **6.** 64

72   **8.** 12   **9.** 36   **10.** 1, 8, 27   **11.** $\sqrt{100}$ **12.** 16 and 25

---

ge 57   M2·5

$9a$ **2.** $2c$ **3.** $-6a$ **4.** $5b$ **5.** 0

$10a + 3b$ **7.** $7p + 7q$ **8.** $10m - 2n$ **9.** $-2a + b$ **10.** b

$2a - 2b$ **12.** $-3x$ **13.** $4p + 6$ **14.** $-4p - 2$ **15.** $4a - 2$

$5x - y$ **17.** $9a - 2$ **18.** $2c - 7$

(a) $13a + 6b - 6$ (b) $5a + 6b - 7$ (c) $8a + 6b - 8$

$5m + 3n - n + 2m$ and $m + 6n - 5n + 6m + n$

$4m^2 + 2n + 8$ **22.** correct   **23.** $9c + 11d + 4$ **24.** $5ab + a$ **25.** $8ab + 5a$

$3xy$ **27.** $3xy - 5$ **28.** $17ab + 6$ **29.** $6xy$ **30.** $10ab - 2a + 4b$

$3xy - 3x$ **32.** $5a^2 + 7$ **33.** $12a^2 - 5a$

---

ge 59   M2·6

$8x$ **2.** $15x$ **3.** $16x$ **4.** $8y$ **5.** $20y$ **6.** $42a$ **7.** $80x$ **8.** $36a$

$18d$ **10.** $24c$ **11.** $36p$ **12.** $45x$ **13.** $14c$ **14.** $27d$ **15.** $48x$ **16.** $2x$

17. $6x$ **18.** $2p$ **19.** $5x$ **20.** $7A$ **21.** $3Q$ **22.** $7n$ **23.** $3A$ **24.** $9N$
25. $4r$ **26.** $10t$ **27.** $12T$ **28.** $7a$ **29.** $8R$ **30.** $4b$ **31.** a^2 **32.** c^2
33. Q^2 **34.** $3c^2$ **35.** $4p^2$ **36.** $5d^2$ **37.** $2r^2$ **38.** B^2 **39.** $5c^2$ **40.** $6a^2$
41. $8ab$ **42.** $18y^2$ **43.** $14a^2$ **44.** $25t^2$

Page 59 *Can you still?*

1. (a) 1, 2, 5, 10 (b) 1, 5, 25 (c) 1, 2, 3, 4, 6, 8, 12, 24
2. 15, 22 **3.** 12, 30, 42 **4.** (a) 28 (b) 18 (c) 24

Page 59 *M2·7*

1. $6ab$ **2.** $18xy$ **3.** $10pq$ **4.** $21e^2$ **5.** $24mn$ **6.** $54c^2$ **7.** $24x^2$ **8.** $16B^2$
9. $45PQ$ **10.** $36uv$ **11.** $4c$ **12.** $5A$ **13.** $8p$ **14.** $8x$ **15.** abc **16.** $12abc$
17. $60xyz$ **18.** $72abcd$ **19.** T **20.** T **21.** F **22.** T **23.** F **24.** T
25. T **26.** T **27.** T **28.** F **29.** F **30.** F **31.** T **32.** F
33. T **34.** $-m^2$ **35.** $-6ab$ **36.** $-20cd$ **37.** $8xy$ **38.** $-3y$ **39.** $3a$ **40.** $-2p$
41. $18cd$ **42.** $-40xy$ **43.** $-7q$ **44.** $-54y$ **45.** $-21a^2$ **46.** $7x$ **47.** $-54ab$ **48.** $54P^2$

Page 61 *M2·8*

1. (a) 3^7 (b) 5^6 (c) 8^6 (d) 7^5 (e) 4^7 (f) 6^7
2. (a) 7^4 (b) 4^3 (c) 3^8 (d) 5^3 (e) 6^3 (f) 4
3. (a) 8^8 (b) 4^{10} (c) 9^3 (d) 6^8 (e) 8^6 (f) 5^3 (g) 3^9 (h) 2^{10} (i) 4^6
4. 2^9
5. (a) 3^6 (b) 6^2 (c) 9^3 (d) 4^2 (e) 9 (f) 4^6 (g) 3^6 (h) 8^5 (i) 4^{12}
6. 3^8
7. (a) 5^{14} (b) 8^{13} (c) 4^4 (d) 7^{10} (e) 8^4 (f) 6^2
8. 5^3 cm
9. (a) T (b) T (c) T (d) F (e) F (f) T

Page 62 *E2·3*

1. (a) 3^8 (b) 5^6 (c) 6^{12} (d) 7^8 (e) 5^{18} (f) 8^{10} (g) 3^{15} (h) 6^{15}
2. same
3. (a) 3^{11} (b) 2^{18} (c) 6^9 (d) 7^3 (e) 5^2 (f) 9^3 (g) 8^2 (h) 4^6 (i) 2^5
4. 1
5. (a) a^7 (b) x^{11} (c) x^5 (d) n^6 (e) a^4 (f) x^9 (g) 1 (h) p^9 (i) m^6
   (j) 1 (k) a^{13} (l) 1
6. $3x^5$
7. (a) $5x^9$ (b) $16x^4$ (c) $10p^5$ (d) $24a^6$ (e) $8a^3$ (f) $5x^2$
8. B
9. (a) x^2 (b) a^4 (c) m (d) a^4 (e) n^2 (f) x^4 (g) x^6 (h) a^4 (i) n^3

Page 64 *M2·9*

1. $2a + 6$ **2.** $16y - 8$ **3.** $24x - 12$ **4.** $15x + 20$ **5.** $21x - 35$ **6.** $28y + 8$
7. $5a - 5b$ **8.** $4a + 2b$ **9.** $21x + 7y$ **10.** $3x + 6y$ **11.** $18x + 12$ **12.** $4p + 4q$
13. $4p + 8q$ **14.** $18a - 30b$ **15.** $36c + 72d$ **16.** $x^2 + xy$ **17.** $2x^2 + xy$ **18.** $ab - ac$
19. $ab + a^2$ **20.** $p^2 - pq$ **21.** $2c^2 + cd$ **22.** $p^2 + 3p$ **23.** $a^2 - 7a$ **24.** $3a^2 + 3a$
25. $5xy + 10x$ **26.** $3bc + 6bd$ **27.** $4a^2 + 8ab$ **28.** $6m^2 - 15mn$ **29.** $24ab - 48ac$ **30.** $6x^2 + 9xy$

ge 65   E2·4

1. $-2x - 12$
2. $-5y + 15$
3. $-3a + 6$
4. $-2x - 8$
5. $-5c - 50$
6. $-6x + 2y$
7. $-12p + 20$
8. $-10a - 5$
9. $-32b + 8$
10. $-6c - 12$
11. $-15a - 6$
12. $-18x + 18$
13. $-20a + 24$
14. $9b - 21$
15. $7 - 14x$
16. $-ab - ac$
17. $-ef + eg$
18. $-x^2 + xy$
19. $-2p^2 - pq$
20. $-3y^2 - yz$
21. $-2x^2 + xy$
22. $-a^2 - ab$
23. $-m^2 + mn$
24. $-3x + y$
25. $-2p - 5q$
26. $-3a^2 - 3ab$
27. $6ab - 4b^2$
28. $15x^2 - 10xy$

ge 65   Can you still?

1. -2
2. -10
3. 1
4. -6
5. -8
6. -4
7. -13
8. -5
9. -3
10. -7
11. -1
12. 1
13. -24
14. 24
15. 30
16. -18
17. -16
18. -4
19. 8
20. -4

ge 65   M2·10

1. $2x + 11$
2. $10x + 8$
3. $14x + 8$
4. $22x + 20$
5. $18x + 13$
6. $4a + 12$
7. $16a + 18$
8. $27y + 12$
9. $9a + 12$
10. $9x + 24$
11. $12x + 18$
12. $14a + 7$
13. $14a + 18$
14. $26x + 25$
15. $6m$
16. $6m + 3$
17. $12a + 28$
18. $12a + 20b + 24$
19. $6n^2 + 3n$
20. $n^2 + 3mn$
21. $an + 5cn$
22. $10m^2 + 2mn$
23. $12a^2 + 12ac$
24. $3x^2 + 21xy$
25. $26d + 32$
26. $18x + 15$
27. $11a + 4$
28. $28x + 5$
29. $22a + 20$
30. $19x + 3$

ge 67   M2·11

1. $3(2a + 5)$
2. $3(3c + 2)$
3. $5(x - 3)$
4. $6(2a + 3)$
5. $5(3m + 4)$
6. $7(n - 5)$
7. $8(x + 4)$
8. $9(x + 4)$
9. $7(2a - 5)$
10. $8(2n - 3)$
11. $9(5x + 4)$
12. $8(6a - 5)$
13. $2(4a + 5)$
14. $3(2x + 9)$
15. $5(x - 4)$
16. $6(m + 7)$
17. $5(5a - 7)$
18. $4(4x - 1)$
19. $9(3p - 2)$
20. $6(3a + 4b)$
21. $8(2x + 5y)$
22. $7(2a - 3b)$
23. $4(6m - 5n)$
24. $7(3x + 4y)$
25. $8(7a + 4b)$
26. $10(2x - y)$
27. $9(4x - 3y)$
28. $8(9c + 5d)$
29. $5(2a + 3b + 5c)$
30. $3(2p + 3q + r)$
31. $7(x + 2y - z)$
32. $3(3a - 3b - 7c)$
33. $4(6m + 3n + 4p)$
34. $7(6a + 5b - 2)$
35. $9(2a - 3b + 4c)$
36. $4(7x - 9y + 4)$

ge 68   M2·12

1. $x(y + z)$
2. $a(b - c)$
3. $x(x + 6)$
4. $a(5 + a)$
5. $3b(b - 4)$
6. $c(d + c)$
7. $3x(y + 5z)$
8. $8b(a - 3c)$
9. $4x(3x - 2)$
10. $m(6m - 1)$
11. $f(e + g)$
12. $p(p + 3)$
13. $a(7 - a)$
14. $x(x - 8)$
15. $a(a + 5)$
16. $2p(q + 2r)$
17. $4b(2a - 3c)$
18. $3y(2x - 3z)$
19. $5x(x - 3)$
20. $5s(t + 7)$
21. $8p(r - 5q)$
22. $2b(3a + 2)$
23. $a(3a + 8)$
24. $4x(3 - 4x)$
25. $x(x + y)$
26. $3x(x + 7y)$
27. $10b(2a - 5)$
28. $a^2(b - c)$
29. $a(a + bc)$
30. $x(5x - 6y)$
31. $10p(2p - 3q)$
32. $4b(9ac - 4b)$
33. $7x(7x + 6y)$
34. $7a(9a - 5b)$
35. Should be $2(3a^2 + ab + 1)$

ge 69   Can you still?

1. $80 = 2 \times 2 \times 2 \times 2 \times 5$
2. (a) $2 \times 3 \times 5$ (b) $2 \times 2 \times 3 \times 3$ (c) $2 \times 5 \times 5$ (d) $2 \times 2 \times 2 \times 2 \times 3 \times 3$
3. (a) 12 (b) 15 (c) 27

12

Page 70 *M2·13*

1. (a) 4 (b) 3 (c) 3 (d) 5 (e) 11 (f) 27 (g) 17 (h) 22
   (i) 10 (j) 7 (k) 3 (l) 16
2. (a) 23 (b) 29 (c) 12 (d) 14 (e) 21 (f) 32 (g) 44 (h) 57
3. (a) 7 (b) 6 (c) 4 (d) 6 (e) 7 (f) 6 (g) 9 (h) 6
   (i) 12 (j) 30 (k) 32 (l) 70 (m) 7 (n) 36 (o) 8
4. 9   5. 8   6. 17   7. 27   8. 9   9. 4
10. (a) 12 (b) 14 (c) 5 (d) 7 (e) 18 (f) 39 (g) 28 (h) 53
    (i) 35 (j) 5 (k) 22 (l) 36

Page 71 *E2·5*

1. (a) -1 (b) -5 (c) -5 (d) -5 (e) 1 (f) -5 (g) -4 (h) -5
   (i) 3 (j) -7 (k) -8 (l) -8
2. (a) -5 (b) -3 (c) -7 (d) -2 (e) -6 (f) -6 (g) -3 (h) -8
   (i) 4 (j) 7 (k) -6 (l) 6
3. (a) -18 (b) -16 (c) -6 (d) -15 (e) -8 (f) -21 (g) -6 (h) 6
   (i) -20 (j) -18 (k) 4 (l) -14
4. (a) $\frac{3}{2}$ (b) $\frac{7}{2}$ (c) $\frac{-1}{2}$ (d) $\frac{-5}{2}$ (e) $\frac{1}{3}$ (f) $\frac{3}{2}$ (g) $\frac{-3}{10}$ (h) $\frac{-9}{2}$
   (i) $\frac{1}{4}$ (j) $\frac{-4}{5}$ (k) $\frac{-1}{7}$ (l) $\frac{-2}{9}$

Page 72 *M2·14*

1. 2   2. 6   3. 5   4. 8   5. 3   6. 2   7. 3   8. 6   9. 4   10. 5
11. 4   12. 4   13. 5   14. 5   15. 3   16. 10   17. 4   18. 8   19. 3   20. 3
21. 10   22. 3   23. 4   24. 6

Page 72 *Can you still?*

1. 25 296   2. 47   3. 17
4. (a) $4·98 \times 10^4$ (b) 9×10^{-2} (c) $8·5 \times 10^{-1}$ 5. $5·6 \times 10^{14}$

Page 73 *E2·6*

1. $1\frac{1}{2}$ 2. $10n = 7, n = \frac{7}{10}$ 3. $\frac{-3}{4}$ 4. -3 5. 2
6. $-10 = 2n, n = -5$ 7. $\frac{2}{3}$ 8. $\frac{4}{5}$ 9. $-\frac{1}{2}$ 10. -1
11. $\frac{-1}{3}$ 12. $\frac{-3}{8}$ 13. $\frac{-5}{6}$ 14. $\frac{-1}{2}$ 15. $\frac{7}{2}$
16. $4n + 2 = 3, n = \frac{1}{4}$ 17. $7n + 5 = 8, n = \frac{3}{7}$ 18. $5n + 11 = 6, n = -1$
19. $2n + 7 = 1, n = -3$ 20. $8n - 4 = -20, n = -2$ 21. $3n + 8 = -7, n = -5$
22. -2 23. -4 24. -3 25. -4 26. -3 27. -2
28. -5 29. -4 30. -3 31. 5   32. -5 33. 4

Page 74 *Wages – overtime*

1. £430   2. £427·50
3. (a) £288   (b) £352   (c) £340   (d) £440   (e) £416
4. £350·40   5. £344·40   6. (a) £343.20   (b) £385   (c) £393·60   (d) £391·60
7. £494   8. £498·75   9. Simon earns £3·50 more   10. 8 hours

. (a) $2n$ (b) $3m - 8$ (c) $3x + 4y$

. (a) 81   (b) 65   (c) 12   (d) -9

   (e) $a = 11$ (f) $V = 124 \cdot 62$ (g) $v = 45$

. (a) $6x + 7y$ (b) $5a + 6b$ (c) $7p + 2$ (d) $6m + 4n$

   (e) $3 + 5x$ (f) $3x^2$ (g) $4a + 5ab$ (h) $15a$

   (i) $6b^2$ (j) $3p$ (k) $9b$ (l) $24mn$

. (a) 6^2 (b) 5^7 (c) 1   (d) 3^6 (e) 4^2 (f) x^2 (g) x^{20} (h) x^2

. (a) $3x + 21$ (b) $12a - 6b$ (c) $5x + 25y$ (d) $pq + 6p$

   (e) $2a^2 - 5a$ (f) $2b^2 + 3bc$ (g) $3xy - 6x^2$ (h) $-8a + 4b$

   (i) $8x + 36$ (j) $23m + 17$

. (a) $5(x + 3)$ (b) $8(a - 3)$ (c) $7(5p - 3)$ (d) $2(2a + 5b - 4c)$

   (e) $c(d + e)$ (f) $x(x - 4y)$ (g) $2q(3p - 5r)$ (h) $5a(a + 6b)$

. (a) 7   (b) 15   (c) 8   (d) 24   (e) -3 (f) 4   (g) 8   (h) 5

   (i) 5   (f) $n - 8 = 19, n = 27$

. (i) $7r$ (ii) $13s - 2t$ **2.** (a) 12   (b) 5

. (i) 4^5 (ii) 6^7 **4.** (a) $4a$ (b) $6b^2$ (c) $6c - 3$

. (a) 4   (b) 12   (c) $-2 \cdot 5$ **6.** 13 cm

. (a) $3a + a^2$ (b) $4(b - 3)$

. (a) 19   (b) 8   (c) $2 \cdot 25$ **9.** (a) 2^8 (b) 3^2 (c) 5^4

. (a) (i) $12g$ (ii) $9x + 3$ (b) $c - 5d$ (c) $2y$

. (a) $2(2x + 5y)$ (b) $x(x + 7)$

. (i) $10w$ (ii) $x + 6$ or $x - 6$ **13.** 2^8 cm^2

. $12t - 4$ **15.** (a) 32   (b) 6

NIT 3

. a, d

. (a) $\dfrac{5}{8}$ (b) $\dfrac{1}{6}$ (c) $\dfrac{1}{4}$ (d) $\dfrac{3}{8}$ (e) $\dfrac{5}{6}$ (f) $\dfrac{7}{9}$ (g) $\dfrac{5}{16}$ (h) $\dfrac{7}{12}$

. (a) $\dfrac{18}{33}$ (b) $\dfrac{15}{33}$

. $\dfrac{3}{5}$ **5.** $\dfrac{5}{30} = \dfrac{1}{6}$ **6.** $\dfrac{5}{14}$ **7.** $\dfrac{7}{21} = \dfrac{1}{3}$

. (a) $\dfrac{10}{100} = \dfrac{1}{10}$ (b) $\dfrac{25}{100} = \dfrac{1}{4}$ (c) $\dfrac{40}{100} = \dfrac{2}{5}$ (d) $\dfrac{3}{100}$

   (e) $\dfrac{65}{100} = \dfrac{13}{20}$ (f) $\dfrac{48}{100} = \dfrac{12}{25}$

. $\dfrac{19}{100}$ **10.** (a) $\dfrac{1}{2}$ (b) $\dfrac{4}{12} = \dfrac{1}{3}$ (c) $\dfrac{9}{16}$

. (a) 3   (b) 7   **2.** (a) 8   (b) 20

. (a) 16   (b) 40   **4.** 8

. £7   **6.** £7   **7.** 6g   **8.** 8   **9.** 24   **10.** £28   **11.** 35   **12.** 30g   **13.** 36 litres

. (a) £48   (b) £84   (c) 850 m   (d) 162   (e) £1866   (f) 125 kg   (g) £7·50   (h) 70 cm

. 63 kg

14

1. £200   **2.** 84 cm   **3.** £7   **4.** 72g   **5.** £12

6. PERFECT   **7.** £99   **8.** Mariana weighs 2 kg more

Page 83 ***Can you still?***

1. $14x + 4y$ **2.** $4a$ **3.** $5p + 5q$ **4.** $9a + 4$

5. $7m + n$ **6.** $2n^2$ **7.** $5a + 5b + 24$ **8.** $14n + 6m + 4$

Page 84 **M3·4**

1. $\dfrac{1}{3}, \dfrac{2}{6}$ **2.** $\dfrac{1}{4}, \dfrac{2}{8}$ **3.** $\dfrac{6}{12}, \dfrac{3}{6}$ **4.** $\dfrac{2}{3}, \dfrac{4}{6}$ **5.** $\dfrac{12}{32}, \dfrac{6}{16}$ **6.** $\dfrac{4}{6}, \dfrac{2}{3}$ **7.** $\dfrac{3}{4}, \dfrac{9}{12}$

8. $\dfrac{2}{6}, \dfrac{4}{12}$ **9.** $\dfrac{1}{4}, \dfrac{25}{100}$ **10.** $\dfrac{2}{12}$ **11.** $\dfrac{14}{16}$ **12.** $\dfrac{4}{8}$ **13.** $\dfrac{12}{20}$ **14.** $\dfrac{16}{20}$

15. $\dfrac{10}{12}$ **16.** $\dfrac{15}{24}$ **17.** $\dfrac{12}{21}$ **18.** $\dfrac{15}{20}$ **19.** $\dfrac{40}{45}$ **20.** $\dfrac{18}{60}$ **21.** $\dfrac{8}{20}$

22. $\dfrac{12}{27}$ **23.** $\dfrac{9}{18}$ **24.** $\dfrac{15}{40}$ **25.** $\dfrac{56}{80}$

Page 85 **M3·5**

1. $\dfrac{5}{6}$ **2.** $\dfrac{1}{8}$ **3.** $\dfrac{4}{5}$ **4.** $\dfrac{2}{3}$ **5.** $\dfrac{1}{3}$ **6.** $\dfrac{1}{3}$ **7.** $\dfrac{1}{2}$ **8.** $\dfrac{3}{4}$

9. (a) $\dfrac{2}{5}$ (b) $\dfrac{2}{5}$ (c) $\dfrac{1}{3}$ (d) $\dfrac{2}{9}$ (e) $\dfrac{1}{3}$ (f) $\dfrac{2}{3}$ (g) $\dfrac{2}{3}$ (h) $\dfrac{5}{6}$

     (i) $\dfrac{8}{9}$ (j) $\dfrac{2}{5}$ (k) $\dfrac{1}{3}$ (l) $\dfrac{3}{5}$ (m) $\dfrac{3}{5}$ (n) $\dfrac{7}{9}$ (o) $\dfrac{1}{2}$

10. (a) CHINA   (b) PEAR   (c) ENGLISH   (d) HOCKEY

Page 86 **M3·6**

1. (a) $\dfrac{1}{2}$ (b) $\dfrac{2}{5}$ **2.** $\dfrac{1}{2} = \dfrac{3}{6}, \dfrac{1}{3} = \dfrac{2}{6}, \dfrac{1}{2}$ **3.** $\dfrac{3}{4} = \dfrac{6}{8}, \dfrac{7}{8}$

4. (a) $\dfrac{1}{3}$ (b) $\dfrac{1}{5}$ (c) $\dfrac{3}{4}$ (e) $\dfrac{2}{5}$ (f) $\dfrac{3}{5}$

5. (a) $\dfrac{1}{6}, \dfrac{1}{3}, \dfrac{1}{2}$ (b) $\dfrac{3}{8}, \dfrac{1}{2}, \dfrac{3}{4}$ (c) $\dfrac{1}{6}, \dfrac{7}{12}, \dfrac{2}{3}$ (d) $\dfrac{3}{10}, \dfrac{2}{5}, \dfrac{1}{2}$ (e) $\dfrac{13}{20}, \dfrac{7}{10}, \dfrac{4}{5}$ (f) $\dfrac{5}{8}, \dfrac{11}{16}, \dfrac{3}{4}$

6. (a) $\dfrac{11}{20}$ (b) $\dfrac{13}{20}$ (c) $\dfrac{3}{4}$ (d) $\dfrac{8}{9}$ (e) $\dfrac{4}{7}$ (f) $\dfrac{7}{40}$

Page 86 ***Can you still?***

1. $5x - 15$ **2.** $8x + 20$ **3.** $35m - 10$ **4.** $28a + 14b$ **5.** $ab + ac$

6. $m^2 - 6m$ **7.** $3a + 9$ **8.** $4n^2 - 28n$ **9.** $15a^2 + 40a$

Page 88 **M3·7**

1. T   **2.** T   **3.** F   **4.** T   **5.** F   **6.** T   **7.** T

8. T   **9.** T   **10.** F   **11.** T   **12.** T   **13.** $0{\cdot}43 = \dfrac{43}{100}$ so correct

14. Correct   **15.** $\dfrac{1}{25}$ **16.** $\dfrac{1}{500}$ **17.** $\dfrac{37}{100}$ **18.** $\dfrac{3}{250}$ **19.** $\dfrac{7}{20}$ **20.** $\dfrac{3}{200}$

21. $\dfrac{9}{25}$ **22.** $\dfrac{3}{8}$ **23.** $\dfrac{8}{10} = 0{\cdot}8$ **24.** $\dfrac{15}{100} = 0{\cdot}15$ **25.** $\dfrac{36}{100} = 0{\cdot}36$

26. $\dfrac{55}{1000} = 0{\cdot}055$ **27.** $0{\cdot}05$ **28.** $0{\cdot}84$ **29.** $0{\cdot}45$ **30.** $0{\cdot}015$

31. $0{\cdot}125$ **32.** $0{\cdot}85$ **33.** $0{\cdot}119$ **34.** $0{\cdot}105$ **35.** $0{\cdot}\dot{6}$

36. $0{\cdot}4\dot{5}$ **37.** $0{\cdot}\dot{2}$ **38.** $0{\cdot}\dot{7}$ **39.** $0{\cdot}1\dot{6}$ **40.** $0{\cdot}8\dot{3}$

ge 89 M3·8

1. Alexis **2.** incorrect **3.** < **4.** < **5.** < **6.** =
7. < **8.** > **9.** < **10.** < **11.** correct **12.** incorrect
13. 0·014, 0·017, 0·1, 0·107 **14.** 0·03, 0·034, 0·303, 0·31, 0·32 **15.** 0·087, 0·806, 0·81, 0·812, 0·82
16. 0·06, 0·061, 0·064, 0·603, 0·61 **17.** 0·015, 0·107, 0·11, 0·121, 0·13 **18.** 3·04, 3·16, 3·18, 3·2, 3·6
19. 8·019, 8·021, 8·1, 8·13, 8·14 **20.** 0·51, 0·53, 5·02, 5·1, 5·17 **21.** 0·19, 1·03, 1·07, 1·16, 1·72
22. EAT MY SHORTS **23.** HOW YOU DOING **24.** Kaitlyn, Addison, Jaden, Edward
25. 28·7 kg **26.** SHARPEN

ge 90 Can you still?

1. 36 **2.** 8 **3.** 26 **4.** 10 **5.** 3 **6.** 20
7. 48 **8.** 12 **9.** 64 **10.** 31 **11.** 2

ge 91 M3·9

1. $3\frac{1}{2}$ **2.** $2\frac{1}{6}$ **3.** $2\frac{3}{4}$ **4.** $3\frac{2}{3}$ **5.** $2\frac{1}{4}$ **6.** $2\frac{1}{7}$ **7.** $3\frac{1}{8}$
8. $1\frac{3}{4}$ **9.** $2\frac{6}{7}$ **10.** $2\frac{1}{9}$ **11.** $2\frac{1}{2}$ **12.** $5\frac{5}{6}$ **13.** $7\frac{2}{3}$ **14.** $8\frac{1}{2}$
15. $5\frac{1}{8}$ **16.** $5\frac{4}{5}$ **17.** $2\frac{5}{6}$ **18.** $3\frac{2}{9}$ **19.** $8\frac{4}{5}$ **20.** $6\frac{3}{4}$

ge 92 M3·10

1. $\frac{7}{3}$ **2.** $\frac{7}{2}$ **3.** $\frac{19}{4}$ **4.** $\frac{17}{3}$ **5.** $\frac{9}{2}$ **6.** $\frac{23}{4}$ **7.** $\frac{19}{3}$
8. $\frac{31}{8}$ **9.** $\frac{14}{3}$ **10.** $\frac{28}{5}$ **11.** $\frac{29}{9}$ **12.** $\frac{31}{7}$ **13.** $\frac{35}{4}$ **14.** $\frac{67}{9}$
15. $\frac{68}{7}$ **16.** $\frac{32}{5}$ **17.** $\frac{62}{7}$ **18.** $\frac{43}{8}$ **19.** correct

ge 93 M3·11

1. (a) $\frac{5}{20}$ (b) $\frac{8}{20}$ (c) $\frac{13}{20}$ **2.** (a) $\frac{30}{35}$ (b) $\frac{21}{35}$ (c) $\frac{9}{35}$
3. $\frac{13}{15}$ **4.** $\frac{13}{28}$ **5.** $\frac{27}{40}$ **6.** $\frac{7}{15}$ **7.** $\frac{3}{8}$
8. $\frac{9}{10}$ **9.** $\frac{5}{6}$ **10.** $\frac{7}{10}$ **11.** $\frac{1}{8}$ **12.** $\frac{1}{12}$
13. $\frac{5}{6}$ **14.** $\frac{11}{12}$ **15.** (c) **16.** (b) **17.** (a)

ge 94 E3·1

1. (a) $\frac{9}{4}$ (b) $2\frac{11}{12}$ **2.** (a) $\frac{11}{5}$ (b) $\frac{7}{4}$ (c) $3\frac{19}{20}$
3. A→R, B→P, C→Q
4. (a) $2\frac{23}{24}$ (b) $2\frac{17}{24}$ (c) $6\frac{1}{10}$ (d) $3\frac{5}{6}$ **5.** (a) $1\frac{13}{30}$ (b) $1\frac{3}{4}$ (c) $2\frac{7}{20}$
6. $4\frac{7}{12}$ km **7.** $\frac{4}{15}$ **8.** $\frac{1}{24}$

ge 94 Can you still?

1. $3(a + 2b)$ **2.** $5(2m - 3n)$ **3.** $a(b - c)$
4. $2a(3b + 2c)$ **5.** $a(a - b)$ **6.** $m(m + 3n)$
7. $2m(2m - n)$ **8.** $3a(2a + 5b)$ **9.** $ab(5c + 6)$
10. $4m(n + 3m)$ **11.** $6mn(m - 3)$ **12.** $3a(2b + 5a)$

Page 95 M3·12

1. (a) $\frac{1}{8}$ (b) $\frac{1}{9}$ (c) $\frac{1}{12}$ (d) $\frac{1}{12}$ 3. (a) $\frac{3}{8}$ (b) $\frac{1}{2}$ (c) $\frac{1}{6}$ (d) $\frac{1}{5}$

4. (a) $\frac{8}{35}$ (b) $\frac{1}{6}$ (c) $\frac{1}{4}$ (d) $\frac{2}{5}$ 5. 7 minutes

6. $\frac{2}{21}$ 7. $\frac{1}{90}$ 8. $\frac{3}{20}$ 9. $\frac{2}{3}$ 10. $\frac{1}{24}$ 11. $\frac{1}{12}$ 12. $\frac{1}{2}$

13. $\frac{1}{12}$ 14. $\frac{1}{36}$ 15. $\frac{1}{12}$ 16. $\frac{1}{3}$ 17. $\frac{1}{6}$ 18. $\frac{3}{40}$

19. (a) 6   (b) 8   (c) 15   (d) $\frac{3}{4}$

Page 96 E3·2

1. $1\frac{1}{20}$ 2. $1\frac{1}{3}$ 3. $\frac{3}{4}$ 4. 2   5. $3\frac{2}{3}$ 6. $7\frac{1}{5}$ 7. 12

8. $\frac{3}{4}$ 9. 6   10. A→R, B→P, C→Q   11. $\frac{6}{25}$ 12. $\frac{3}{40}$ cm²

Page 98 M3·13

1. $\frac{3}{4}$ 2. $\frac{18}{35}$ 3. $\frac{7}{40}$ 4. 27   5. 4   6. 32   7. 30   8. $1\frac{1}{2}$

9. $1\frac{3}{5}$ 10. $\frac{5}{27}$ 11. $\frac{5}{14}$ 12. A→R, B→P, C→Q   13. 9   14. 32 weeks

Page 98 E3·3

1. 4   2. $6\frac{3}{7}$ 3. $\frac{21}{32}$ 4. $2\frac{3}{20}$ 5. $5\frac{1}{4}$ 6. $1\frac{5}{23}$ 7. $\frac{4}{7}$

8. $\frac{49}{106}$ 9. $11\frac{1}{5}$ 10. $2\frac{2}{17}$ 11. $1\frac{3}{5}$ 12. $2\frac{13}{14}$ 13. 15   14. 48 days

Page 99 E3·4

1. (a) 0·2 or $\frac{1}{5}$ (b) 0·125 or $\frac{1}{8}$ (c) 2   (d) 5   (e) 9   (f) 10

2. 1·25   3. 7   4. 16   5. n 6. $\frac{3}{2}$ or 1·5

7. (a) $\frac{5}{3}$ (b) $\frac{9}{4}$ or 2·25   (c) $\frac{13}{2}$ or 6·5   (d) $\frac{2}{5}$ or 0·4   (e) 20

Page 100 *Pitch the tent*

Task A

early June at Halby Coombe, total cost £78

Task B

latest train from Denby is 1442 and the total journey time will 3 hours 27 minutes

Page 102 *Test yourself on Unit 3*

1. (a) $\frac{5}{9}$ (b) $\frac{2}{7}$ 2. (a) £300   (b) £390

3. (a) $\frac{21}{24}$ (b) $\frac{10}{35}$ (c) $\frac{4}{5}$ (d) $\frac{3}{8}$ (e) $\frac{3}{7}$ (f) $\frac{3}{4}$ (g) $\frac{1}{3}$

4. (a) $\frac{1}{4}, \frac{3}{8}, \frac{2}{5}$ (b) $\frac{7}{12}, \frac{2}{3}, \frac{3}{4}, \frac{5}{6}$

5. (a) 0·35   (b) 0·08   (c) $0·\dot{5}$ (d) $\frac{37}{100}$ (e) $\frac{7}{250}$ (f) $\frac{7}{10}$ (g) $\frac{21}{50}$

6. (a) 0·3   (b) 0·17   (c) 0·062, 0·064, 0·6, 0·63   (d) 2·049, 2·14, 2·183, 2·318, 2·714, 2·83

7. (a) $5\frac{3}{4}$ (b) $4\frac{1}{2}$ (c) $3\frac{2}{5}$ (d) $6\frac{2}{5}$ (e) $\frac{9}{4}$ (f) $\frac{17}{3}$ (g) $\frac{23}{7}$ (h) $\frac{35}{8}$

(a) $\frac{13}{35}$ (b) $\frac{11}{12}$ (c) $4\frac{1}{12}$ (d) $1\frac{5}{12}$ **9.** (a) $\frac{1}{24}$ (b) $\frac{3}{14}$ (c) $6\frac{3}{5}$ (d) $10\frac{2}{3}$

(a) $\frac{8}{9}$ (b) $\frac{18}{35}$ (c) $1\frac{9}{25}$ (d) $1\frac{5}{6}$ **11.** (a) $\frac{1}{10}$ (b) 2

ge 104 Mixed examination questions

(a) $\frac{3}{5}$ (b) $4\frac{2}{3}$ tins **2.** $\frac{1}{4}$ **3.** 0·05, 0·16, 0·4, 0·59

4 **5.** $\frac{8}{10}, \frac{20}{25}$ **6.** (a) $\frac{1}{3}$ (b) $4\frac{1}{15}$

4·072, 4·079, 4·17, 4·7, 4·712 **8.** $\frac{1}{7}$ **9.** 60p cheaper

(a) $\frac{3}{8}$ (b) $4\frac{3}{8}$ **11.** $\frac{5}{9}$

(a) $-0·3, \frac{1}{3}, 3·03, 33·3$ (b) not correct (difference = 33·6)

(a) $\frac{7}{24}$ (b) 7 hours

NIT 4

ge 107 M4·1

(a) Obtuse (b) Acute (c) Reflex (d) Reflex (e) Obtuse (f) Acute
(g) Reflex (h) Obtuse (i) Acute (j) Obtuse
(a) Acute (b) Obtuse (c) Acute (d) Obtuse (e) Obtuse (f) Reflex
(c) no **4.** Obtuse
(a) $I\hat{A}B, B\hat{C}D, C\hat{D}E, D\hat{E}F, F\hat{G}H$, (Any 3) (b) $A\hat{B}C, E\hat{F}G, G\hat{H}I, H\hat{I}A$ (Any 3)
(c) Obtuse (d) Acute

ge 108 M4·2

40° **2.** 160° **3.** 75° **4.** 45° **5.** 50° **6.** 160°
155° **8.** 90° **9.** 70° **10.** 328° **11.** 145° **12.** 39°

ge 109 M4·3

a 120° **2.** b 40°, c 140° **3.** d 50° **4.** e 30° **5.** f 85°
g 25° **7.** h 80°, i 100° **8.** j 50°, k 50° **9.** l 60°, m 60° **10.** n 58°, p 58°
q 46°, r 62° **12.** s 67°, t 42° **13.** EF, IJ

ge 110 M4·4

a 50° **2.** g 65° **3.** c 80°, d 20° **4.** e 40°, f 100°
g 75°, h 30° **6.** i 50°, j 50° **7.** k 70°, l 110° **8.** m 25°, n 130°, p 155°
q 33°, r 114°, s 114° **10.** t 85°, u 85°, v 85° **11.** w 42°, x 96°, y 96° **12.** z 60°, a 120°
$C\hat{B}D = 45°, A\hat{B}D = 135°$ **14.** $P\hat{R}Q = 60°, S\hat{R}T = 60°$

ge 112 M4·5

a 80° **2.** b 125° **3.** c 35° **4.** d 50°, e 130°
f 60°, g 120° **6.** h 25°, i 155° **7.** j 42°, k 138° **8.** l 37°, m 37°, n 143°
p 71°, q 71°, r 80°, s 100° **10.** t 67°, u 113°, v 56°, w 124°
x 90°, y 117°, z 117° **12.** a 30°, b 80°, c 70°
BE and CD **14.** $P\hat{Q}S = T\hat{R}S$ or $Q\hat{P}S = R\hat{T}S$
(a) 38° (b) 100° (c) 142°

18

Page 112 **Can you still?**

1. $42x$
2. $28a$
3. $9y^2$
4. $5n$
5. $24mn$
6. $3n^2$
7. $a^2 + 2ab$
8. $3n^2 - 6n$
9. $10m^2 - 5m$
10. $6xy + 15x^2$
11. $2(2a + 3b)$
12. $m(n - y)$
13. $3m(4 + 3n)$
14. $x(x - 4)$
15. $a(a + 6b)$
16. $5m(3m - 4n)$

Page 113 **M4·6**

1. a, c, d, f
2. a, c, f

Page 115 **M4·7**

1. 3
2. 1
3. 2
4. 1
5. 4
6. 2
7. 4
8. 2
9. 5
10. 8
11. 6
12. 6
13. 4
14. 4

Page 115 **M4·8**

1. A, B, D, F
2. (a) Equal/90° (b) equal
4. (b) 4
5. (a) yes (b) 4 (c) 4
6. (a) equal (b) equal
8. (a) 2
9. (a) yes (b) 2
10. B, F
12. (b) 2
13. (a) yes (b) 2 (c) 2
15. (a) 0 (c) 0
16. (a) yes (b) 2 (c) 2
17. D
21. (a) 1 (c) 1
22. 90°
23. (a) a, c, f (b) a, b (c) a, c

Page 115 **Can you still?**

1. true
2. false
3. true
4. true
5. true
6. true
7. true
8. false

Page 119 **M4·9**

1. a 60°
2. b 120°
3. c 35°
4. d 125°
5. e 96°, f 84°
6. g 42°, h 138°
7. i 57°, j 115°
8. k 50°
9. l 91°, m 91°
10. n 107°, p 107°
11. q 115°, r 115°, s 40°
12. t 115°
13. (a) 100° (b) 80° (c) 80° (d) 20°
14. 30°

Page 119 **Can you still?**

1. 6
2. 2×5^2
3. 3^3
4. $4 \times (2 + 3) - 2 = 18$
5. 15

Page 121 **M4·10**

1. (a) 108° (b) 90° (c) 120° (d) 144°
2. (a) 76° (b) 141° (c) 122° (d) 67° (e) 51° (f) 128°
   (g) 113° (h) 122° (i) 85° (j) 92° (k) 88°
3. (a) 30° (b) 150°
4. (a) 40° (b) 140°
5. (a) 24° (b) 18° (c) 6° (d) 4°
6. (a) 156° (b) 162° (c) 174° (d) 176°
7. 45
8. 18
9. 30
10. 165°
11. $x = 36°, y = 144°$

Page 123 **E4·1**

1. Sum of angles = 1080°
2. (a) 1260° (b) 1800°
3. $x = 80°$
4. 110°
5. 85°
6. 90°
7. 79°
8. 62°
9. 144°
10. 3780°
11. 168°

Page 124 **Can you still?**

1. $8n + 9$
2. $14x + 27$
3. 4
4. $15a^2$
5. $4(9m - 4n)$
6. 3·5
7. x^7
8. m^8

ze 125 **M4·11**

A, H, M; B, E, N; C, O, Q; D, I, L; F, P, R; G, J, S; K, T, U

ze 127 **M4·12**

I LOVE BLING **2.** (5, 2) (2, 2) (6, 3) (5, 1) (0, 1) (5, 2) (2, 2) (6, 3) (5, 3) (4, 4) (5, 5)

WHAT LIES AT THE BOTTOM OF THE SEA AND SHIVERS? A NERVOUS WRECK

(a) top square (5, 11), top parallelogram (11, 7), rectangle (7, 7) bottom parallelogram (7, 3), bottom square (9, 0)

(b) top square (3, 10), top parallelogram $\left(10\frac{1}{2}, 9\frac{1}{2}\right)$, rectangle (4, 6) bottom parallelogram (4, 2), bottom square (9, 2)

ze 127 *Can you still?*

$\frac{8}{21}$ **2.** $\frac{5}{16}$ **3.** 12   **4.** $4\frac{1}{12}$ **5.** $\frac{14}{15}$ **6.** $5\frac{17}{20}$ **7.** 11 : 21

ze 129 **E4·2**

THIS IS EASY   **2.** (a) $(-4, 0)$ (b) $(1, 0)$ (c) $(3, 1)$ (d) $(2, 1)$

ze 131 **M4·13**

(a) $\begin{pmatrix} -3 \\ -1 \end{pmatrix}$ (b) $\begin{pmatrix} 1 \\ -4 \end{pmatrix}$ (c) $\begin{pmatrix} -2 \\ -2 \end{pmatrix}$ (d) $\begin{pmatrix} 3 \\ -2 \end{pmatrix}$

(e) $\begin{pmatrix} -3 \\ 2 \end{pmatrix}$ (f) $\begin{pmatrix} 1 \\ 2 \end{pmatrix}$ (g) $\begin{pmatrix} -4 \\ 0 \end{pmatrix}$ (h) $\begin{pmatrix} 4 \\ -3 \end{pmatrix}$

(a) $\begin{pmatrix} 1 \\ -3 \end{pmatrix}$ (b) $\begin{pmatrix} 3 \\ -7 \end{pmatrix}$ (c) $\begin{pmatrix} -4 \\ -9 \end{pmatrix}$

(d) $\begin{pmatrix} 1 \\ -10 \end{pmatrix}$ (e) $\begin{pmatrix} 0 \\ -6 \end{pmatrix}$ (f) $\begin{pmatrix} 2 \\ -8 \end{pmatrix}$

(g) $\begin{pmatrix} 5 \\ 0 \end{pmatrix}$ (h) $\begin{pmatrix} 4 \\ 3 \end{pmatrix}$ (i) $\begin{pmatrix} -2 \\ -4 \end{pmatrix}$

(j) $\begin{pmatrix} -7 \\ 2 \end{pmatrix}$ (k) $\begin{pmatrix} -5 \\ -6 \end{pmatrix}$ (l) $\begin{pmatrix} 9 \\ 0 \end{pmatrix}$

(m) $\begin{pmatrix} 7 \\ 4 \end{pmatrix}$ (n) $\begin{pmatrix} -3 \\ 4 \end{pmatrix}$ (o) $\begin{pmatrix} -2 \\ -3 \end{pmatrix}$

(p) $\begin{pmatrix} -9 \\ 6 \end{pmatrix}$ (q) $\begin{pmatrix} 5 \\ 6 \end{pmatrix}$ (r) $\begin{pmatrix} -5 \\ 7 \end{pmatrix}$

(f) $\begin{pmatrix} 4 \\ 4 \end{pmatrix}$ (g) $\begin{pmatrix} -2 \\ -8 \end{pmatrix}$ (h) $\begin{pmatrix} 0 \\ 8 \end{pmatrix}$

ze 133 *Can you still?*

$8m - 20$ **2.** $4n^2 + 12n$ **3.** 0·74   **4.** $3p^2 + 3$ **5.** n^{14} **6.** $y = a + 7$

ze 135 **M4·15**

(d) reflect in x-axis   **4.** (d) reflect in y-axis

ze 136 *Can you still?*

8330   **2.** 18   **3.** $4·28 \times 10^4$ **4.** -8 **5.** 6×10^{19}

ze 139 **M4·17**

(a) 3   (b) 27   (c) 9 times larger = (scale factor)^2

(a) 3   (c) 12   (d) 4 times larger = (scale factor)^2

(c) (1, 1), (1, 3), (5, 3)

Page 141   **Mobile phones Task**

5. 300   **6.** £12   **7.** Tariff P   **8.** Tariff Q

9. (b) 200   (c) Tariff Z   (d) Tariff Y

Page 143   **Test yourself on Unit 4**

1. (a) ABD   (b) obtuse   **2.** a 39°, b 141°, c 123°, d 64°, e 52°, f 52°

3. (a) (i) 2 (ii) 2   (b) (i) 4 (ii) 4   (c) (i) 1 (ii) 1

4. (a) trapezium (i) 0 (ii) 1   (b) rhombus (i) 2 (ii) 2   (c) kite (i) 1 (ii) 1

  (d) parallelogram (i) 0 (ii) 2

5. a 70° b 80° c 100°   **6.** a 60°, b 120°, c 95°   **7.** B

8. (a) (2, 3)   (b) (2, 0)   (c) A(1, 2) or M(3, 2) or B(2, 3)

9. (a) $\begin{pmatrix} -5 \\ -4 \end{pmatrix}$ (b) $\begin{pmatrix} -1 \\ -5 \end{pmatrix}$ (c) $\begin{pmatrix} -4 \\ 4 \end{pmatrix}$ (d) $\begin{pmatrix} 5 \\ 1 \end{pmatrix}$

Page 146   **Mixed examination questions**

1. 45°   **2.** (b) 6   **4.** 100°

5. (i) C, D   (ii) B, D   (iii) A, E

6. (a) $p = 55°, q = 125°$ (b) 9   **9.** 105°

UNIT 5

Page 150   **M5·1**

1. (a) 32   (b) 38·55   (c) 13·39   (d) 11·3   (e) 5·56   (f) 11·4

2. 0·71 + 0·29,   0·54 + 0·46,   0·96 + 0·04,   0·37 + 0·63,   0·22 + 0·78,

  0·8 + 0·2,   0·41 + 0·59,   0·61 + 0·39

3. (a) 4·97   (b) 10·15   (c) 3·152   (d) 6·31   (e) 12·47   (f) 52·44

  (g) 25·5   (h) 34·9   (i) 22·4   (j) 2·6   (k) 5·7   (l) 2·31

4. 3 cups of coffee and 2 cakes **5.** £10·63   **6.** Yes, £24·31

7. 0·281 + 0·019,   0·049 + 0·251,   0·213 + 0·087,   0·12 + 0·18,   0·17 + 0·13,

  0·28 + 0·02,   0·06 + 0·24,   0·202 + 0·098

8. £105·50   **9.** B

10. (a) 8·56 − 4·83 = 3·73 (b)   4·07 + 4·96 = 9·03 (c) 3·176 − 2·428 = 0·748

Page 153   **M5·2**

1. (a) 2·66   (b) 0·234   (c) 51·6   (d) 0·0493   (e) 2·914   (f) 9·184

  (g) 2·2284   (h) 5·13   (i) 0·0835   (j) 8·672

2. (a) 0·36   (b) −0·16   (c) 0·021   (d) 0·016   (e) −0·018   (f) 0·0035

3. £16·53   **4.** £21·16   **5.** £165·96   **6.** £8·82   **7.** £7·68

8. (a) 0·3   (b) −0·06   **9.** £8·64

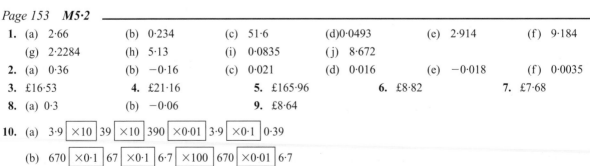

10. (a) 3·9 ×10 39 ×10 390 ×0·01 3·9 ×0·1 0·39

  (b) 670 ×0·1 67 ×0·1 6·7 ×100 670 ×0·01 6·7

  (c) 83·2 ×100 8320 ×0·1 832 ×0·01 8·32 ×0·1 0·832

  (d) 0·24 ×100 24 ×0·1 2·4 ×100 240 ×0·001 0·24

ge 153   Can you still?

, 25   **2.** 21   **3.** 20   **4.** 63   **5.** £576   **6.** £72

ge 154   M5·3

, 6·2   **2.** 9·12   **3.** 3·41   **4.** 2·56   **5.** 4·9   **6.** 4·35
, 4·63   **8.** 2·47   **9.** 34·2   **10.** −3·155   **11.** 0·217   **12.** −3·81
, 0·49   **14.** 10·04   **15.** −1·74   **16.** −0·0725   **17.** 0·00392   **18.** 0·0532
, £12·45   **20.** £5·75   **21.** 48·25 kg   **22.** 4p   **23.** 47 cm   **24.** £69·75

ge 156   M5·4

, 3·4
, (a) 6·3   (b) 5·8   (c) 8·4   (d) 6·8   (e) 0·4   (f) 9·8   (g) 12·6   (h) 15·7
, 7·319, 7·31, 7·341 and 7·33
, (a) 2·35   (b) 7·05   (c) 13·33   (d) 2·07   (e) 0·24   (f) 23·68   (g) 0·94   (h) 7·09
, 8·164, 8·1623, 8·1649
, (a) 2·168   (b) 5·641   (c) 8·326   (d) 4·232   (e) 7·252   (f) 13·711   (g) 17·330   (h) 41·614
, (a) 1·39   (b) 0·31   (c) 6·60   (d) 7·66   (e) 0·33   (f) 1·14   (g) 2·02   (h) 0·76
, (i) 0·01   (j) 2·76   (k) 4·12   (l) 0·16
, (a) A 5·2, 6, 3·7; B 3·7, 4, 4   (b) 14·9, 11·7
, Kavya is correct

ge 158   M5·5

, (a) £14, £19   (b) £14·95, £20·29 both smaller
, A→Q, B→S, C→P, D→T, E→R   **3.** £5000   **4.** 12 000 KCals
, (a) B   (b) A   (c) A   (d) C   (e) A   (f) B
, (g) C   (h) B   (i) B   (j) A   (k) C   (l) B
, true ≈ 600 ÷ 8 × £1·60   **7.** 210 cm^3 **8.** not correct ≈ 20·268   **9.** true

ge 160   Can you still?

, (a) 80°   (b) 100°   **2.** (a) 114°   (b) 66°
, (a) 71°   (b) 102°   **4.** (a) 51°   (b) 51°   (c) 51°

ge 161   M5·6

, (a) 8   (b) 8   (c) 2   (d) 38   (e) 1   (f) 18
, (g) 58   (h) 30   (i) 20   (j) 2   (k) 13
, Across Answers
, **1.** 6·92   **3.** 11·9   **5.** 40·12   **7.** 735   **9.** 49   **10.** 34·8   **11.** 81   **12.** 245
, Down Answers
, **1.** 6·8   **2.** 250·848   **3.** 11·27   **4.** 94·65   **6.** 91·68   **8.** 31·45   **10.** 34

ge 162   M5·7

, A→R, B→P, C→S, D→U, E→Q, F→T
, (a) 136·68   (b) 0·28   (c) 3·50   (d) 3·84   (e) 5·15
, (f) 5·15   (g) 0·62   (h) 0·31   (i) 3·47   (j) 47·82

3.

+	$\frac{3}{8}$	$\frac{7}{20}$	$2\frac{1}{2}$	$1\frac{2}{3}$
$\frac{1}{4}$	$\frac{5}{8}$	$\frac{3}{5}$	$2\frac{3}{4}$	$1\frac{11}{12}$
$\frac{3}{5}$	$\frac{39}{40}$	$\frac{19}{20}$	$3\frac{1}{10}$	$2\frac{4}{15}$
$2\frac{1}{3}$	$2\frac{17}{24}$	$2\frac{41}{60}$	$4\frac{5}{6}$	4
$2\frac{3}{10}$	$2\frac{27}{40}$	$2\frac{13}{20}$	$4\frac{4}{5}$	$3\frac{29}{30}$

4.

H		L	E	G	I	B	L	E
E				E			O	
D	O	I	L		G	O	B	
G				H	I	S		
E		B			B	E	D	
H	B	O	G				I	
O		O			S	G		
G	O	Z		H				
	B	E	S	I	E	G	E	

Page 164 **M5·8**

1. 3·9639, 3·9641, 3·9568

2. (a) 14 (b) 8 (c) 6·4 (d) 0·836 (e) 1740
(f) 51·4 (g) 32 000 (h) 0·055 (i) 30 000 (j) 73·63

3. Across Answers

1. 17·97 **3.** 11 **6.** 830 **8.** 14·52 **9.** 224 **11.** 11 **12.** 8·8 **13.** 31·8 **14.**

Down Answers

1. 1·98 **2.** 900 **4.** 138·268 **5.** 0·041 **7.** 3·02 **9.** 2·23 **10.** 418 **12.**

Page 164 *Can you still?*

1. $2a^2$ **2.** a^4 **3.** $9m + 1$ **4.** m^{12} **5.** $m^2 + 4m$
6. $8a^2 - 6a$ **7.** $2(4n - 3)$ **8.** $m(m + 5)$ **9.** $2a(2b + 5)$ **10.** $5n(n - 4)$

Page 166 **M5·9**

1. (a) 1850, 1850 ÷ 20 = 92·5 (b) 4952, 4952 ÷ 328 = 14 (c) 50·4, 50·4 + 12 6 = 63
(d) 31·6, 31·6 × 7 = 221·2 (e) 42·3, 42·3 × 9·1 = 384·93 (f) 39·51 − 25·8 = 13·71
(g) 21·2, 21·2 × 4·5 = 95·4 (h) 42·4, both ways (i) 6·2449, check by squaring
(j) 29·63, both ways

2. A→T, B→P, C→S, D→R, E→Q

3. (a) 281 (b) 36 (c) 101·16

4. £1000 **5.** 6 times

6. (a) 5 (b) 100 (c) £3000 (d) 1 (i) 0·2 kg
(f) 2 (g) 100 (h) £2000 (i) 400

Page 168 **M5·10**

1. 5% **2.** 30% **3.** 12% **4.** (a) $\frac{37}{100}$ (b) 37%

5. (a) $\frac{1}{10}$ (b) $\frac{3}{100}$ (c) $\frac{11}{100}$ (d) $\frac{2}{5}$ (e) $\frac{3}{4}$ (f) $\frac{3}{20}$
(g) $\frac{4}{5}$ (h) $\frac{11}{50}$ (i) $\frac{8}{25}$ (j) $\frac{19}{20}$ (k) $\frac{12}{25}$ (l) $\frac{1}{20}$

6. $\frac{3}{10}$ **7.** $\frac{4}{5}$ **8.** 33%

9. (a) 25% (b) 35% (c) 12% (d) 36% (e) 70% (f) 85% (g) 42%

10. 12% more **11.** 11%

12. (a) 71% (b) 28% (c) 31%

13. 59% **14.** 27% **15.** 0·4, 42%, $\frac{11}{25}$, $\frac{9}{20}$

ge 170 **Can you still?**

, 2   **2.** 2   **3.** 135°   **4.** 125°   **5.** 18

ge 171 **M5·11**

(a) 35%   (b) 45%   (c) 20%   **2.** (a) 65%   (b) 36%   (c) Maths

, 41%   **4.** Survey B greater by 5%

, English 85% Maths 56% Science 46% Art 65% Geog. 70% Meg.   **6.** 69%   **7.** 42%

(a) 9%   (b) 16%   (c) 21%   **9.** (a) 8%   (b) 36%   **10.** 14%

ge 172 **Can you still?**

(a) 8   (b) 3   (c) −80   (d) 32   (e) −16   (f) 25

(a) −3   (b) −9   (c) 6 or −6   (d) −2

(a) 8   (b) −2   (c) 16   (d) 8

ge 173 **M5·12**

, (b)   **2.** (b)   **3.** (a) 10%   (b) 15 g

(a) 12   (b) 9   (c) 18   (d) 30   (e) 7·5   (f) 4·5

, £270   **6.** £5600   **7.** £882   **8.** 825 g

(a) £120   (b) £480   **10.** (a) £9   (b) £81

(a) £22·50   (b) £67·50   **12.** (a) £60   (b) £20

(a) £46   (b) £46   **14.** (a) £126   (b) £294

(a) £30   (b) £60   **16.** (a) £140   (b) £210

(a) £48   (b) £16   **18.** £22 880

ge 175 **M5·13**

, 29 760   **2.** 689   **3.** A→R, B→P, C→Q

(a) £2·11   (b) £23·66   (c) £18·19   (d) £8·86   (e) £30·09

(f) £5·14   (g) £11·31   (h) 85p   (i) £4·77

, £479·40

(a) £69·75   (b) £292·80   (c) £8·21   (d) £19·68   (e) £60·48

(f) £1·53   (g) £175·94   (h) £9·53

, £945·14   **8.** £7·72   **9.** 11 270   **10.** £338   **11.** £494·40

(a) £330   (b) £280·50   **13.** 640

(a) £2784   (b) £2032·32   **15.** £765·84

ge 176 **Can you still?**

→U, B→Q, C→T, D→V, E→S, F→P

ge 178 **E5·1**

, B   **2.** R

(a) £36   (b) £96   (c) £150   (d) £117

, 56 days   **5.** £36   **6.** Alyssa earns £350 more

ge 179 **E5·2**

(a) 0·75   (b) £80   **2.** (a) 1·5   (b) £600

(a) £80   (b) £200   (c) £90   (d) £400

, £140   **5.** 20 mm by 14 mm   **6.** £550

, computer £800, cooker £750, bike £300   **8.** 400

24

Page 180 **Can you still?** ────────────────────────────

1. $\dfrac{1}{20}$　　　2. $\dfrac{5}{12}$　　　3. $\dfrac{5}{12}$　　　4. $\dfrac{6}{7}$　　　5. $\dfrac{5}{22}$　　　6. $\dfrac{22}{35}$

7. $\dfrac{9}{40}$　　　8. $\dfrac{11}{30}$　　　9. $\dfrac{1}{20}$　　　10. $\dfrac{56}{45} = 1\dfrac{11}{45}$　　　11. 6　　　12. $\dfrac{5}{27}$

Page 181 **M5·14** ────────────────────────────

1. a, d, f, h are true

2. (a) 84%　　　(b) 67%　　　(c) 2%　　　(d) 80%　　　(e) 20%　　　(f) 8%

3. $A \rightarrow T,\ B \rightarrow R,\ C \rightarrow U,\ D \rightarrow Q,\ E \rightarrow P$

4. (a) 0·035　　　(b) 0·067　　　(c) 1　　　(d) 1·2　　　(e) 2·48　　　(f) 1·92

5. $21\% = 0·21 = \dfrac{21}{100}$,　$7\% = 0·07 = \dfrac{7}{100}$,　$19\% = 0·19 = \dfrac{19}{100}$,　$25\% = 0·25 = \dfrac{1}{4}$,

$30\% = 0·3 = \dfrac{3}{10}$,　$70\% = 0·7 = \dfrac{7}{10}$

6. Toni correct

7. $0·32 = 32\% = \dfrac{8}{25}$,　$0·43 = 43\% = \dfrac{43}{100}$,　$0·06 = 6\% = \dfrac{3}{50}$,　$0·14 = 14\% = \dfrac{7}{50}$,

$0·8 = 80\% = \dfrac{4}{5}$,　$0·15 = 15\% = \dfrac{3}{20}$

Page 183 **M5·15** ────────────────────────────

1. £102　　　2. £228　　　3. £508　　　4. £1820　　　5. £8·75　　　6. £1680

7. (a) £3068　　　(b) £7210　　　(c) £1615　　　(d) £10 165

8. £5258

Page 184 **Can you still?** ────────────────────────────

2. (d) (0, 6)

Page 185 **M5·16** ────────────────────────────

1. 4 : 3　　　2. 3 : 4　　　3. 4 : 1　　　4. (b) not correct　　　6. 2 : 5

7. (a) 1 : 5　　(b) 2 : 1　　(c) 1 : 5　　　8. (a) 3 : 1　　(b) 1 : 6　　(c) 1 : 3　　(d) 9 : 4

9. (a) 8　　(b) 9　　(c) 6　　(d) 12　　(e) 6 white 9 red

10. (a) 2 : 1　　(b) correct

Page 187 **M5·17** ────────────────────────────

1. (a) 3 : 2　　(b) 2 : 3　　(c) 3 : 5　　(d) 5 : 11　　(e) 3 : 2　　(f) 6 : 7　　(g) 3 : 4　　(h) 7 : 4

　(i) 3 : 4　　(j) 3 : 5　　(k) 8 : 5　　(l) 2 : 5　　(m) 4 : 2 : 1　　(n) 2 : 3 : 4　　(o) 8 : 3 : 5　　(p) 4 : 9 : 7

2. 8 : 5　　　　3. yes　　　　4. 6 : 1　　　　5. 4 : 5

6. (a) 1 : 2　　(b) 5 : 1　　(c) 10 : 1　　(d) 6 : 1　　(e) 1 : 8　　(f) 1 : 4　　(g) 25 : 2

　(h) 1 : 40　　(i) 1 : 4　　(j) 1 : 10　　(k) 1 : 40　　(l) 1 : 10

7. (a) 5 : 9　　(b) 23 : 52　　(c) 5 : 2　　(d) 88 : 185

8. A is the odd one out　　　　9. Q

Page 188 **M5·18** ────────────────────────────

1. £9　　　2. £35　　　3. 55p　　　4. £48　　　5. £4·50

6. 1125 g　　　7. 1·90, 15·20, 61·75, 142·50　　　8. 1·65, 8·25, 24·75, 206·25, 104·61

9. £95·90　　　10. 400 g　　　11. 300 g　　　12. 750 g

13. 450 g cheese, 900 g flour, 750 g Margarine, 3 onions, 9 eggs, 90 g butter, 9 Table spoons water

14. 330 g butter, 330 g sugar, 3 Table spoons water, 6 eggs, 330 g flour, 3 Table spoons cocoa

5. 180 g flour, 420 mℓ milk, 3 eggs

6. 450 g cheese, 324 g dough, 270 mℓ tomato sauce, 45 g pepperoni

7. €107·10

Page 189 Can you still?

1. (a) $7·8 \times 10^{-2}$ (b) $1·19 \times 10^{-3}$ (c) $1·69 \times 10^{3}$ (d) $1·867 \times 10^{2}$

2. $7·4 \times 10^{-6}$

3. (a) $1·702 \times 10^{18}$ (b) $6·2658 \times 10^{-8}$ (c) 2×10^{13}

Page 191 M5·19

1. (a) 90 g : 210 g   (b) 350 g : 100 g   (c) 45 min : 15 min
   (d) £500 : £100 : £200   (e) £80 : £120 : £160   (f) 2000 g : 1250 g : 1750 g

2. Colin 14, Lily 21

3. 6 cm, 21 cm   4. (a) 260   (b) 325   (c) 390

5. Omar £120, Molly £40, Sachin £160

6. BMW 48 litres, Mini 27 litres

7. (a) 54 mℓ   (b) 10 mℓ   8. £165

9. (a) 18   (b) 20   10. 10

11. (a) 24 ℓ   (b) 24 ℓ   (c) 32 ℓ Red, 48 ℓ Yellow

12. 4   13. (a) 29 g   (b) 10·5 kg

14. 540 g flour, 180 g sugar

Page 192 E5·3

1. $x = 100°$, $y = 20°$, $z = 60°$ 2. £60   3. 5 : 4

4. £5200   5. (a) 75   (b) 4

6. 49 litres   7. 6   8. $p = 108°$, $q = 36°$, $r = 72°$, $s = 144°$ 9. £72 000

Page 194 Money for your holiday Task

1. 290 E   2. 6944 Pesos   3. 358·50 Aus$

4. 10 782 Rand   5. £165   6. £600

7. £68   8. 3105·36 riyals   9. £700

10. £1500   11. Japan   12. Australia

13. Shabina   14. £76·80   15. £38·80

Page 195 Test yourself on Unit 5

1. (a) 0·018   (b) 0·48   (c) 0·49   (d) 6·36   (e) bus cheaper by 40p

2. (a) 2·25   (b) 0·128   (c) 0·72   (d) £15·75

3. (a) (i) 8·2   (ii) 6·4   (iii) 4·2   (iv) 14·3   (v) 8·2
   (b) (i) 3·39   (ii) 2·19   (iii) 15·38   (iv) 0·90   (v) 28·18

4. (a) C   (b) A   (c) B   (d) A   (e) 4   (f) 4624   (g) $5\frac{32}{35}$ (h) 16

5. (a) 17·8   (b) 24   (c) 31·7   (d) 213 000   (e) 380   (f) 0·611

6. (a) yes   (b) yes   (c) yes   (d) 3·86

7. (a) 51%   (b) 30%   (c) 28%   (d) 55%   (e) 40%   (f) Ned by 8·4%   (g) 8%

8. (a) £392   (b) £753·60   (c) £634·40   (d) £338·80

9. (a) £80   (b) £500

10. (a) 75% = 0·75, 0·7 = 70%, 0·07 = 7%, 0·34 = 34%, 1·4 = 140%   (b) 0·02 greater

11. (a) £408   (b) £944

12. (a) 4 : 5   (b) 1 : 3   (c) 3 : 8   (d) 4 : 1   (e) 1 : 4   (f) 1 : 12   (g) 2 : 5

13. (a) £2·94 (b) 16 (c) 200 g is better value
14. (a) Ally (£1650), Jane (£600), Rob (£750) (b) 9 mℓ (c) 18 litres (d) 35

Page 199   *Mixed examination questions*

1. £1·29 **2.** Total = £2120, VAT = £424, Total = £2544 **3.** 3 litres **4.** 5%
5. size B **6.** (a) 900 euros (b) £5 **7.** not enough cement
8. (a) 1·437 398 936 (b) 1·44 **9.** no, only 92% attendance
10. £408·48 **11.** £30 **12.** 60
13. (a) 800 (b) 6 (c) 9 **14.** £30 **15.** better value at farm shop

UNIT 6

WATCH YOUR MONEY 1

Page 203   *WYM 6·1*

1. £40·19 **2.** £47·25 **3.** £116·52
4. (a) 17 − 26 − 19 (b) 32718425 (c) www.sb.co.uk (d) 419327
(e) the amount figure and words do not agree **5.** £35·14

Page 205   *WYM 6·2*

1. £353·15 **2.** £1044·98 **3.** £1016·34 **4.** £125·60 **5.** £785·29 **6.** £65
7. £807·03 **8.** £785·08 **9.** £785·08 **10.** money taken to pay bills
11. money taken from a cash machine **12.** amount overdrawn (owed to bank)

Page 207   *WYM 6·3*

1. (a) £42 (b) £504 (c) £546 (d) £126
2. (a) £84 (b) £558 (c) £642 (d) £82
3. (a) Total credit price £820. Extra cost £85 (b) £440, £50 (c) £13 752, £1352
(d) £250, £20 (e) £594·64, £129·64
4. £988 **5.** £980

Page 209   *WYM 6·4*

1. £149·90 **2.** £3037·57 **3.** £3057·57 **4.** £1942·43 **5.** £4936·57
6. £246·83 **7.** £46·83 **8.** £5001·73 **9.** £5021·73

UNIT 7

Page 211   *M7·1*

1. (a) 14 (b) 7 (c) 13 **2.** 18, 22, (+4), yes
3. 15, 17, (+2), yes **4.** 39, 47, (+8), yes **5.** 4, 1, (−3), yes
6. 7, 3, (−4), yes **7.** 41, 50, (+9), yes **8.** 28, 34, (+6), yes
9. 46, 55, (+9), yes **10.** 19, 25, (+1 to previous difference), no
11. 11, 16, (+1 to previous difference), no **12.** 8, 3, (subtract 1 more each time), no
13. 30, 5, (subtract 5 more each time), no **14.** −3, −5, (−2), yes **15.** −6, −8, (−2), yes
16. 15, 23 **17.** 14, 20 **18.** 11, 1
19. 14, 8 **20.** 19, 33 **21.** −6, −2
22. −3, −9 **23.** 49, 45 **24.** 4, −4
25. 14, 19 **26.** 15, 21

(a) 16   (b) 20

(a) 21   (b) 26   (c) no

16, 32, (×2), no

50, 25, (÷2), no

15, 21, (triangular), no

20,000, 200,000, (×10), no

250, 432, $(2n^3)$, no

28. (a) 13   (b) 17

30. (a) 13   (b) 16   (c) yes

32. 81, 243, (×3), no

35. 26, 37, $(n^2 + 1)$, no

38. 162, 486, (×3), no

41. 125, 216, (n^3), no

44. 55, 66, (triangular), no

33. 25, 36, (n^2), no

36. $2\frac{1}{2}$, 3, $(+\frac{1}{2})$, yes

39. 3, 1, (÷3), no

42. 2·9, 3·3, (+0·4), yes

45. 0·03, 0,003, (÷10), no

---

ge 213   M7·2

5n − 2   **2.** (a) 8   (b) 2   (c) 2n + 6

(a) 6n − 3   (b) 7n − 3   (c) 10n + 3   (d) 14 − 2n   (e) 8n − 7

(f) 21 − 4n   (g) 49 − 9n   (h) 0·5n + 2   **4.** (a) 283   (b) 2

(a) 17   (b) 4   **6.** (a) −6   (b) ÷2   (c) +1·5   (d) ×3

---

ge 213   Can you still?

−60   **2.** 25   **3.** 21   **4.** −20   **5.** 16   **6.** −3   **7.** −10

20   **9.** −56   **10.** 4   **11.** 35   **12.** −5   **13.** 6   **14.** $\frac{3}{7}$

---

ge 215   M7·3

(b) 23   (c) w = 5n + 3   (d) 103   **2.** (c) s = 6n − 2   (d) 298

(c) s = 2n + 1   (d) 101   **4.** (c) s = 8n − 4   (d) 396

(c) s = 4n + 1   (d) 201   **6.** (c) s = 9n + 1   (d) 451

(b) p = 3n + 2   (c) 62   **8.** (c) y = 2n + 6   (d) 106   (e) yes (n = 9)

---

ge 217   E7·1

x − 5 = y   **2.** x − 8 = y   **3.** a + 3 = b   **4.** a − 9 = b   **5.** $\frac{a}{6} = b$ **6.** x + 2 = y

(a) x = y + 9   (b) x = 12y   (c) x = y − 6   (d) x = y − 20   (e) $x = \frac{y}{8}$ (f) $x = \frac{y}{10}$

(g) x = y + 4   (h) x = y + 25   (i) x = 3y   (j) x = 15y   (k) x = y − 100   (l) $x = \frac{y}{18}$

A→Q, B→P, C→S   **9.** $q = \frac{p}{3}$ **10.** $b = \frac{a}{7}$ **11.** y = 9x

(a) $y = \frac{x - 2}{3}$ (b) $y = \frac{x + 9}{4}$

$b = \frac{a + 5}{2}$ **14.** $q = \frac{p - 7}{9}$ **15.** $b = \frac{a - 1}{7}$ **16.** $y = \frac{x + 10}{3}$

(a) $\frac{y - 8}{2}$ (b) $\frac{y + 5}{6}$ (c) $\frac{y + 10}{8}$ (d) 3(y − 2)   (e) 5(y + 6)   (f) 2(y + 4)

---

ge 218   M7·4

A, x = 1; B, $x = 4\frac{1}{2}$; C, x = −3   **2.** P, y = 1; Q, $y = 3\frac{1}{2}$; R, y = −3; S, $y = -1\frac{1}{2}$

(c) (i) x = 4   (ii) x = −3   (iii) y = 3

(a) A   (b) L   (c) B D   (d) E J G K   (e) 2   (f) J   (g) L

y = 1, y = 5, y = 9, x = 1, x = 3, x = 7, x = 9

---

ge 219   Can you still?

12ab   **2.** $35a^2$ **3.** $2a^2$ **4.** a^4 **5.** m^6

$3n^2 + 3n$ **7.** 4a − 4c   **8.** $m^2 + 3mn$ **9.** $2a^2 − 8ab$ **10.** $15n^2 − 10np$

3(2m + 3n)   **12.** b(a − c)   **13.** a(a − 7)   **14.** 5n(3n + 2m)

Page 220   *M7·5*

1. $(0, 4)$ $(1, 5)$ $(2, 6)$ $(3, 7)$

2. $(0, 0)$ $(1, 2)$ $(2, 4)$ $(3, 6)$

3. $(0, 1)$ $(1, 4)$ $(2, 7)$ $(3, 10)$

4. $(0, 6)$ $(1, 5)$ $(2, 4)$ $(3, 3)$

5. (b) $(2, 2)$ **6.** (a) 1   (b) -6 (c) -4 (d) -4 (e) -1

7. (a) -2 (b) -6 (c) -6 (d) -9 (e) -11

8. $(-2, -4)(-1, -3)(0, -2)(1, -1)(2, 0)$

9. $(-2, 0)(-1, 2)(0, 4)(1, 6)(2, 8)$

10. (a) $(-2, -8)(-1, -5)(0, -2)(1, 1)(2, 4)$ (b) $x \approx -1\cdot3$

11. (a) $(-3, 9)(-2, 7)(-1, 5)(0, 3)(1, 1)(2, -1)(3, -3)$ (b) $x \approx -0\cdot5$

Page 223   *M7·6*

1. 1   **2.** $\frac{1}{2}$ **3.** 3   **4.** 1   **5.** $\frac{1}{3}$ **6.** $\frac{3}{4}$

7. (A) 4, (B) $1\frac{1}{2}$, (C) $\frac{1}{4}$ **8.** (a) 3   (b) $\frac{1}{4}$ (c) $\frac{2}{3}$

3. -3 **10.** $-\frac{1}{2}$ **11.** -1 **12.** (A) -2, (B) -5, (C) $-\frac{1}{3}$, (D) $\frac{3}{2}$, (E) $\frac{5}{2}$

Page 224   *Can you still?*

1. a $140°$ **2.** b $42°$, c $42°$ **3.** d $80°$ **4.** e $38°$, f $142°$ **5.** g $65°$ **6.** h $53°$ **7.** $144°$

Page 225   *M7·7*

1. (e) all gradients $= 2$ **2.** (e) all gradients $= -3$ **3.** $(0, -5)$

Page 225   *Can you still?*

1. $0\cdot024$ **2.** $1\cdot24$ **3.** $14\cdot84$ **4.** $1\cdot17$ **5.** £$3\cdot05$ **6.** $0\cdot084, 0\cdot09, 0\cdot79, 0\cdot8, 0\cdot82$

Page 226   *M7·8*

1. $y = 3x + 1, y = 3x - 2, y = 7 + 3x$

2. (a) 3, 4   (b) 2, -5 (c) 8, -1 (d) 1, 6   (e) $-4, -2$ (f) $-4, 3$

(g) $-1, -2$ (h) $-5, 2$ (i) $-1, 3$ (j) $-2, 4$ (k) $\frac{1}{3}, -7$ (l) $-4, \frac{1}{2}$

3. A: $y = 3x - 1$, B: $y = \frac{1}{2}x + 1$, C: $y = -x - 2$ **4.** $y = 3 + 4x$ and $y = 4x - 2$

Page 227   *M7·9*

1. $(-3, 9)$ $(-2, 4)$ $(-1, 1)$ $(0, 0)$ $(1, 1)$ $(2, 4)$ $(3, 9)$

2. $(-3, 10)$ $(-2, 5)$ $(-1, 2)$ $(0, 1)$ $(1, 2)$ $(2, 5)$ $(3, 10)$

3. $(-3, 6)$ $(-2, 1)$ $(-1, -2)$ $(0, -3)$ $(1, -2)$ $(2, 1)$ $(3, 6)$

4. $(-3, 18)$ $(-2, 8)$ $(-1, 2)$ $(0, 0)$ $(1, 2)$ $(2, 8)$ $(3, 18)$

5. $(-3, 27)$ $(-2, 12)$ $(-1, 3)$ $(0, 0)$ $(1, 3)$ $(2, 12)$ $(3, 27)$

6. $(-3, 19)$ $(-2, 9)$ $(-1, 3)$ $(0, 1)$ $(1, 3)$ $(2, 9)$ $(3, 19)$

7. $(-3, 25)$ $(-2, 10)$ $(-1, 1)$ $(0, -2)$ $(1, 1)$ $(2, 10)$ $(3, 25)$

Page 229   *E7·2*

1. (a) $(-4, 14)$ $(-3, 8)$ $(-2, 4)$ $(-1, 2)$ $(0, 2)$ $(1, 4)$ $(2, 8)$

2. (a) $(-3, 3)$ $(-2, 0)$ $(-1, -1)$ $(0, 0)$ $(1, 3)$ $(2, 8)$ $(3, 15)$

3. (a) $(-3, 14)$ $(-2, 8)$ $(-1, 4)$ $(0, 2)$ $(1, 2)$ $(2, 4)$ $(3, 8)$ (b) $1\cdot75$

Page 229   *M7·10*

1. (a) 40   (b) 30   (c) 10   (d) 55   (e) 11am–12 noon, 20 cars

2. (a) 28   (b) 112   (c) 70   (d) 336   (e) 40   (f) 60   (g) 100   (h) 400   (i) 110

3. (a) 160   (b) 120   (c) 6.30 pm   (d) 8.30 pm   (e) $1\frac{1}{2}$ hrs.   (f) the first

1. (a) 100 m   (b) 150 m   (c) 400 m   (d) 20 secs   (e) 35 secs   (f) 45 secs   (g) Kris
2. (a) 60 km/h   (b) 20 km/h
3. (a) 13.00   (b) 15 mins.   (c) 10.15   (d) 75 mins.   (e) 25 km/h   (f) 70 km/h   (g) 60 km/h
4. A 3, B 1, C 2   6. A 5, B 1, C 6, D 3, E 2, F 4

1. £15 600   2. 40%   3. £51   4. $\dfrac{6}{25}$ 5. £5580

sk A

1. £719   2. £952   3. £789   4. £1350

sk B

1. (a) £5403·35   (b) £65·45   2. £150·06

1. (a) R   (b) Both could be correct   (c) (i)   10, 5   (ii)   13, 10   (iii)   27, 38
2. (a) $3n + 1$ (b) $5n - 2$ (c) $w = 4n + 2$ (d) 82
3. (a) $x = y - 3$ (b) $x = \dfrac{y}{4}$ (c) $x = y + 9$ (d) $x = \dfrac{y - 1}{2}$
   (e) $x = \dfrac{y + 2}{5}$ (f) $x = 5y$ (g) $x = 7y$ (h) $x = 3(y - 4)$
4. (a) (0, 1) (1, 5) (2, 9)   (b) (0, 7) (1, 6) (2, 5) (3, 4)   (c) (2, 5)
5. (a) $\dfrac{1}{3}$ (b) $-\dfrac{2}{3}$ (c) -4 (d) $\dfrac{5}{2}$
   (e) $y = 2x + 3$ (f) $y = 5x - 4,\ y = 1 + 5x$ (g) -1
6. (a) (−3, 11) (−2, 6) (−1, 3) (0, 2) (1, 3) (2, 6) (3, 11)
   (b) (−3, 21) (−2, 11) (−1, 5) (0, 3) (1, 5) (2, 11) (3, 21)
7. (a) 61·5 kg   (b) 65 kg   (c) 64 kg   (d) July
   (e) 62 kg   (f) August 63·5 kg   (g) 2·5 kg   (h) 1 kg

1. (a) 12   11   (b) 41   (c) $4n + 1$ 2. (−1, −5) (0, −2) (1, 1) (2, 4) (3, 7)
3. (a) Katie has stopped   (b) 7·5 km   (c) 16 minutes   (d) home   (e) 15 km/h
   (f) first 40 minutes   (g) 84 minutes   4. $t = \dfrac{v - u}{5}$
5. (a) (i)   19   (ii)   18   (b) (i)   5   16   8   (ii)   44 or 7
6. (a) 7, 2, −1, −2, −1, 2, 7   7. $y = \dfrac{1}{2}x + 4$

NIT 8

1. even chance   2. unlikely   3. unlikely   4. likely   5. unlikely
6. certain   7. certain   8. unlikely   9. impossible   10. unlikely

1. $x = y - 6$ 2. $x = \dfrac{y}{12}$ 3. $x = 5y$ 4. $x = m + 7$
5. $x = \dfrac{m + 9}{2}$ 6. $x = \dfrac{a - 1}{5}$ 7. $x = 4(m - 6)$ 8. $x = 3(y + 4)$

Page 244 M8·2

1. (a) 50 (b) 0·71 (c) No, pupils' explanations
2. (a) 50 (b) 0·18 (c) Janice (throws more dice) (d) Yes, pupils' explanation
3. (a) 0·39 (b) 122 (c) 0·61
4. (a) 0·2 (b) Cottage pie 270, Chicken kurma 180, Spaghetti bolognese 450.
5. (a) 50 (b) 1, 0·088; 2, 0·096; 3, 0·102; 4, 0·1; 5, 0·094;
   6, 0·104; 7, 0·08; 8, 0·164; 9, 0·09; 10, 0·082
   (c) No, pupils' explanations (d) throw even more dice

Page 245 *Can you still?*

1. (c) translation $\begin{pmatrix} 3 \\ -4 \end{pmatrix}$ (d) B and C

Page 246 M8·3

1. $\frac{2}{5}$
2. (a) $\frac{1}{6}$ (b) $\frac{1}{6}$ (c) $\frac{1}{6}$ (d) $\frac{2}{6}$
3. (a) $\frac{1}{9}$ (b) $\frac{2}{9}$ (c) $\frac{3}{9}$
4. (a) $\frac{4}{11}$ (b) $\frac{5}{11}$ (c) $\frac{6}{11}$
5. (a) $\frac{1}{5}$ (b) $\frac{2}{5}$ (c) $\frac{3}{5}$
6. (a) $\frac{5}{10}$ (b) $\frac{3}{10}$ (c) $\frac{5}{10}$
7. (a) $\frac{5}{13}\left(\frac{1}{3}\right)$ (b) $\frac{3}{15}\left(\frac{1}{5}\right)$ (c) $\frac{10}{15}\left(\frac{2}{3}\right)$ (d) 0
8. (a) $\frac{1}{10}$ (b) $\frac{4}{10}$ (c) $\frac{5}{10}$
9. (a) $\frac{1}{52}$ (b) $\frac{26}{52}\left(\frac{1}{2}\right)$ (c) $\frac{13}{52}\left(\frac{1}{4}\right)$
10. (a) $\frac{5}{12}$ (b) $\frac{7}{12}$

Page 248 E8·1

1. 60
2. (a) 30 (b) 30 (c) 90 (d) 60
3. 30
4. 5
5. 15
6. 24
7. 4
8. (a) 28 (b) 20 (c) 32
9. 48
10. 180
11. 12
12. (a) 1 (c) black
13. 25
14. (a) $\frac{1}{4}$ (b) 1 (c)
15. bag B
16. 9, 9, 9
17. (a) 40 (b) $\frac{7}{10}$

Page 250 *Can you still?*

1. 189 g : 351 g
2. 64 : 105
3. £7385
4. yes
5. 500 mℓ
6. 1 : 60

Page 251 M8·4

1. Cereal + Juice, Cereal + tea, toast + juice, toast + tea
2. H1, H2, H3, H4, H5, H6, T1, T2, T3, T4, T5, T6
3. (a) (2, 1) (2, 4) (2, 9) (2, 16) (3, 1) (3, 4) (3, 9) (3, 16) (5, 1) (5, 4) (5, 9) (5, 16) (7, 1) (7, 4) (7, 9) (7, 16)
   (b) 16
4. CC, CV, CR, VV, VR, RR
5. MLC, MTC, MPC, SLC, STC, SPC, MLA, MTA, MPA, SLA, STA, SPA, MLR, MTR, MPR, SLR, STR, SPR
6. Tom Sasha : Tom Becky : Tom Ronnie : Sasha Becky : Sasha Ronnie : Becky Ronnie
7. HHH, HHT, HTH, HTT, THH, THT, TTH, TTT. $\frac{1}{8}$.
8. Coke Fanta; Coke sprite, Coke Diet coke, Fanta sprite, Fanta Diet coke, Sprite Diet Coke
9. (a) 6 (b) $\frac{1}{3}$

(a)

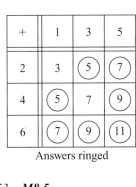

+	1	3	5
2	3	(5)	(7)
4	(5)	7	(9)
6	(7)	(9)	(11)

Answers ringed

(b) $\frac{3}{9}$

(c) incorrect. Same probability for both.

11. (b) $\frac{5}{36}$ (c) $\frac{1}{2}$ (d) $\frac{1}{6}$

---

age 253 **M8·5** ────────────────────────────────

. $31 \to 17, 14 \to 11, 6, 3, 11$

2. (a) $150 \to 53, 97 \to 16, 37, 48, 49$ (b) $\frac{48}{97}$

.

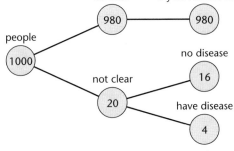

people
(1000)

all clear
(980)

5 year routine check
(980)

not clear
(20)

no disease
(16)

have disease
(4)

4. (a) $200 \to 120, 80 \to 6, 114, 12, 68$

(b) $\frac{114}{120} = \frac{19}{20}$

---

age 255 **M8·6** ────────────────────────────────

. b, c, f

2. (a) 0·8   (b) 0·2

3. (a) 0·9   (b) 0·1

. (a) 0·4   (b) 0·2   (c) 12

5. (a) 0·2   (b) 0·2   (c) 15

. $\frac{12}{13}$

7. (a) $\frac{3}{8}$ (b) $\frac{15}{16}$ (c) $\frac{9}{16}$ (d) 2

. 0·2

9. (a) 0·3   (b) 0·85

. (a) 0·6   (b) 0·15   (c) 15

11. $\frac{2}{3}$

12. $\frac{1}{4}$

---

age 258 **Can you still?** ────────────────────────

rrot

---

age 259 **M8·7** ────────────────────────────────

. (a) 2   (b) 6   (c) 2

2. (a) 17   (b) 12   (c) 7   (d) 21

. $\mathcal{E}$

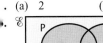

P 7 3 9 L
82

4. $\mathcal{E}$

T 30 18 11 C
41

.

---

age 260 **Can you still?** ────────────────────────

. 12   **2.** $\frac{41}{63}$ **3.** $\frac{2}{9}$ **4.** 16

---

age 261 **M8·8** ────────────────────────────────

. (a) $\frac{23}{50}$ (b) $\frac{7}{10}$ (c) $\frac{7}{50}$

2. (a) $\frac{7}{16}$ (b) $\frac{1}{2}$ (c) $\frac{9}{16}$

. (a) $\frac{123}{200}$ (b) $\frac{129}{200}$ (c) $\frac{23}{200}$

4. (a) $\frac{19}{50}$ (b) $\frac{59}{75}$ (c) $\frac{1}{2}$

. (a) $\frac{49}{120}$ (b) $\frac{1}{2}$ (c) $\frac{1}{5}$

Page 263   **Trim it**

Task A

1. and **2.** Jasmine   BMI 26·4   (overweight)
      Rory   BMI 18·7   (underweight)
      Mark   BMI 32·7   (obese)

Task B

1. Jasmine 3069 calories, Mark 4510 calories so Mark will burn off 1441 more extra calories.

2. 601 g   **3.** 2·9 weeks

Page 265   **Test yourself on Unit 8**

2. (a) 0·32   (b) 0·42   (c) 0·26   (d) 84

3. (a) (i) $\frac{1}{8}$ (ii) $\frac{3}{8}$ (iii) $\frac{2}{8}\left(\frac{1}{4}\right)$ (iv) $\frac{3}{8}$

      (b) (i) $\frac{4}{12}$ (ii) $\frac{2}{12}$ (iii) $\frac{7}{12}$ (c) (i) 5   (ii) 25   (iii) 25

4. (a) (1, 1) (1, 2) (1, 3) (1, 4) (2, 1) (2, 2) (2, 3) (2, 4) (3, 1) (3, 2) (3, 3) (3, 4) (4, 1) (4, 2) (4, 3) (4, 4)
          (5, 1) (5, 2) (5, 3) (5, 4) (6, 1) (6, 2) (6, 3) (6, 4)

      (b) French History Art; French History dt; French Geography Art; French Geography dt; German History Art; German
          History dt; German Geography Art; Ferman Geography dt; Spanish History Art; Spanish History dt; Spanish Geography
          Art; Spanish Geography dt.

      (c) 12

5. 50→15, 35→6, 9, 28, 7

6. (a) 0·99   (b) (i) $\frac{5}{6}$ (ii) $\frac{1}{6}$ (c) (i) 0·2   (ii) 0·3   (iii) 25

7. (a) $\frac{3}{40}$ (b) $\frac{129}{200}$

Page 268   **Mixed examination questions**

1. (a) $\frac{1}{26}$ (b) $\frac{8}{26} = \frac{4}{13}$ **2.** 45%   **3.** $\frac{1}{8}$ **4.** $\frac{15}{50} = \frac{3}{10}$

5. (a) 0·24   (b) 75   **6.** (a) 60→40, 20→16, 16, 8, 3, 7, 10   (b) $\frac{42}{60} = \frac{7}{10}$

7. (a) 0·4   (b) Blue 0·55   (c) did not ask enough girls

UNIT 9

Page 270   **M9·1**

1. (a) A 26 g, B 38 g   (b) 12 g   **2.** (a) A 54 cm, B 72 cm   (b) 18 cm
3. (a) A 18, B 33   (b) 15   **4.** (a) A 260, B 480   (b) 220
5. (a) A 72, B 96   (b) 24   **6.** (a) A 70, B 240   (b) 170
7. 4·5 kg   **8.** 150 g   **9.** 2·5 g   **10.** 7·5 kg   **11.** 4·5 ℓ   **12.** 26 kg
13. 1 : 15   **14.** 8 : 30   **15.** 10 : 05   **16** 9 : 20   **17.** 3 : 45   **18.** 7 : 50

Page 272   **M9·2**

1. (a) A 7·4, B 8·8   (b) 1·4   **2.** (a) A 4·8, B 5·6   (b) 0·8
3. (a) A 2·41, B 5·61   (b) 3·21   **4.** (a) A 16·4 m, B 17·4 m   (b) 1 m
5. (a) A 0·341, B 0·561   (b) 0·221   **6.** (a) A 24·8 mℓ, B 26·2 mℓ   (b) 1·4 mℓ
7. (a) A 42·2 mℓ, B 45·8 mℓ   (b) 3·6 mℓ   **8.** (a) A 0·038 kg, B 0·053 kg   (b) 0·015 kg
9. (a) A 6·8 kg, B 8·2 kg   (b) 1·4 kg   **10.** (a) A 25·5 cm, B 26·75 cm   (b) 1·25 cm
11. (a) A 0·42 kg, B 0·54 kg   (b) 0·12 kg   **12.** (a) A 750 mℓ, B 1200 mℓ   (b) 450 mℓ
13. 37·5 ℓ   **14.** 201   **15.** 9·6 kg   **16.** 3·25 ℓ   **17.** 840 mℓ   **18.** 0·56 kg

──────────────

. kg | **2.** m | **3.** mℓ | **4.** m | **5.** tonnes | **6.** g

. (a) 700 cm | (b) 450 cm | (c) 162 cm | (d) 5 cm | (e) 30 cm

. (a) 5000 g | (b) 3600 g | (c) 9200 g | (d) 632 g | (e) 6420 g

. (a) 3000 mℓ | (b) 24 mℓ | (c) 143 mℓ | (d) 9600 mℓ | (e) 3125 mℓ

. (a) 4 kg | (b) 0·7 l | (c) 60 kg | (d) 2 m | (e) 16 cm | (f) 330 mℓ

. 300 g | **12.** 1200 mℓ | **13.** 173 cm | **14.** 2·5 tonnes

─────────────────────

. (c) 3 | **2.** (b) *y*-values: 4, −1, −4, −5, −4, −1, 4 | (c) ±2·4 (or ±2·5)

──────────────

. 0·28 m | **2.** 0·01 m | **3.** 3·2 m | **4.** 0·09 m | **5.** 6 cm | **6.** 20 cm | **7.** 0·8 cm

. 2·5 km | **9.** 0·35 km | **10.** 9 km | **11.** 3000 g | **12.** 9500 g | **13.** 375 g | **14.** 0·575 kg

. 1·849 kg | **16.** 6000 kg | **17.** 0·53 ℓ | **18.** 1·832 ℓ | **19.** 5·5 ℓ | **20.** 4500 mℓ | **21.** 0·065 ℓ

. 2·43 kg | **23.** 1050 g | **24.** 33·6 cm | **25.** 220 | **26.** 12 | **27.** yes

. (a) 0·19 km | (b) 71 mm | (c) 2·3 tonnes | (d) 9·4 litres | (e) 5·7 m

. (f) 0·04 kg | (g) 70 cm | (h) 0·8 g | (i) 65 cℓ | (j) 380 mℓ

──────────────

. (a) 11:15 | (b) 14:45 | (c) 17:30 | (d) 09:40 | (e) 18:50 | (f) 21:32

. (a) 10.40 am | (b) 4.20 pm | (c) 7.35 pm | (d) 9.10 pm | (e) 2.05 am | (f) 8.05 am

. 9.05 am (09:05) | **4.** 8.40 am (08:40) | **5.** 8 hrs 50 minutes | **6.** 1 hr 45 mins

. (a) 52 wks | (b) 260 wks | (c) 24 months | (d) 120 months | (e) 730 days | (f) 1095 days

. 36 months | **9.** 2 hrs 50 mins | **10.** 2 hrs 35 mins

. 15:25→17:05; 16:24→18:09; 11:38→14:28

. 18:05 | **13.** 23:25 | **14.** 8:20 | **15.** 11:30

	Train 1	Train 2	Train 3	Train 4	Train 5	Train 6
Henton	09:00	09:57	10:30	11:23	12:15	13:12
Oldhill	09:08	10:05	10:38	11:31	12:23	13:20
Eastham	09:23	10:20	10:53	11:46	12:38	13:35
Colston	09:40	10:37	11:10	12:03	12:55	13:52
Todwick	09:55	10:52	11:25	12:18	13:10	14:07

──────────────

. 36 miles | **2.** 140 km/h | **3.** 20 miles | **4.** 9·5 hours | **5.** $1\frac{1}{2}$ hours

. 19·5 m | **7.** 2·5 hrs | **8.** 11 miles | **9.** $1\frac{1}{4}$ hrs | **10.** 52 mph

──────────────

. (a) 15 m/s | (b) 25 m/s | (c) 5·56 m/s | (d) 216 km/h | (e) 36 km/h | (f) 35 m/s

. 18 km | **3.** 60 mph, 36 mph, 45 mph, 72 mph, 40 mph | **4.** 12 mph | **5.** 11:35

. 100 m | **7.** 18 km/h | **8.** 20 sec | **9.** (a) 4 hrs | (b) 33·75 km/h

─────────────────────

. 1, 9 | **2.** 12 | **3.** 7 | **4.** 5·2 × 10⁴ | **5.** correct | **6.** e.g. 7 and 13 | **7.** 34

Page 281   *M9·7*

2. 38 cm   **3.** (a) 9 cm   (b) 19 cm   (c) 10·5 cm   **4.** 5 cm   **5.** 9 cm   **6.** 12 cm
7. (a) 5 cm   (b) 3 cm   (c) 42 cm   **8.** 44   **9.** 42   **10.** 46   **11.** 52
12. 66   **13.** 58   **14.** 14 cm

Page 284   *M9·8*

1. 20 cm^2 **2.** 36 cm^2 **3.** 450 cm^2 **4.** 21 cm^2 **5.** 44 cm^2 **6.** 31·5 cm^2
7. 24 cm^2 **8.** 6 cm   **9.** 41 cm^2 **10.** 81 cm^2 **11.** 66 cm^2 **12.** 192 cm^2
13. 164 cm^2 **14.** 132 cm^2 **15.** 62 cm^2 **16.** 140 cm^2 **17.** 88 cm^2 **18.** 180 cm^2
19. 35 cm^2 **20.** 23   **21.** 175 cm^2 **22.** 82 cm^2 **23.** 96 cm^2

Page 284   *Can you still?*

1. $2n$ **2.** 70   **3.** $8n + 9$ **4.** $27n^2$ **5.** m^5 **6.** $12m^2 - 6mn$ **7.** $5(2n + 3)$

Page 287   *M9·9*

1. 42 cm^2 **2.** 40 cm^2 **3.** 48 cm^2 **4.** 50 cm^2 **5.** 154 cm^2 **6.** 50 cm^2 **7.** 74 m^2
8. 9:10   **9.** 69 cm^2 **10.** 3·03 m^2 **11.** $\frac{1}{2}$ m^2 **12.** 180 m^2 **13.** 7 cm   **14.** £119

Page 289   *Can you still?*

1. 30°   **2.** 85°   **3.** 150°

Page 290   *M9·10*

1. (a) 113·1 cm   (b) 44·0 cm   (c) 25·1 mm   (d) 72·3 cm   **2.** square   **3.** 1571 m

Page 291   *E9·2*

1. 43·7 cm   **2.** 61·7 cm   **3.** 90·0 cm   **4.** 25·0 cm   **5.** 388·5 m   **6.** 41·7 cm
7. 33·6 cm   **8.** 64·3 cm   **9.** 253·4 cm   **10.** 43·6 cm   **11.** 2042 cm   **12.** 94
13. 370·2 cm   **14.** (a) 257·6 cm   (b) 1940   **15.** 29 cm

Page 293   *M9·10*

1. (b) chord   (c) diameter   **2.** (a) 2290·2 cm^2 (b) 1963·5 cm^2 (c) 10·2 cm^2
4. 7·1 m^2 **5.** circle (by 3·52 cm^2)   **6.** (a) 4π (b) 9π (c) 100π

Page 294   *Can you still?*

1. 15, 21   **2.** (a) 3   (b) $3n + 4$ **3.** 7   **4.** $x = y + 4$
5. $x = \dfrac{m}{8}$ **6.** $x = \dfrac{m - 9}{5}$ **7.** $x = \dfrac{a + 6}{2}$

Page 295   *E9·3*

1. 100·5 cm^2 **2.** 44·2 cm^2 **3.** 377·4 cm^2 **4.** 183·4 cm^2 **5.** 330·3 cm^2
6. 126·6 cm^2 **7.** 10·5 cm^2 **8.** 15·9 cm^2 **9.** 27·5 cm^2 **10.** 6·5 cm^2
11. 35·3 cm^2 **12.** 33·5 cm^2 **13.** 75·4 cm^2 **14.** 11·6 cm^2 **15.** 2 boxes for £85

Page 297   *M9·11*

1. (a) 166 cm^2 (b) 216 cm^2 **2.** (a) 140 cm^3 (b) 180 cm^3
3. C   **4.** 120   **5.** 2:3   **6.** 810

Page 298   **M9·12** ——————————————————————————————

1. a, b, d, g, h   **2.** 216 cm³   **3.** 84 cm³   **4.** 220 cm³
5. 432 m³   **6.** 768 m³   **7.** 816 cm³   **8.** 20·14 m³
9. 23·625 tonnes   **10.** 200 cm   **11.** 132 cm²   **12.** 1324 cm²

Page 300   **Can you still?** ——————————————————————————————

1. (a) $\frac{9}{19}$ (b) $\frac{7}{19}$ (c) $\frac{10}{19}$ **2.** $\frac{10}{21}$ **3.** (a) 40   (b) 80

Page 301   **M9·13** ——————————————————————————————

1. 1244·1 cm³   **2.** 1399·6 cm³   **3.** 384·8 cm³   **4.** 8595·4 litres   **5.** 23·3 cm³   **6.** 40π
7. A larger by 35·3 cm²   **8.** (a) 628·3   (b) 1963·5   (c) 175·9   **9.** 10
10. 419 seconds   **11.** (a) 16·2 m²   (b) 4854·4 m³   **12.** yes

Page 302   **Can you still?** ——————————————————————————————

1. £80   **2.** 0·17   **3.** 102·3 kg   **4.** $\frac{13}{36}$

Page 303   **M9·14** ——————————————————————————————

1. C and E   **2.** Scale factor 1·5 for each side   **3.** (a) 6 cm   (b) 10 m   (c) 5 cm   (d) 9 cm

Page 305   **Which is better value?** ——————————————————————————————

1. A   **2.** B   **3.** B   **4.** A
5. Plates : 1 pack of 50 + 1 pack of 20 − cups : 1 pack of 30 + 4 packs of 12
6. A   **7.** B

Page 306   **Test yourself on Unit 9** ——————————————————————————————

1. (a) 180 cm   (b) 0·05 kg   (c) 2·8 ℓ   (d) 1·67 kg   (e) 44 cm
2. (a) 762 kg   (b) 1265 mℓ
3. (a) Afternoon   (b) 4 hrs 55 mins   (c) 22:05 or 10:05 pm
    (d) 14:10   (e) 15 hrs 45 mins
4. (a) 15 km   (b) 4·5 hrs   (c) 17 miles   (d) 12·5 m/s   (e) 72 km/h
5. (a) 48 cm   (b) 54 cm   (c) 19 cm   **6.** (a) 28 cm²   (b) 100 cm²   (c) 288 cm²
7. (a) 351 cm²   (b) 60 cm²   (c) 128 cm²   **8.** (a) 50·3 cm   (b) 22·6 cm   (c) 77·1 cm
9. (a) 254·5 cm²   (b) 855·3 cm²   (c) 28·3 cm²   (d) 138·2 cm²
10. (a) (i) 280 cm³   (ii) 292 cm²   (b) (i) 240 cm³   (ii) 332 cm²   (c) 3·2 cm
11. (a) 210 cm³   (b) 270 cm²   **12.** (a) 1308·5 cm³   (b) 5·19 m³   (c) 37 minutes
13. Q and S

Page 310   **Mixed examination questions** ——————————————————————————————

1. 120 cm²   **2.** (a) 64 cm   (b) 60 cm²   **3.** 7·22 km
4. woman 50 kg, glass 270 mℓ, man 180 cm, distance 266 km
5. 5   **6.** (a) 9:47   (b) 40 minutes   (c) 16:47
7. 1256·6 cm³   **8.** No   **9.** 380 cm³
10. (a) 11309·7 cm² (1·13 m²)   (b) 791·7 litres   **11.** 12 096 litres

Page 314   **M10·1** ——————————————————————————————

1. (a) 7   (b) 5   (c) 6   (d) 6
2. £240   **3.** 5·6 cm   **4.** 13   **5.** 6°C
6. (a) 13   (b) 14   (c) 13·4   **7.** (a) 6   (b) 6   (c) 5 and 9   (d) 7
8. £3

Page 316   E10·1

1. (a) 7   (b) 7·35 Mode is better – most common size
2. (a) 11   (b) 1   (c) Median because 70 distorts the data
5. 6, 12   6. 312
7. (a) median   (b) £7050   8. (a) £30   (b) £6
9. 75%   10. 29, 42, 43   11. 1   12. 8
13. (a) 3200 cm   (b) 159 cm
14. 31   15. 32   16. median

Page 318   Can you still?

Across: 1. 551   4. 595   5. 804   7. 14   8. 32
Down: 1. 525   2. 1560   3. 45   5. 84   6. 43

Page 319   M10·2

1. (a) 30   (b) 25   (c) 35   (d) 20   (e) 20%
4. (a) 350   (b) 340   (c) 280   (d) Swindon   (e) Swindon   (f) 100
   (g) 140   (h) 1920
6. (a) 42%   (b) 34%   (c) 27→28%   (d) 26%   (e) 12%   (f) 6%
7. (a) frequencies: 7, 10, 9, 8, 6, 2   (c) 16   (d) 5–9

Page 322   M10·3

1. (b) 18   2. (b) 27   (c) 28   (d) 9   (e) $\frac{19}{27}$
3. (a) 1·75 litres   (b) 1·4 litres   4. (a) 88   (b) 23   (c) 40%
5. Holland Bank: median = 47, range = 39

   Grindley High School: median = 36, range = 38

   The age range is similar for both schools but the median age is lower at Grindley H.S.

Page 323   Can you still?

1. 0·137, 0·37, 0·4, 0·703, 0·73   2. (a) $\frac{5}{21}$ (b) $\frac{4}{5}$ (c) $3\frac{3}{10}$ (d) 18
3. 63°, 81°   4. £49·28

Page 325   M10·4

1. (a) 40   (b) 9°   (c) 63°, 72°, 36°, 54°, 135°
2. 156°, 96°, 51°, 36°, 21°   3. 88°, 108°, 48°, 72°, 44°
4. frequencies 25, 4, 10, 15, 6; angles 150°, 24°, 60°, 90°, 36°

Page 327   M10·5

1. (a) 20   (b) 40   (c) 8   (d) 12   2. (a) £225   (b) £150   (c) £525
3. (a) 50   (b) 30   (c) 18   (d) 90   (e) 40   (f) 12
4. (a) 2h   (b) 6h   (c) 8h   (d) 1h   (e) 2h   (f) 5h
5. (a) 90°   (b) 144°   (c) 72°   (d) 54°
6. (a) wrong. 10 more at Hatton Green   (b) wrong. 10 more at Holland Bank
7. (a) wrong   (b) true   (c) wrong   8. (a) 108°   (b) 72°   (c) 18°   (d) 162°
9. (a) depends on population   (b) depends on population   (c) true

Page 329   Can you still?

1. C   2. 21:20   3. 14 cm

18	17	12	47
15	10	8	33
33	27	20	80

(b) 27   (c) $\dfrac{27}{80}$

(a)

107	83	15	5	210
12	16	141	121	290
119	99	156	126	500

(b) 25·2%

(a)

123	481	604
65	637	702
98	396	494
286	1514	1800

(b) 15·9%

8   **5.** 19   **6.** 37

(b)   strong negative   (c) $\dfrac{1}{3}$ **2.** (b) positive

A no correlation,   B strong negative,   C no correlation,   D strong positive
(b)   weak negative

Vertical scale does not start at 0, gaps between bars not equal, no label on vertical scale.
eg. did they play the same number of games?
eg. do not know how many dentists were asked so how reliable?

eg. large intervals on the vertical axis make the differences between each bar appear smaller then they really are.
labelling on vertical axis not consistent, day 4 is not included in the line graph.
It says 'up to' so will not definitely save anything like £80 a month.

The area of the 2015 symbol is four times larger than the 2014 symbol but statement says that sales only doubled.
The break in the vertical axis makes the heights of the bars misleading.
The graph is extended up to 2050 but the value of the house might just as easily fall rather than rise before then.

18   **2.** $5a + 15b$ **3.** $\dfrac{1}{2}$ **4.** $3a + 3ab$

$n(4 - 7m)$ **6.** $26m + 16$ **7.** a^{14}

(a) 1   (b) 1   **2.** (a) 14–21, 1 visit : 65+, 2 visits   (b) over 65
(a) 8–9 lbs   (b) 6–7 lbs
(a) Easitech 11–15, compfix 7–10 (b)   Easitech, higher median
(a) 40–49   (b) 40–49

65°   **3.** parallelogram   **4.** translation with $\begin{pmatrix} 5 \\ -4 \end{pmatrix}$

Page 339 **M10·10**

1. (a) 30   (b) 2   2. (a) 225   (b) 2·25
3. (a) Paradise 16·53, Devere 16·46, Tropic 16·36   (b) Paradise
4. (a) 3·48   (b) 5

Page 341 **Can you still?**

1. $-7, -10$ 3. $x = \dfrac{y-3}{4}$ 4. $5n + 2$ 5. $5, 0, -3, -4, -3, 0, 5$

Page 342 **M10·11**

1. (b) 91   (c) about 4·55   2. (b) 2900   (c) 14·5
3. (a) Kabinseal   (b) about £14 500   4. (b) 7250   (c) 29
5. about 27 hours   6. 38·9

Page 343 **Can you still?**

1. 56 mph   2. 08:18   3. 57·6 km/h   4. No. She needs another 170 mℓ

Page 344 **M10·12**

1. Truman; median 67 kg, range 36 kg; Jenkins; median 69 kg, range 44 kg; Truman median *smaller*. Truman range smaller, Truman weights *less* spread out.

2. 16 yr olds mean £5·01, range £1·80.

    17 yr olds mean £5·27, range £1·30.

    16 yr olds mean is smaller, range greater. So 16 yr old hourly rate is more spread out.

3. Wolves median 22·5, range 9

    Sentinels median 22, range 10

    Wolves median is greater and the range is smaller. So the ages for the Wolves are less spread out.

Page 345 **Can you still?**

1. 1200 cm³   2. 7 cm²   3. 1288 cm²

Page 346 **M10·13**

1. (a) 10 A median 69, range 45 : 10   B median 65, range 51
2. (a) yr. 10 mean 7·1 haircuts, range = 4   (b) yr. 11 mean 7·1 haircuts, range = 3
3. boys : mean = 61·5 kg, range = 35 kg
4. (a) Ash Lane mean 1·75, range = 4   (b) Tibbs Drive mean 2·1, range = 4
5. Team A: mean = 20, range = 25,   team B: mean = 17·5, range = 30 or use another average

Page 348   **Feed the dogs**

Breed		food (daily)	cost (weekly)
ST	dry	2 cups	1·75
C	dry	$\frac{1}{2}$ cup	0·44
L	mix	3 cups $1\frac{1}{2}$ cans	7·04
SS	mix	2 cups, 1 can	4·69
B	dry	$3\frac{1}{2}$ cups	3·06
YT	dry	$\frac{1}{2}$ cup	0·44
L	mix	3 cups, $1\frac{1}{2}$ cans	7·04
GD	dry	8 cups	7
GR	mix	3 cups, $1\frac{1}{2}$ cans	7·04

total weekly food cost	£38·50
weeky booster cost	£4·92
weekly cost for worming/fleas	£21·14
weekly insurance cost	£17·54
total weekly cost	£82·10

Ans. Alex and Kate are wrong

weekly cost is around £82.

Page 349   **Test yourself on Unit 10**

1. (a) (i) 7   (ii) 6   (iii) 5   (iv) 8   (b) both the same (7)

2. (a) 12–21, 22–35   (b) 66%   (c) 52%   (d) 4%

3. (b) 36   (c) 43

4. (a) (i) 90   (ii) 4°   (iii) 60°, 112°, 80°, 68°, 40°
     (b) (i) 18   (ii) 36   (iii) 12   (iv) 42

5. (a)

23	32	16	71
24	8	17	49
47	40	33	120

   (b) $\frac{1}{3}$ (c) 51·5%

6. (a) positive correlation   (b) no correlation   (c) strong negative correlation

7. eg. vertical scale does not start at 0, inconsistent scale on the vertical axis, gaps between bars are not equal, no label on the vertical scale.

8. (a) 2   (b) 2   **9.** 13·5 hours

10. (a) mean 11·5, range 9   (b) compare with 19 year-olds' mean = 7·6 and range = 12

Page 353   **Mixed examination questions**

1. (a) 15   (b) 14·5   (c) 25   **2.** (b) positive correlation

3. 11   **4.** Select Lizzie (mean = 26·4, range = 0·5, median = 26·3) as opposed to
       Megan (mean = 26·5, range = 0·8, median = 26·5)

5. 2·48   **6.** 1, 3, 3, 6, 7, 8, 9   **7.** $\frac{1}{5}$

8. (a) 24·625   (b) no, only 68·75%   **9.** 150°, 60°, 90°, 30°, 30°

10. (a) 1   (b) 5   (c) 29

UNIT 11

Page 356 ***M11·1*** _____

1. (a) 0·5   (b) 2·5   (c) 3·5   (d) 5   (e) 6·5   (f) 8·5

2. 7·7, 4·6   **3.** 6·6, 2·0, 3·8   **4.** (a) 14·8 cm   (b) 9·4 cm   (c) 8·7 cm

Page 357 ***M11·2*** _____

1. 60°   **2.** 50°   **3.** 45°   **4.** 110°   **5.** 23°   **6.** 102°   **7.** 107°   **8.** 72°   **9.** 294°

Page 358 ***M11·3*** _____

4. 70°   **5.** 60°   **6.** 6·7 cm (accept 6·6–6·8)   **7.** 5·9 cm

8. 6·6 cm   **9.** 7·25 cm   **10.** 5 cm   **11.** 10·2 cm

Page 359 ***Can you still?*** _____

2. 23°   **4.** 10

Page 360 ***M11·4*** _____

1. 57°   **2.** 51°   **3.** 55°   **5.** 6·2 cm

6. $X\hat{Y}Z = 79°$, $Y\hat{Z}X = 42°$, $Z\hat{X}Y = 59°$ **7.** must have $\triangle$ height = 4 cm

8. eg. base = 2 cm, height = 20 cm or base = 5 cm, height = 8 cm   **11.** 50°   **12.** 5·7 cm

Page 361 ***M11·5*** _____

3. 15 m   **5.** 3·6 cm

Page 362 ***Can you still?*** _____

1. $(-2)^2$ larger by 1   **2.** eg. 5 cm, 7 cm, 13 cm   **3.** 18

4. £92 880   **5.** 3

Page 363 ***M11·6*** _____

1. B, C, E   **3.** (a) 4 cm   (b) 2 cm   (c) 2 cm   (d) 16 cm³   **4.** 7

5. (b)   (c)

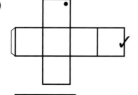

7. eg.

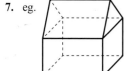

8. A5, B6, C4   **9.** B

Page 364 ***Can you still?*** _____

1. $2ab$ **2.** 7   **3.** (i) $6a + 2b$ (ii) $a(2a + b) = 2a^2 + ab$

4. $3(n - 7) = 3n - 21$ **5.** (i) $3(a + 4)$ (ii) $2a(3a - 5b)$

Page 366 ***M11·8*** _____

1. cone   **2.** cylinder   **3.** cuboid

4. A larger by 2 cm³   **5.** triangular prism   **6.** 7

41

Page 367 ***Can you still?***

1. (a) 4   (b) 3   (c) 267   (d) 3   2. eg. 1, 1, 10, 11, 12

Page 368 ***M11·9***

1. 8 m
3. 150 km
5. (missing numbers) 4·8, 200, 18, 8, 4, 3·5
7. (a) 66 km   (b) 114 km   (c) 84 km
8. 5·5 cm

2. 2 km
4. 2·5 km
6. 9 cm

9. 12 cm

Page 370 ***M11·10***

1. (a) 090°   (b) 135°   (c) 270°   (d) 045°   (e) 225°   (f) 315°   (g) 180°   (h) 000°
2. A 031°, B 056°, C 338°, D 279°, E 311°, F 073°
3. (a) 135°   (b) 025°   (c) 205°   (d) 255°   (e) 315°   (f) 075°
4. A 043°, B 202°, C 249°, D 129°, E 104°, F 214°, G 303°

Page 371 ***M11·11***

2. (a) 213°   (b) 080°   (c) 310°   (d) 260°   3. (a) 032°   (b) 081°   (c) 238°
4. (b) 2·9 km   (c) 115°   5. (a) 115°   (b) 040°   (c) 195°   (d) 330°
6. 11·5 km   7. 10·4 km   8. (a) 125°   (b) 305°

Page 373 ***Can you still?***

-values: 11, 6, 3, 2, 3, 6, 11

Page 374 ***M11·12***

1. (b) (3, 2)   (c) (0, −1)   (d) 18 square units   (e) stays same
2. (a) AB $\left(4, 7\frac{1}{2}\right)$, CD $\left(2, 3\frac{1}{2}\right)$, EF $\left(4\frac{1}{2}, 5\frac{1}{2}\right)$, GH (4, 4), IJ $\left(6\frac{1}{2}, 4\right)$, KL $\left(7\frac{1}{2}, 1\frac{1}{2}\right)$
   (b) 4 square units   (c) (4, 2)
3. (b) (−1, −2)   (c) (0, 0)   (d) 20 square units   (e) a 2 × 10 rectangle
4. (a) (1, 1)   (b) (6, 5)   (c) (6, 2)
5. many possibilities   6. (b) (3, 1), (5, 3), (3, 5), (−3, 3)

Page 375 ***Can you still?***

1. 2·13 × 10⁴   2. $6n + 60 = 180, n = 20°$ 3. 4 years   4. $\frac{1}{5}$

Page 377 ***Car insurance Task***

1. £20·67   2. £57·70   3. £31·67   4. £504, £42   5. £1071, £89·25
6. £562·50, £46·88   7. £748, £62·33   8. £348, £29   9. £848, £70·67
10. £42·67   (b) £64   (c) £21·33   11. £34·25

Page 378 ***Test yourself on Unit 11***

. (a) 6·5 cm   (b) 10·6 cm   (c) (i) 115°   (ii) 80°
. (a) 55°   (b) 54°
. (a) triangular prism
. (a) (square based) pyramid   (b) 54 square units
. (a) 6 cm   (b) 7·5 km
. (a) (i) 260°   (ii) 307°   (iii) 043°   (iv) 080°   (b) (ii) 298°
. (c) D(−3, −3)   (d) $\left(0, \frac{-1}{2}\right)$ (e) (−1, 2)   (f) 3 : 2

42

1. A Cube, B Pyramid, C Cuboid, D Triangular Prism
4. (a) 045° (b) South-West (c) 115° (d) 80 km
5. Many possibilities
6. (a) Zoo (b) Hospital (c) 065°
7. (a) S(3, 2) (b) T (?, −1) where ? can be any value